Reviewing Biology

With Sample Examinations

Revised Edition

Carl M. Raab

Director of Academic Initiatives for the Office of
School Programs and Support Services
New York City Board of Education, NY
Former Assistant Principal, Supervision Science Department
Fort Hamilton High School, Brooklyn, NY

When ordering this book, please specify:
either **R 454 P** *or* REVIEWING BIOLOGY

AMSCO SCHOOL PUBLICATIONS, INC.
315 Hudson Street / New York, N. Y. 10013

NOTE TO STUDENTS:

Text and diagrams that are extended area materials are marked with a large asterisk (✻). This material is tested in Part II of the exams.

NOTE TO THE TEACHER:

The books of this series—*Reviewing Biology, Reviewing Earth Science, Reviewing Chemistry,* and *Reviewing Physics*—offer an innovative format that comprehensively reviews and supplements the study of science as it is usually taught at the high school level. Each book is readily correlated with the standard textbooks for this level. The series is specifically geared to the needs of students who want to refresh their memory and review the material in preparation for final exams.

Reviewing Biology contains a review of the one-year introductory biology course for college-bound students. The material is divided into seven units, each of which is subdivided into major topic sections. The book is abundantly illustrated with clearly labeled drawings and diagrams that illuminate and reinforce the subject matter. Important science terms are boldfaced and are defined in the text. Other terms that may be unfamiliar to students are italicized for emphasis. In addition, the large work-text format makes *Reviewing Biology* easy for students to read.

Within each unit are several sets of multiple-choice and essay questions that test students' knowledge and reasoning while provoking thought. Questions are often accompanied by diagrams that aid in reviewing and testing the materials. The almost 700 questions found in the text can be used for topic review throughout the year, as well as for final exams and homework assignments.

A section called Laboratory Skills follows the seven topic units. This special section reviews the skills that all students should master in the course of completing one year of biology instruction at this level. *Reviewing Biology* also contains a full Glossary, where students can find concise definitions of significant scientific terms. The extensive Index should be used by students to locate fuller text discussions of these and other biological terms. The four exams at the back of the book can be used for extra practice and review.

Also included in this revised edition of *Reviewing Biology* are seven special end-of-book features that explore current controversial issues in biological science, technology, and society. Reading comprehension, free response, and research questions presented at the end of each feature encourage students to evaluate the issues, and to make their own decisions about the impact of science and technology on society, the environment, and their lives.

Cover Photos: Scarlet Macaw, Parrot Jungle, Florida, by Andrea Pistolesi, courtesy of The Image Bank; Desert Bighorn Sheep, North America, by Shelly Grossman; African Lion, Masai Mara, Kenya, by Jose Azel; and Forest Floor, Southeast Alaska, by Gary Braasch, all courtesy of Woodfin Camp & Associates, Inc.

ISBN 0-87720-050-5

Printed in the United States of America

Contents

Unit 7: Ecology

Laboratory Skills 94

Science, Technology, and Society

UNIT 1 Unity and Diversity Among Living Things

CONCEPT OF LIFE

Scientists have not agreed on a single definition of life. Thus "life" is often defined in terms of certain activities, or life functions, performed by all living things.

Life Functions.

All living organisms carry on the following life functions:

1. **Nutrition** includes the activities involved in **ingestion** (obtaining food from the environment) and **digestion** (processing food for use by the organism). It also includes **egestion** (removal of solid wastes).

2. **Transport** includes the **absorption** of materials through cell membranes and the circulation, or distribution, of materials to all the cells of the organism.

3. **Respiration** includes the chemical activities that release energy from organic molecules for use by the cells. During respiration, glucose is broken down, and the energy released is stored in the compound ATP. Energy released by the breakdown of ATP is used by organisms to perform all the life functions.

4. **Excretion** includes all those activities involved in the elimination of cellular waste products from the organism. These wastes include water, carbon dioxide, salts, and nitrogen-containing compounds.

5. **Synthesis** involves chemical reactions in which small molecules combine to form larger ones.

6. **Growth** is an increase in size brought about by increases in cell size and cell number. The raw materials for growth are the products of synthesis.

7. **Regulation** involves the control and coordination of the life functions.

8. **Reproduction** results in the production of new individuals. Since each organism has a limited life span, reproduction is necessary for the survival of each **species**, or kind of organism.

Metabolism.

All the chemical activities that an organism must carry on to sustain life are its **metabolism**.

Homeostasis.

The maintenance of a stable internal environment in spite of changes in the external environment is known as **homeostasis**. An example of homeostasis is the maintenance of a constant body temperature in spite of the temperature changes in the environment.

QUESTIONS

1. The tendency of an organism to maintain a stable internal environment is called (1) homeostasis (2) cell theory (3) reproduction (4) synthesis
2. The energy available for use by the cell is obtained from the life function of (1) reproduction (2) respiration (3) transport (4) synthesis
3. The chemical process by which complex molecules of protein are made from simple molecules is called (1) regulation (2) respiration (3) synthesis (4) excretion
4. Which life function includes the absorption and circulation of essential substances throughout an organism? (1) transport (2) excretion (3) ingestion (4) nutrition
5. Which term includes all of the chemical activities carried on by an organism? (1) regulation (2) metabolism (3) digestion (4) respiration
6. Which life activity is *not* required for the survival of an individual organism? (1) nutrition (2) respiration (3) reproduction (4) synthesis
7. In an ameba, materials are taken from its environment and then moved throughout its cytoplasm. These processes are known as (1) absorption and circulation (2) food processing and energy release (3) energy release and synthesis (4) coordination and regulation
8. In an organism, the coordination of the activities that maintain homeostasis in a constantly changing environment is a process known as (1) digestion (2) regulation (3) synthesis (4) respiration
9. Which life function provides substances that may be used by an organism for its growth and for the repair of its tissues? (1) excretion (2) reproduction (3) nutrition (4) regulation
10. Why are both bacteria and humans considered to be organisms? Write a brief paragraph explaining why scientists have difficulty including viruses in the category of organisms.

DIVERSITY OF LIFE

Necessity for Classification.

The fact that all organisms carry out the same life functions is said to illustrate the **unity of life**. The fact that organisms show a wide variety of adaptations for carrying out the life functions is said to illustrate the **diversity of life**. To study the unity and diversity of living things in an organized fashion, biologists classify, or group, organisms according to certain common characteristics.

Organisms are grouped together lagely on the basis of similarities in structure. Similarities in chemical and genetic makeup and in embryonic development are also important considerations. Organisms classified in the same group are thought to share a common ancestry. In other words, these organisms may have evolved, or developed, from the same ancestral organism.

A Classification System.

Biologists have not agreed on a single system for classification. One modern classification system places organisms in five major groups, or **kingdoms—Monera, Protista, Fungi, Plant,** and **Animal.** The criteria considered in grouping organisms in this five-kingdom system are: the presence or absence of a nucleus surrounded by a nuclear membrane in the cell, unicellularity or multicellularity, and type of nutrition.

Each kingdom is subdivided into major groups called **phyla** (singular, *phylum*). Table 1-1 lists some major phyla in each kingdom, their characteristics, and representative organisms.

Within each phylum, the organisms are separated into smaller and smaller classification groups. From larger to smaller, these groups are **class, order, family, genus,** and **species.** With each smaller group, the organisms show greater similarity in structure and function. The smallest classification group, the species, includes only one kind of organism.

Scientific Names.

For convenience and for accuracy in identifying organisms, each kind of organism has a two-part scientific name consisting of its genus and species. Scientific names are generally in Latin. This system of naming organisms is called **binomial nomenclature,** and it was developed by **Carolus Linnaeus,** a Swedish botanist. A scientific name is generally printed in italics. The genus name begins with a capital letter, the species name with a lowercase letter. For example, dogs belong to the genus *Canis* and species *familiaris.* Thus the scientific name for dogs is *Canis familiaris.* The wolf, *Canis lupus,* belongs to the same genus but a different species. Organisms belonging to the same species can mate and produce fertile offspring.

Table 1-1. The Five-Kingdom System of Classification

Kingdoms and Major Phyla	Characteristics	Examples
Monera	Primitive cell structure; lack nuclear membrane and all organelles except ribosomes	
Bacteria	Very small cells; some photosynthetic	*Escherichia, Salmonella*
Blue-green bacteria	Photosynthetic; chlorophyll in cytoplasm	*Anabaena*
Protista	Mostly unicellular; nucleus surrounded by nuclear membrane; many kinds of organelles; some are plantlike, some are animallike	
Protozoa	Animallike nutrition	paramecium, ameba
Algae	Plantlike nutrition	spirogyra, elodea
Fungi	Structure usually in the form of branched, multinucleated filaments that absorb digested food from the environment	yeast (unicellular), bread mold, mushroom
Plants	Multicellular; all but a few are photosynthetic	
Bryophytes	Lack vascular tissue and true roots, stems, and leaves	moss, liverwort
Tracheophytes	Have vascular tissue and true roots, stems, and leaves	geranium, fern, bean, corn, pine tree, maple tree
Animals	Multicellular; ingest food	
Coelenterates	Hollow body with two cell layers	hydra, jellyfish
Annelids	Segmented body wall	earthworm, sandworm
Arthropods	Exoskeleton with jointed appendages	grasshopper, lobster, spider
Chordates	Dorsal nerve cord	shark, frog, human

CELLULAR STRUCTURE OF LIVING THINGS

1. According to one classification system, which term includes all of the others? (1) algae (2) ameba (3) protozoa (4) protists

2. A modern classification system should reflect (1) the types of habitats in which organisms live (2) evolutionary relationships (3) color and size relationships (4) the eating habits of organisms

3. Among many species, those most closely related to each other would probably (1) live in the same geographic area (2) contain similar enzymes and hormones (3) have similar food requirements (4) live during the same time period

4. Which two classification groups indicate the scientific name of an organism? (1) kingdom and phylum (2) class and order (3) family and genus (4) genus and species

5. The classification group that shows the greatest similarity among its members is the (1) phylum (2) kingdom (3) genus (4) species

6. The mosquito *Anopheles quadrimaculatus* is most closely related in structure to (1) *Aedes sollicitans* (2) *Culex pipiens* (3) *Aedes aegypti* (4) *Anopheles punctulatus*

7. In one modern classification system, organisms are grouped into five (1) kingdoms (2) phyla (3) genera (4) species

8. In which kingdom is an organism classified if it *lacks* a membrane separating its genetic material from its cytoplasm? (1) protist (2) monera (3) plant (4) animal

9. Which is true of organisms that are classified in the same genus? (1) They must be in the same phylum, but may be of different species. (2) They must be of the same species, but may be in different phyla. (3) They must be in the same phylum, but may be in different kingdoms. (4) They must be in the same kingdom, but may be in different phyla.

10. Which group of organisms in the animal kingdom is characterized by jointed appendages and exoskeletons? (1) arthropods (2) chordates (3) annelids (4) coelenterates

11. The correct order used in classifying organisms is (1) phylum, kingdom, genus, species (2) kingdom, phylum, genus, species (3) kingdom, species, phylum, genus (4) phylum, genus, species, kingdom

12. Fish, frogs, and humans are examples of (1) coelenterates (2) annelids (3) arthropods (4) chordates

13. The scientific classification of animals is based primarily on similarities in (1) where the organisms live (2) size (3) the food the organisms eat (4) structure

14. A multicellular photosynthetic organism would probably be classified as a (1) moneran (2) protist (3) plant (4) fungus

15. Explain the criteria used by scientists to classify living things. Explain the relationship between the science of classification and evolution.

All living things are composed of **cells**. Some organisms consist of only one cell, while others consist of billions of cells. The processes essential for the survival of the organism are performed by the cells.

The Cell Theory. The cell theory, which is one of the major theories of biology, can be stated as follows:

1. The cell is the basic unit of structure in all living things. Every organism is made up of one or more cells.

2. The cell is the basic unit of function in living things. For example, cells synthesize proteins and release energy. Every organism functions through the activities of its cells.

3. All cells come only from preexisting cells. New cells are formed when existing cells divide.

Development of the Cell Theory. During the last four centuries, improvements in the microscope and the development of other techniques have made it possible for biologists to observe and study cells. The cell theory was developed from the work of a number of scientists.

Anton van Leeuwenhoek (1632–1723) made powerful simple microscopes (magnifying glasses) that he used to study samples of living material. Van Leeuwenhoek was the first to see sperm cells, bacteria, and protozoa.

Robert Hooke (1635–1703) made compound microscopes (microscopes with two or more lenses) that he used to observe thin slices of cork. He used the term "cells" for the small compartments that make up cork.

Robert Brown, in 1831, concluded from his studies that all plant cells contain a nucleus.

Matthias Schleiden, in 1838, concluded that all plants are made up of cells.

Theodor Schwann, in 1839, concluded that all animals are made up of cells.

Rudolph Virchow, in 1855, concluded that all cells arise only from preexisting cells.

Exceptions to the Cell Theory. Recent discoveries have led scientists to identify several exceptions to the cell theory.

1. Mitochondria and chloroplasts, which are cell organelles, contain genetic material (DNA) and can duplicate themselves in living cells.

2. A virus is not a cell. It consists of an outer coat of protein surrounding a core of DNA or RNA. A virus can reproduce inside a living host cell, but outside the cell, it shows no sign of life.

3. The first living cells on earth must have developed from noncellular matter.

QUESTIONS

1. The unit of structure and function of all living things is a(n) (1) organ (2) atom (3) cell (4) nucleolus

2. According to the cell theory, which statement is correct? (1) Viruses are true cells. (2) Cells are basically unlike in structure. (3) Mitochondria are found only in plant cells. (4) Cells come from preexisting cells.

3. Chloroplasts and mitochondria are examples of (1) cells (2) tissue (3) organelles (4) organs

4. Give one example of how technology has enhanced our understanding of the structure of living things.

Cell Structure.
Cells contain a variety of small structures, called **organelles,** that perform specific functions (Figure 1-1).

1. The **cell membrane,** or **plasma membrane,** surrounds and protects the cell and separates the cell contents from the environment. The membrane consists of a double lipid layer in which large protein molecules float. The cell membrane is *semipermeable*—some substances can pass through it, while others cannot. In this way, it regulates the passage of materials into and out of the cell and controls the cell's chemical makeup.

2. The **cytoplasm** is the fluidlike material that fills the space between the cell membrane and the nucleus. Many metabolic reactions occur in the cytoplasm, which consists mainly of water. The organelles are suspended in the cytoplasm.

3. The **nucleus** is the control center of the cell. It is surrounded by a nuclear membrane and contains the genetic material, which is found in the **chromosomes.** The chromosomes are made of DNA (deoxyribonucleic acid) and protein.

4. The **nucleolus** is a dense granular structure found in the nucleus. The components of ribosomes are synthesized in nucleoli.

5. The **ribosomes** are tiny organelles that are suspended in the cytoplasm and attached to the membranes of the endoplasmic reticulum. Protein synthesis takes place at the ribosomes.

6. The **endoplasmic reticulum** is a network of interconnecting, membrane-lined channels that divide the cytoplasm into chemically separate regions. Various substances are synthesized, stored, secreted, and transported in these channels.

7. **Mitochondria** are the sites of most of the reactions of aerobic cellular respiration, the process by which energy is released from nutrient molecules. Most of the ATP produced by aerobic respiration is synthesized in the mitochondria.

8. The **Golgi complex** consists of a stack of flattened membranes and vesicles that are involved in the synthesis, packaging, and secretion of cell products. These products may be secreted into the cytoplasm or to the outside of the cell.

9. **Lysosomes** are small, membrane-bounded organelles that contain digestive enzymes. In

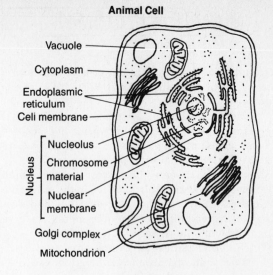

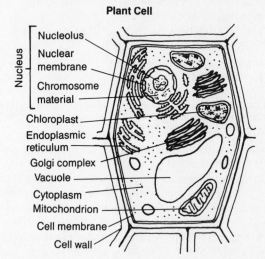

Figure 1-1. Generalized animal and plant cells.

one-celled organisms, such as the paramecium, a lysosome fuses with and releases its enzymes into a food vacuole, where digestion takes place. In multicellular organisms, lysosomes function in the breakdown of older cells and cell parts.

10. **Vacuoles** are fluid-filled organelles surrounded by membranes. In one-celled organisms, digestion occurs in food vacuoles, and excess water collects in contractile vacuoles, which pump it out of the cell. Plant cells contain very large vacuoles that may fill much of the cell interior. In animal cells, there are relatively few vacuoles, and they are small.

11. **Centrioles** are cylindrical structures that are found in pairs near the nucleus of animal cells. They play an important role in cell division.

12. **Chloroplasts** are small, pigment-containing organelles found in the cytoplasm of green plants, algae, and some protists. Photosynthesis takes place in chloroplasts.

13. The **cell wall** is a nonliving structure found outside the cell membrane in the cells of plants, algae, and fungi. It provides strength and rigidity,

but does not interfere with the passage of materials into or out of the cell.

QUESTIONS

1. The term "semipermeable" is used in reference to the (1) nucleolus (2) cell wall (3) cytoplasm (4) cell membrane
2. The canals that connect the cell membrane with the nuclear membrane are the (1) ribosomes (2) lysosomes (3) endoplasmic reticulum (4) nuclei
3. The part of a cell that is in most direct contact with the environment is the (1) nucleus (2) cell membrane (3) mitochondrion (4) centrioles
4. Plant cell organelles that contain photosynthetic pigments are (1) chloroplasts (2) centrioles (3) chromosomes (4) cell walls
5. A student could tell the difference between onion skin cells and cheek cells because the onion skin cells have a (1) cell membrane (2) nucleus (3) centriole (4) cell wall
6. The sites of protein synthesis in the cytoplasm are the (1) ribosomes (2) lysosomes (3) nuclei (4) centrioles
7. The watery environment in which most life activities of a cell take place is the (1) cell membrane (2) chloroplast (3) cytoplasm (4) vacuole
8. Intracellular transport of materials is most closely associated with which cell organelle? (1) cell membrane (2) cell wall (3) ribosome (4) endoplasmic reticulum
9. Centrioles are normally present in the (1) cytoplasm of onion cells (2) cytoplasm of cheek cells (3) nuclei of liver cells (4) nuclei of bean cells
10. Which organelle contains hereditary material and controls most cell activities? (1) nucleus (2) cell membrane (3) vacuole (4) endoplasmic reticulum
11. Centrioles are cell structures involved primarily in (1) cell division (2) storage of fats (3) enzyme production (4) cellular respiration
12. The cell organelles that are the sites of aerobic cellular respiration in both plant and animal cells are (1) mitochondria (2) centrioles (3) chloroplasts (4) nuclei
13. An increase in the concentration of ATP in a muscle cell is a direct result of which life function? (1) respiration (2) reproduction (3) digestion (4) excretion
14. An organelle found within the cell nucleus is a (1) centriole (2) nucleolus (3) chloroplast (4) mitochondrion
15. An organelle that is present in the cells of a mouse but *not* present in the cells of a bean plant is a (1) cell wall (2) chloroplast (3) cell membrane (4) centriole
16. A nonliving cell structure is a (1) cell membrane (2) nucleus (3) cell wall (4) Golgi complex
17. Research how the study of human cells has helped scientists learn how to fight diseases.

METHODS OF CELL STUDY

Compound Light Microscope. A microscope that uses two lenses or sets of lenses to form an enlarged image is called a **compound microscope**. Light passes through the specimen, the objective lens, and the ocular lens, or eyepiece, before reaching the eye. The objective lens produces a magnified image that is further enlarged by the ocular lens.

The main parts of a compound light microscope are shown in Figure 1-2. The functions of these parts are listed in Table 1-2 (page 6).

Magnifying Power and Resolution. The amount of enlargement of the image produced by the lenses of a microscope is the **magnifying power**. For a compound microscope, magnifying power is found by multiplying the magnifying power of the objective lens by the magnifying power of the ocular lens. For example, if the magnifying power of the objective is $40\times$ (40 times) and that of the ocular is $10\times$, the total magnification is $40 \times 10 = 400\times$. The greater the magnification, the smaller the field of vision, or observable area, of the specimen.

Resolution, or **resolving power**, is the capacity of the microscope to show as separate two points that are close together.

Dissecting Microscope. A microscope that has an ocular lens and an objective lens for each eye is called a **binocular**, or **dissecting**, **microscope**. Dissecting microscopes, which produce a three-dimensional image, have relatively low magnifying power, and are used for viewing fairly large, opaque specimens.

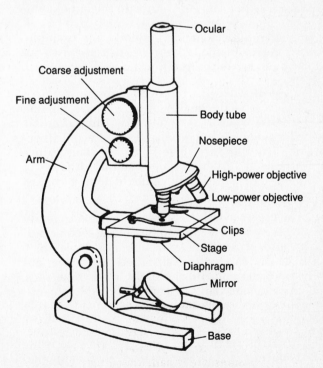

Figure 1-2. The compound light microscope.

Table 1-2. Parts of the Compound Light Microscope and Their Functions

Part	Function
Base	Supports the microscope
Arm	Used to carry microscope; the base, stage, and body tube are attached to the arm
Body tube	Holds the objective lens and eyepiece
Stage	Platform on which the glass slide with the specimen is placed; slide is positioned so that the specimen is over the hole in the stage through which light passes
Clips	Hold the slide in position on the stage
Nosepiece	Holds the objective lenses; rotates so that the different objective lenses can be moved in line with the specimen and eyepiece
Coarse adjustment	Larger knob used for rough-focusing with the low-power objective
Fine adjustment	Smaller knob used for all focusing with the high-power objective and for final focusing with the low-power objective
Mirror	Directs light to the specimen
Diaphragm	Controls the amount of light reaching the specimen
Objective lenses	Lenses mounted on the nosepiece
Ocular lens	Lens at the top of the body tube; commonly known as the *eyepiece*

Phase-Contrast Microscope.

Unstained, living cells can be observed with a phase-contrast microscope, which makes visible parts that cannot be seen with an ordinary light microscope.

Electron Microscope.

The most powerful kind of microscope is the **electron microscope,** which can magnify an object more than 400,000×. Unlike other microscopes, the electron microscope uses an electron beam focused by electromagnets, instead of light and lenses. One disadvantage of the electron microscope is that only dead specimens can be viewed.

Microdissection Instruments.

Tiny instruments that can be used, with the aid of a microscope, to remove or transfer the parts of a cell are **microdissection instruments.** For example, with the use of microdissection instruments, a nucleus can be transferred from one cell to another.

Ultracentrifuge.

The laboratory instrument used to separate small particles or materials on the basis of density is the **ultracentrifuge.** Various cell organelles can be isolated by ultracentrifugation. The ultracentrifuge spins the sample in a test tube at very high speeds so that particles of different densities settle to the bottom of the test tube in layers.

Staining.

Cell structures can be made clearly visible by the use of various staining techniques. Because of differences in chemical makeup, a particular stain will be absorbed only by certain parts of the cell. For example, methylene blue and iodine are stains that are absorbed by the nucleus. Other parts of the cell can be made visible with other stains.

Measurement.

The unit used in measuring structures that can be viewed with a compound light microscope is the **micrometer** (μm). One micrometer equals 0.001 millimeter; 1,000 micrometers equal 1 millimeter. The diameter of the low-power field of a compound light microscope is commonly about 1,500 μm. A paramecium is about 250 micrometers (0.25 millimeter) long. (Measurement with a microscope is discussed in greater detail on page 98.)

QUESTIONS

1. Which of the following plant cell structures could not be seen using the 10× objective of a compound microscope? (1) nucleus (2) cell wall (3) cytoplasm (4) endoplasmic reticulum

2. A microscope reveals one hundred similar cells arranged end-to-end in a space of 1 millimeter. The average length of each cell must be (1) 0.1 micrometer (2) 10 micrometers (3) 100 micrometers (4) 1,000 micrometers

3. Which instrument would provide the most detailed information about the internal structure of a chloroplast? (1) a compound light microscope (2) a phase-contrast microscope (3) an electron microscope (4) an ultracentrifuge

4. If the low-power objective and the eyepiece both have a magnifying power of 10×, the total magnifying power of the microscope is (1) 10× (2) 100× (3) 1× (4) 20×

5. To separate the parts of a cell by differences in density, a biologist would probably use (1) a microdissection instrument (2) an ultracentrifuge (3) a phase-contrast microscope (4) an electron microscope

6. Which microscope magnification should be used to observe the largest field of view of an insect wing? (1) 20× (2) 100× (3) 400× (4) 900×

7. The diameter of the field of vision of a compound light microscope is 1.5 millimeters. This may also be expressed as (1) 15 micrometers (2) 150 micrometers (3) 1,500 micrometers (4) 15,000 micrometers

8. To transplant a nucleus from one cell to another cell, a scientist would use (1) an electron microscope (2) an ultracentrifuge (3) microdissection instruments (4) staining techniques

9. A student using a compound microscope measured the diameters of several red blood cells and found that the average cell length was 0.008 millimeter. What is the average length of a single red blood cell in micrometers? (1) 0.8 (2) 8 (3) 80 (4) 800

10. A student using a compound microscope estimated the diameter of a cheek cell to be 50 micrometers. What is the diameter of this cheek cell in millimeters? (1) 0.050 mm (2) 0.500 mm (3) 5.00 mm (4) 50.9 mm

11. A student has a microscope with a $10\times$ eyepiece and $10\times$ and $40\times$ objectives. She observed 40 onion epidermal cells across the diameter of the low-power field. How many cells would she observe under high power? (1) 1 (2) 40 (3) 10 (4) 4

12. After examining cells from an onion root tip under high power, a student switches to the low-power objective without moving the slide. He would most likely see (1) more cells and less detail (2) more cells and more detail (3) fewer cells and less detail (4) fewer cells and more detail

13. A slide of the letters F and R is placed on the stage of a microscope in the position shown in the diagram below. How would the image of the letters appear when the slide is viewed under the lower power of a compound light microscope?

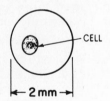

(1) **RF**   (2) **ᖷᴚ**   (3) **ᖴᴚ**   (4) **ᴚᖴ**

14. The diagram below represents the field of vision of a microscope. What is the approximate diameter of the cell shown in the field? (1) 50 micrometers (2) 500 micrometers (3) 1,000 micrometers (4) 2,000 micrometers

CELL

|← 2 mm →|

BIOCHEMISTRY

The chemical reactions necessary to sustain life take place in the cells. The study of the chemical reactions of living things is called **biochemistry**.

Elements.
A substance that cannot be broken down into simpler substances is an **element**. Examples of elements include hydrogen, oxygen, sodium, and potassium. In all, there are about 110

Table 1-3. Some Chemical Elements and Their Symbols

Element	Symbol	Element	Symbol
Carbon	C	Iodine	I
Hydrogen	H	Iron	Fe
Oxygen	O	Calcium	Ca
Nitrogen	N	Sodium	Na
Sulfur	S	Chlorine	Cl
Phosphorus	P	Potassium	K
Magnesium	Mg		

known elements. Table 1-3 lists some of the elements found in living things, along with their chemical symbols.

The most abundant elements in living things are carbon, hydrogen, oxygen, and nitrogen. Elements found in lesser amounts include sulfur, phosphorus, magnesium, iodine, iron, calcium, chlorine, potassium, and others.

Atoms.
All elements are made up of particles called **atoms**. Each element has a different kind of atom.

An atom contains a dense central portion called the **nucleus**. Within the nucleus are positively charged particles called **protons** and electrically neutral particles called **neutrons**. Negatively charged particles called **electrons** are found in the space around the nucleus. The electrons occupy specific energy levels, or shells, at varying distances from the nucleus.

The atoms of different elements differ in the numbers of protons, neutrons, and electrons they contain. Every atom of a given element has the same number of protons in its nucleus. The number of electrons equals the number of protons so that the atom is electrically neutral. For example, oxygen atoms have 8 protons, 8 electrons, and 8 neutrons. Hydrogen atoms have 1 proton, 1 electron, and no neutrons.

A **compound** is formed when two or more elements combine chemically. For example, water (H_2O) is formed by the chemical combination of two hydrogen atoms and one oxygen atom.

Chemical Bonding.
The formation of compounds involves either the transfer or sharing of electrons between atoms, resulting in the formation of **chemical bonds**. When an atom loses or gains electrons, it becomes an electrically charged particle called an **ion**. The force of attraction between oppositely charged ions is called an **ionic bond**. A **covalent bond** is formed when atoms share electrons.

Chemical Formulas.
A chemical formula shows which elements are found in a compound. A **molecular formula** shows how many of each kind of atom are present in a molecule of a compound. A **structural formula** shows how the atoms of a molecule are bonded together. Figure 1-3

shows the molecular and structural formulas for some common compounds.

✳Figure 1-3. Molecular and structural formulas of water (H_2O), carbon dioxide (CO_2), and glucose ($C_6H_{12}O_6$).

Inorganic and Organic Compounds.
There are two basic classes of chemical compounds—inorganic and organic compounds. Both types are found in living things.

Compounds that do not contain both carbon and hydrogen atoms are **inorganic compounds**. Inorganic compounds found in cells include water, salts, carbon dioxide, and inorganic acids, such as hydrochloric acid (HCl).

Compounds that contain both carbon and hydrogen atoms are **organic compounds**. Because carbon atoms can form four covalent bonds with other atoms, organic compounds are often large and complex. The major categories of organic compounds are carbohydrates, proteins, lipids, and nucleic acids. (Nucleic acids—DNA and RNA—are discussed in Unit 5, page 71.)

Carbohydrates.
Sugars and starches, which are used primarily as sources of energy and as food-storage compounds, are **carbohydrates**. These substances are made up of carbon, hydrogen, and oxygen, and the ratio of hydrogen to oxygen is 2 to 1.

Monosaccharides. The simplest carbohydrates are the **monosaccharides**, or **simple sugars**. Glu-cose, galactose, and fructose, each with the formula $C_6H_{12}O_6$, are simple sugars.

Disaccharides. Maltose and sucrose (both $C_{12}H_{22}O_{11}$) are **disaccharides**, sugars whose molecules are made up of two monosaccharide molecules bonded together. For example, a maltose molecule is formed from two glucose molecules bonded together.

Polysaccharides. Complex carbohydrates made up of chains of monosaccharides are **polysaccharides. Starch, cellulose,** and **glycogen** are polysaccharides made up of chains of glucose molecules. Starch is a food-storage compound in plants; cellulose makes up the cell walls of plants; and glycogen is a food-storage compound in animals.

Dehydration Synthesis.
The chemical process by which simple molecules are joined to form larger molecules with the removal of water is called **dehydration synthesis**. In this type of reaction, two molecules are joined by the removal of a hydrogen atom (H) from one molecule and a hydroxyl group (OH) from the other, producing a molecule of water (HOH). The remaining parts of the two molecules become bonded together where the H and OH were removed. Figure 1-4 shows the formation of a disaccharide by dehydration synthesis.

Proteins.
Enzymes, hormones, and various structural parts of organisms are **proteins**. Proteins are made of smaller subunits called **amino acids**.

Structure of Amino Acids. Amino acids contain the elements carbon, hydrogen, oxygen, and nitrogen. Some also contain sulfur. Figure 1-5 shows the generalized structure of an amino acid. The —NH_2 is an **amino group;** the —COOH is a **carboxyl,** or **acid, group;** and the R represents a variable group. The R group is the part of the amino acid structure that differs from one amino acid to another. Twenty different amino acids are found in the cells of living things.

Dipeptides and Polypeptides. Like carbohydrates, amino acids combine chemically by de-

✳Figure 1-4. The formation of maltose by dehydration synthesis.

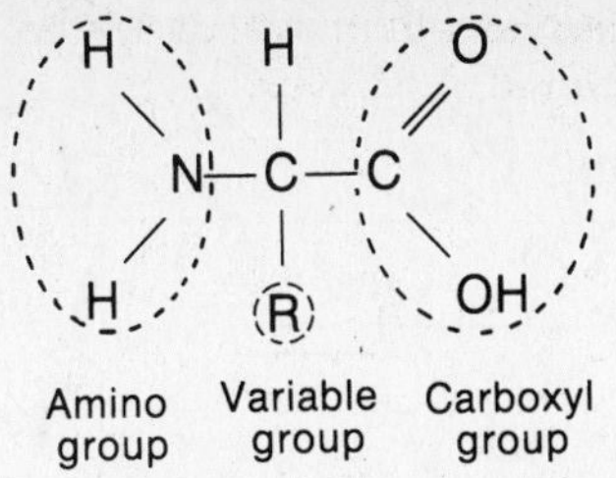

Amino group   Variable group   Carboxyl group

*Figure 1-5. Generalized structure of an amino acid.

hydration synthesis to form more complex molecules. When two amino acids combine by dehydration synthesis, they form a **dipeptide** (Figure 1-6). The bond that holds the amino acids together is called a **peptide bond**. More amino acids may combine by dehydration synthesis with a dipeptide to form a **polypeptide**. A protein is made up of one or more polypeptide chains.

There is a tremendous variety of protein molecules in living things. These molecules differ in the number, kinds, and sequence of amino acids they contain.

Lipids. Fats, oils, and waxes belong to a class of organic compounds called **lipids**. They serve mainly as sources of energy and as components of structures such as cell membranes. Lipids that are solid at room temperature are **fats**, while those that are liquid are **oils**. Lipids contain carbon, hydrogen, and oxygen. The ratio of hydrogen atoms to oxygen atoms is greater than 2 to 1, and varies from one lipid to another.

Lipid molecules are produced in cells by dehydration synthesis. Many lipids consist of one glycerol molecule and three fatty acid molecules. Figure 1-7 shows the formation of a lipid by dehydration synthesis. For each lipid molecule formed, three water molecules are released. Lipids that are made up of fatty acids and an alcohol other than glycerol are called **waxes**.

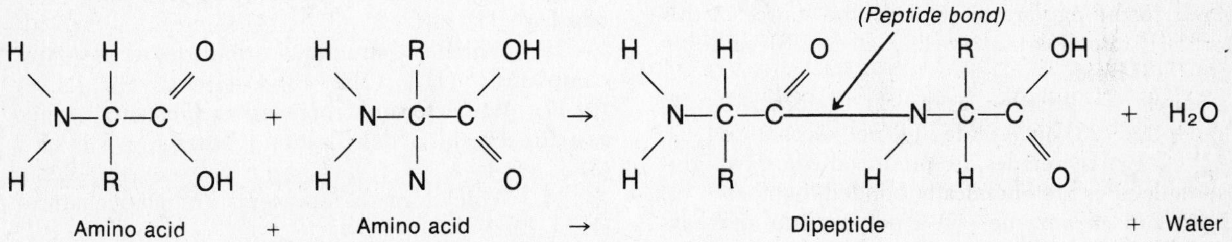

Amino acid   +   Amino acid   →   Dipeptide   +   Water

*Figure 1-6. Formation of a dipeptide by dehydration synthesis.

Glycerol   +   3 Fatty acids   →   Lipid   +   Water

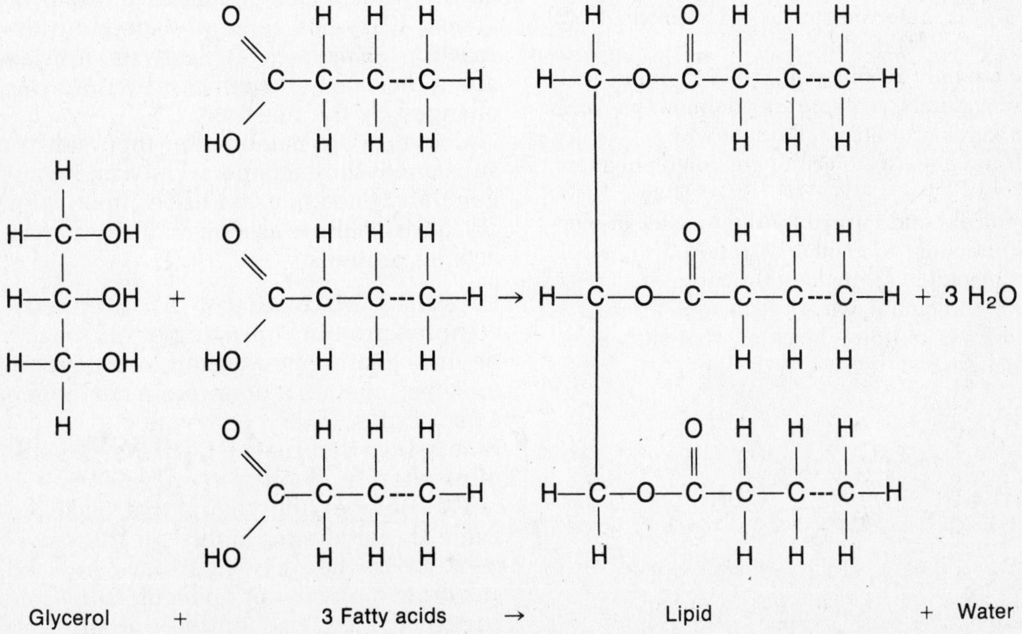

*Figure 1-7. Formation of a lipid by dehydration synthesis.

QUESTIONS

1. What is the principal inorganic solvent in cells? (1) salt (2) water (3) alcohol (4) carbon dioxide

2. Fats that are stored in human tissue contain molecules of (1) glycerol and fatty acids (2) amino acids (3) monosaccharides and disaccharides (4) nucleotides

3. One of the carbon compounds found in a cell has twice as many hydrogen atoms as oxygen atoms. This compound most likely belongs to the group of substances known as (1) nucleic acids (2) lipids (3) proteins (4) carbohydrates

4. Which formula represents an organic compound? (1) NH_3 (2) H_2O (3) $NaCl$ (4) $C_{12}H_{22}O_{11}$

5. When two molecules are joined together chemically, a molecule of water is released. This process is known as (1) dehydration synthesis (2) hydrolysis (3) absorption (4) transpiration pull

6. A rotten egg may give off a foul-smelling gas containing sulfur. Which decomposing chemical compounds in the egg are most likely the source of this odor? (1) proteins (2) nucleic acids (3) carbohydrates (4) lipids

7. Starch is classified as a (1) disaccharide (2) polypeptide (3) nucleotide (4) polysaccharide

8. What two molecules are produced when two glucose molecules are chemically bonded together? (1) a lipid and an enzyme (2) a polypeptide and oxygen (3) a polysaccharide and carbon dioxide (4) a disaccharide and water

9. Which organic compound is correctly matched with the subunit that composes it? (1) maltose—amino acid (2) starch—glucose (3) protein—fatty acid (4) lipid—sucrose

10. A chemical bond in which two atoms share a pair of electrons is referred to as (1) covalent (2) acidic (3) ionic (4) double

11. There are only 20 different kinds of amino acids found in living things, yet there are enormous numbers of different kinds of proteins. Explain why.

12. Starch and protein molecules are called polymers. Explain why.

13. A chemical bond formed by the transfer of electrons from one atom to another is referred to as (1) covalent (2) acidic (3) ionic (4) double

✱ 14. The compound whose structural formula is shown below is a building block of what class of organic compounds?

(1) proteins (2) carbohydrates (3) lipids (4) starches

✱ Base your answers to questions 15 through 18 on the structural formulas shown below.

✱ 15. Which is a structural formula for a component of a fat? (1) 1 (2) 2 (3) 3 (4) 4

✱ 16. Which is a structural formula for an inorganic compound? (1) 1 (2) 2 (3) 3 (4) 4

✱ 17. Which formula represents a substance formed as a direct result of dehydration synthesis? (1) 1 (2) 2 (3) 3 (4) 4

✱ 18. Which formula represents a monosaccharide? (1) 1 (2) 2 (3) 3 (4) 4

ENZYMES

Role of Enzymes.
Chemical reactions occur continuously in living things. Each reaction requires the presence of a special protein called an **enzyme**, which regulates the rate of the reaction. Enzymes generally speed up the rate of reactions. Enzymes are **catalysts**, substances that affect the rates of chemical reactions but are unchanged by the reactions.

Enzymes are named after their **substrates**, the substances they act upon. The name of an enzyme generally ends in *ase*. For example, a lipase acts on lipids, maltase acts on maltose, and a protease acts on proteins.

Enzyme Structure.
An enzyme is a large, complex protein consisting of one or more polypeptide chains. In addition to the protein, some enzymes contain a nonprotein component called a **coenzyme**. If the coenzyme part of an enzyme is missing, the enzyme will not function. **Vitamins** often function as coenzymes.

The polypeptide chains that make up an enzyme are folded in a highly specific way, forming pockets on the enzyme surface into which the substrate molecule or molecules fit. The specific part of the enzyme where the substrate fits is called the **active site**.

Lock-and-Key Model of Enzyme Action.
The mechanism of enzyme action is explained on the basis of a lock-and-key model. The active site on an enzyme has a unique three-dimensional shape that can form a complex only with one type of substrate. The substrate fits the active site as a key fits a lock (Figure 1-8).

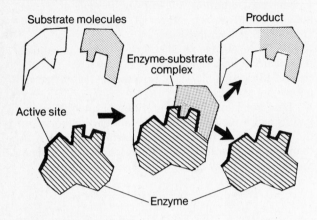

Figure 1-8. Lock-and-key model of enzyme action.

For an enzyme to affect the rate of a chemical reaction, the substrate must become attached to the active site of the enzyme, forming an **enzyme-substrate complex**. The enzyme's action occurs while the enzyme and substrate are bound together. At this time, bonds of the substrate may be weakened, causing it to break apart, or bonds may form between substrate molecules, joining them together. After the reaction is complete, the enzyme and product(s) separate, and the enzyme molecule becomes available to act on other substrate molecules.

Factors Influencing Enzyme Action.
The rate of enzyme action is affected by temperature, concentrations of enzyme and substrate, and pH.

✳ **Temperature.** The rate of enzyme action varies with temperature. Up to a point, the rate increases with increasing temperature (Figure 1-9). The temperature at which the enzyme functions most efficiently is called the **optimum temperature**. If the temperature is raised above the optimum, the rate of enzyme action begins to decrease. The decrease in enzyme action occurs because the higher temperature destroys the three-dimensional shape of the enzyme protein, a process known as **denaturation**. In denaturation, the shape of the enzyme's active site is altered so that it no longer fits the substrate. In humans, the normal body temperature is 37°C, which is also the optimum temperature for most human enzymes. Denaturation of these enzymes begins at about 40°C.

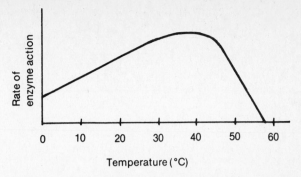

✳Figure 1-9. The effect of changing temperature on the rate of enzyme action.

✳ **Enzyme and Substrate Concentrations.** The rate of enzyme action varies with the amount of available substrate. With a high concentration of enzyme and a low concentration of substrate, the rate of enzyme action increases as the substrate concentration increases (Figure 1-10). At the point where all enzyme molecules are reacting, the rate levels off, and addition of more substrate has no further effect.

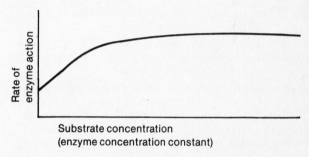

✳Figure 1-10. The effect of changing substrate concentration on the rate of enzyme action.

✳ **pH.** The rate of enzyme action varies with the pH of the environment. The **pH scale** is a measure of the hydrogen ion (H^+) concentration of a solution. Solutions with a pH of 7 are neutral. Those with a pH below 7 are acids, while those with a pH above 7 are bases (Figure 1-11).

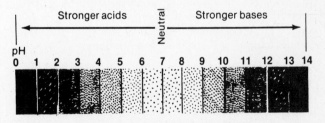

✳Figure 1-11. The pH scale.

✳ Each enzyme has a particular pH at which it functions most efficiently. For example, most enzymes in human blood function best in neutral solutions. Pepsin, an enzyme found in the stomach, works best at a pH of 2. Trypsin, which is found in the small intestine, works most effectively at a pH of 8 (Figure 1-12).

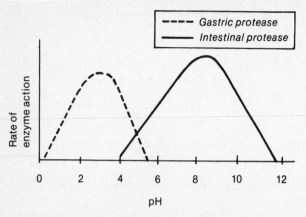

*Figure 1-12. The effect of pH on the rate of enzyme action.

QUESTIONS

1. Which of the following is characteristic of an enzyme? (1) It is an inorganic catalyst. (2) It is destroyed after each chemical reaction. (3) It provides energy for any chemical reaction (4) It regulates the rate of a specific chemical reaction.

2. The "lock-and-key" model of enzyme action illustrates that a particular enzyme molecule (1) forms a permanent enzyme-substrate complex (2) may be destroyed and resynthesized several times (3) interacts with a specific type of substrate molecule (4) reacts at identical rates under all conditions

3. An enzyme-substrate complex may result from the interaction of molecules of (1) glucose and lipase (2) fat and amylase (3) sucrose and maltase (4) protein and protease

4. The part of the enzyme molecule into which the substrate fits is called the (1) active site (2) coenzyme (3) polypeptide (4) protease

5. A nonprotein molecule necessary for the functioning of a certain enzyme is called a (1) catalyst (2) polypeptide (3) coenzyme (4) substrate

6. Which of the following variables has the *least* direct effect on the rate of an enzyme-regulated reaction? (1) temperature (2) pH (3) carbon dioxide concentration (4) enzyme concentration

* Base your answers to questions 7 through 9 on the graph below and on your knowledge of biology. The graph represents the rate of enzyme action when different concentrations of enzyme are added to a system with a fixed amount of substrate.

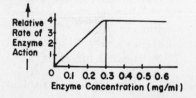

* 7. At which enzyme concentration does all of the available substrate react with the enzyme? (1) 0.1 mg/ml (2) 0.2 mg/ml (3) 0.3 mg/ml (4) 0.05 mg/ml

* 8. When the enzyme concentration is increased from 0.5 mg/ml to 0.6 mg/ml, the rate of enzyme action (1) decreases (2) increases (3) remains the same

* 9. If more substrate is added to the system at an enzyme concentration of 0.4 mg/ml, the rate of the reaction would most likely (1) decrease (2) increase (3) remain the same

* 10. The change in shape of enzyme molecules that occurs at high temperatures is known as (1) synthesis (2) specificity (3) replication (4) denaturation

* Base your answers to questions 11 and 12 on the graphs below. Graph I shows the relationship between the relative rates of activity of enzymes A and B and temperature. Graph II shows the relationship between the rates of activity of enzymes A and B and pH.

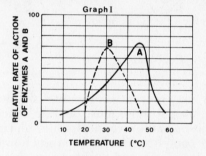

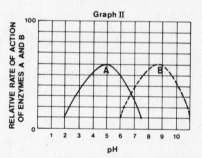

* 11. Under which conditions is enzyme A most effective? (1) at 40°C and a pH of 5 (2) at 45°C and a pH of 5 (3) at 45°C and a pH of 9 (4) at 50°C and a pH of 9

* 12. The optimum environment for enzyme B is (1) a basic medium (2) an acidic medium (3) either an acidic or a basic medium (4) a neutral medium

13. Draw a diagram illustrating how the enzyme maltase combines with two glucose molecules during dehydration synthesis to form maltose. Label the enzyme, the substrate, the enzyme-substrate complex, and the end product.

Maintenance in Living Things

Most living organisms perform the same life functions. They obtain and process food and distribute nutrients and other essential materials to the cells. They get rid of wastes produced by cell metabolism. All of the life functions must be regulated.

Different kinds of organisms have specific structures and behavioral patterns that enable them to perform the life functions efficiently in their own environments. These structures and behavioral patterns are called **adaptations**.

NUTRITION

Nutrition includes those activities by which organisms obtain and process food for use by the cells. The cells use nutrients from foods for energy, growth, repair, and regulation. Nutrition may be autotrophic or heterotrophic. In **autotrophic nutrition**, the organism can synthesize organic substances (nutrients) from inorganic substances obtained from the environment. In **heterotrophic nutrition**, the organism must ingest needed organic substances from other organisms in the environment.

Photosynthesis.
The most common type of autotrophic nutrition is **photosynthesis**, which occurs in all green plants and in some bacteria and protists (including all algae). In photosynthesis, the organism uses carbon dioxide and water taken from the environment and energy from sunlight to synthesize the organic compound glucose. Most of the chemical energy available to living organisms comes directly or indirectly from photosynthesis. Also, most of the oxygen in the air comes from photosynthesis.

Photosynthetic Pigments. Photosynthesis requires the presence of certain colored substances called **pigments**, which "trap" light energy and convert it to a form of chemical energy that can be used by living things. **Chlorophylls** are the green photosynthetic pigments found in most photosynthetic organisms. In most of these organisms, the chlorophyll is found in chloroplasts. In addition to the chlorophylls, chloroplasts may contain a variety of other pigments. These pigments can be separated and identified by a technique called **chromatography**.

White light, such as sunlight, is made up of all different wavelengths of visible light. When chlorophyll is exposed to white light, it absorbs most of the red and the blue wavelengths and reflects green and yellow wavelengths. Because the red and blue wavelengths are absorbed, they are most effective for photosynthesis. Because the green and yellow wavelengths are reflected, they are least effective for photosynthesis. The reflection of these wavelengths gives plants their green color.

Chemistry of Photosynthesis. The process of photosynthesis is complex, involving several series of reactions. However, it can be summarized by the following equation:

$$\text{carbon dioxide} + \text{water} \xrightarrow[\substack{\text{chlorophyll} \\ \text{enzymes}}]{\text{light energy}} \text{glucose} + \text{water} + \text{oxygen}$$

$$6CO_2 + 12H_2O \xrightarrow[\substack{\text{chlorophyll} \\ \text{enzymes}}]{\text{light energy}} C_6H_{12}O_6 + 6H_2O + 6O_2$$

Carbon dioxide and water are the raw materials of photosynthesis. Light energy absorbed by the chlorophyll is converted to chemical energy, which is used to synthesize glucose from the raw materials.

The glucose produced by photosynthesis is used, when needed, as an energy source in cellular respiration. It can also be converted by dehydration synthesis to starch, an insoluble food storage compound. Before starch can be used in any cellular process, it must first be broken down by enzymes within the cell (intracellular digestion) to glucose. The glucose can be used in the synthesis of other organic compounds, such as lipids and proteins.

✱ **Light Reactions.** Detailed studies of photosynthesis have shown that the process has two sets of reactions; the first set requires light, the second does not.
✱ The first set of reactions, known as the **light**, or **photochemical**, **reactions**, takes place in the *grana* of the chloroplasts (Figure 2-1). These

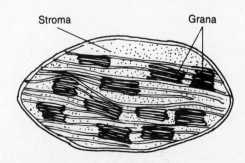

Figure 2-1. The structure of a chloroplast.

stacks of membranes contain the enzymes and chlorophyll necessary for the light reactions. In the light reactions, water is broken down and ATP molecules are produced.

✳ When light energy is absorbed by the chlorophyll, some of it is used to split water molecules, producing hydrogen atoms and oxygen gas (Figure 2-2). The splitting of water using energy from light is called **photolysis**. Studies using the isotope oxygen-18 have shown that all the oxygen given off during photosynthesis comes from the breakdown of water.

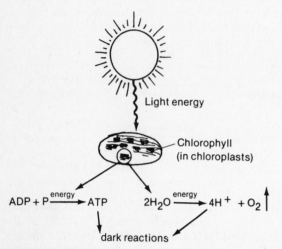

Light energy

Chlorophyll
(in chloroplasts)

$ADP + P \xrightarrow{\text{energy}} ATP$ $2H_2O \xrightarrow{\text{energy}} 4H^+ + O_2\uparrow$

dark reactions

✳**Figure 2-2.** The light reactions of photosynthesis.

✳ In the second part of the light reactions, some of the light energy absorbed by the chlorophyll is used to produce ATP (adenosine triphosphate) from ADP (adenosine diphosphate) and phosphates. The ATP and hydrogen atoms produced by the splitting of water are needed for the second set of reactions of photosynthesis, the dark reactions.

✳ **Dark Reactions.** In the **dark reactions**, also known as the **carbon-fixation reactions**, glucose is synthesized from carbon dioxide and hydrogen atoms (Figure 2-3). The dark reactions take place in the *stroma* of the chloroplasts. The stroma is the dense solution that fills the space outside the

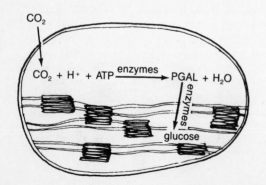

CO_2

$CO_2 + H^+ + ATP \xrightarrow{\text{enzymes}} PGAL + H_2O$

enzymes

glucose

✳**Figure 2-3.** The dark reactions of photosynthesis.

grana. In the dark reactions, carbon dioxide absorbed from the air combines with hydrogen atoms from the light reactions to produce **PGAL**, a three-carbon compound. The energy for these reactions comes from the ATP produced by the light reactions. Glucose and other organic compounds are then synthesized from the PGAL. The process in which inorganic carbon dioxide molecules are converted to organic compounds, such as PGAL, is called *carbon fixation*. The radioactive isotope carbon-14 was used to trace the pathways of the dark reactions.

QUESTIONS

1. By which process are CO_2 and H_2O converted to carbohydrates? (1) transpiration (2) respiration (3) fermentation (4) photosynthesis
2. Which process is represented below?

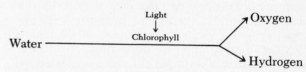

Light

Chlorophyll

Water

Oxygen

Hydrogen

(1) aerobic respiration (2) dehydration synthesis (3) photolysis (4) carbon fixation
3. The conversion of light energy into chemical bond energy occurs within the cells of (1) molds (2) yeasts (3) algae (4) grasshoppers
4. Glucose molecules may be stored in plants in the form of (1) oxygen (2) starch (3) nucleic acids (4) amino acids
5. Knowing that red glass transmits mainly red light, green glass mainly green light, yellow glass mainly yellow light, and orange glass mainly orange light, a student set up an experiment to determine the effect of light color on glucose production. She selected jars of each of the above colors and grew a bean plant in each jar under controlled conditions in the presence of natural light. The greatest amount of glucose would most likely be produced by the bean plant growing in the jar whose color was (1) red (2) yellow (3) green (4) orange
6. Organisms capable of manufacturing organic molecules from inorganic raw materials are classified as (1) autotrophs (2) heterotrophs (3) aerobes (4) anaerobes
7. The basic raw materials for photosynthesis are (1) water and carbon dioxide (2) oxygen and water (3) sugar and carbon dioxide (4) water and oxygen
8. In autotrophic plants, stored starch may be converted into small organic molecules by the process of (1) transpiration (2) aerobic respiration (3) intracellular digestion (4) extracellular digestion
9. Which word equation represents the process of photosynthesis?
(1) carbon dioxide + water → glucose + oxygen + water
(2) glucose → alcohol + carbon dioxide

Reviewing Biology: Unit 2

(3) maltose + water → glucose + glucose

(4) glucose + oxygen → carbon dioxide + water

10. Autotrophic activity in green plant cells is most closely associated with organelles called (1) mitochondria (2) ribosomes (3) vacuoles (4) chloroplasts

11. Bromthymol blue turns to bromthymol yellow in the presence of carbon dioxide. When the carbon dioxide is removed, the solution will return to a blue color. Two green water plants were placed in separate test tubes, each containing water and bromthymol yellow. Both test tubes were corked. One tube was placed in the light, the other in the dark. After several days, the liquid in the tube exposed to the light turned blue.

This demonstration illustrates that, during photosynthesis, green plants (1) take in carbon dioxide (2) need bromthymol blue (3) give off oxygen gas (4) form ATP molecules

12. A functional difference between animals and green plants is that green plants are able to (1) synthesize glucose (2) break down carbohydrates (3) carry on aerobic respiration (4) form ATP molecules

* **13.** Which compound is formed in the process of photosynthesis? (1) DNA (2) PGAL (3) colchicine (4) ammonia

* **14.** A scientist uses the isotope carbon-14 to trace the path of carbon through the reactions of photosynthesis. In which sequence would the carbon-14 most likely be found?

(1) water → free oxygen → glucose

(2) carbon dioxide → pyruvic acid → glucose

(3) carbon dioxide → PGAL → glucose

(4) ammonia → nitrates → plant proteins

* For each statement in questions 15 through 17, select the phrase, chosen from the list below, that is most closely associated with the statement.

Reactions of Photosynthesis

A. photochemical reactions, only

B. carbon-fixation reactions, only

C. both the photochemical and carbon-fixation reactions

D. neither the photochemical nor carbon-fixation reactions

* **15.** Light energy is absorbed by chlorophyll in (1) *A* (2) *B* (3) *C* (4) *D*

* **16.** Oxygen gas is used in (1) *A* (2) *B* (3) *C* (4) *D*

* **17.** Carbon dioxide is used in (1) *A* (2) *B* (3) *C* (4) *D*

* Base your answers to questions 18 through 22 on the word equation below, which represents a summary of the two major sets of reactions occurring during photosynthesis.

* **18.** Which form of energy is absorbed by green plants during phase I? (1) heat energy (2) light energy (3) nuclear energy (4) chemical energy

* **19.** The oxygen present in the water molecule in phase I is (1) released as molecular oxygen (2) released as chemical energy (3) incorporated into PGAL (4) incorporated into glucose

* **20.** Phase II is often referred to as (1) oxidation (2) hydrolysis (3) carbon fixation (4) aerobic respiration

* **21.** A three-carbon sugar formed during phase II is (1) carbon dioxide (2) glucose (3) ATP (4) PGAL

* **22.** The reaction in phase I occurs in the (1) grana (2) stroma (3) Golgi apparatus (4) cell wall

* **23.** Which statement correctly describes part of the photosynthetic process in plants? (1) Oxygen is used in the dark reactions. (2) Carbon dioxide is released in the dark reactions. (3) Water is split in the light reactions. (4) Alcohol is produced by the light reactions.

* **24.** During photosynthesis, molecules of oxygen are liberated from the "splitting" of water molecules due to the (1) dark reactions (2) light reactions (3) formation of PGAL (4) formation of CO_2

25. Summarize the light and dark reactions and discuss how they are dependent on one another.

Adaptations for Photosynthesis.

Algae and green plants are autotrophic organisms that carry on photosynthesis. A large percentage of the earth's photosynthesis occurs in unicellular algae present in the oceans. The raw materials necessary for photosynthesis are absorbed directly from the water into the cells of the algae. Most photosynthesis in terrestrial (land-dwelling) plants occurs in leaves.

Structure of Leaves. Most leaves are thin and flat, providing the maximum surface area for the absorption of light.

The outermost cell layer of the leaf is the **epidermis**, which protects the internal tissues from water loss, mechanical injury, and attack by fungi (Figure 2-4). In some plants, the epidermis is covered by a waxy coating called the **cuticle**, which provides additional protection against water loss and infection.

There are many tiny openings in the epidermis and cuticle, mainly on the undersurface of the leaf. These openings, called **stomates**, allow the exchange of carbon dioxide, oxygen, and water vapor between the environment and the moist, inner tissues of the leaf. Each stomate is surrounded by a pair of chloroplast-containing **guard**

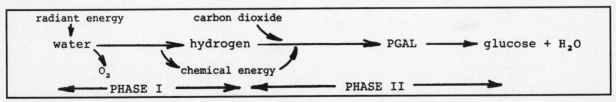

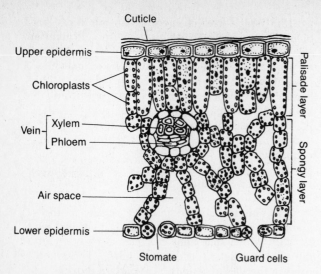

Figure 2-4. Cross section of a leaf.

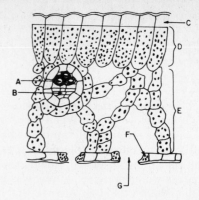

4. Which letter indicates the area where carbon dioxide passes out of the leaf? (1) A (2) G (3) C (4) D

5. Which letter indicates a structure that regulates the size of a stomate? (1) A (2) B (3) F (4) G

6. Water and dissolved nutrients are carried by the tissues labeled (1) D and E (2) C and D (3) A and B (4) E and F

7. Explain why a cactus's leaves are not broad and flat but are reduced in size in the form of spines.

8. How is the leaf adapted for carrying on photosynthesis? Include the roles of the parts of a leaf in your answer.

Heterotrophic Nutrition.

Organisms that cannot synthesize organic molecules from inorganic raw materials are **heterotrophs,** and must obtain preformed organic molecules from the environment. Heterotrophic organisms include most bacteria, some protists, and all fungi and animals. Heterotrophic nutrition involves the processes of ingestion, digestion, and egestion. Heterotrophic nutrition generally begins with the mechanical breakdown of food, during which large pieces of food are broken down into smaller pieces by cutting, grinding, and tearing. The smaller pieces provide greater surface area for the action of enzymes during chemical digestion.

Digestion. In some heterotrophs, such as protists, chemical digestion is **intracellular**—it occurs within the cells of the organism. In most heterotrophs, however, digestion is **extracellular**—it occurs in a sac or tube outside the cells. The end products of digestion are absorbed into cells.

Enzymatic Hydrolysis. Large, insoluble food molecules are broken down into smaller, soluble molecules by the enzyme-regulated process of **hydrolysis.** Hydrolysis is the reverse of dehydration synthesis (page 33). In hydrolysis, large molecules are broken down into small ones by the addition of water.

The end products of enzymatic hydrolysis are similar in all organisms: carbohydrates are broken down into simple sugars; lipids are broken down into fatty acids and glycerol; and proteins are broken down into amino acids.

Some molecules in the food of heterotrophs are indigestible. They cannot be digested because the necessary enzymes are not present. Other

cells. By changing shape, the guard cells open or close the stomate opening.

Beneath the upper epidermis is the **palisade layer,** which is made up of tall, tightly packed cells filled with chloroplasts. Most of the photosynthetic activity of the leaf occurs in this layer. The cells of the epidermis are clear, so that light striking the leaf passes through to the chloroplasts in the palisade layer.

Between the palisade layer and the lower epidermis of the leaf is the **spongy layer,** which is made up of loosely arranged cells separated by interconnecting air spaces. The air spaces are continuous with the stomates. Gases from the environment enter the leaf through the stomates, then diffuse from the air spaces into the cells. Other gases diffuse out of the cells into the air spaces and then out of the leaf through the stomates. The cells of the spongy layer contain chloroplasts and carry on some photosynthesis.

The conducting tissues of the leaf are found in bundles called **veins.** The conducting tissues carry water and dissolved minerals from the roots through the stems to the leaves, and they carry food from the leaves to the rest of the plant.

QUESTIONS

1. Water is lost from the leaves of a plant through (1) lenticels (2) root hairs (3) veins (4) stomates

2. The waxy covering over the surface of a leaf is the (1) cuticle (2) epidermis (3) palisade layer (4) spongy layer

Base your answers to questions 3 through 6 on the following diagram, which shows a leaf cross section, and on your knowledge of biology.

3. Which letter indicates the principal region of food manufacture? (1) E (2) B (3) C (4) D

foods may not remain in the digestive tract long enough for digestion to be completed. Indigestible and undigested foods are eliminated from the organism.

QUESTIONS

1. During chemical digestion, large food molecules are broken down to smaller molecules by the process of (1) synthesis (2) absorption (3) hydrolysis (4) excretion
2. Based on their pattern of nutrition, most animals are classified as (1) autotrophic (2) heterotrophic (3) photosynthetic (4) phagocytic
3. Which occurs as a result of the action of hydrolytic enzymes? (1) Inorganic substances are converted directly to organic substances. (2) Complex organic molecules are made more soluble. (3) Glucose molecules are converted to starches. (4) Glucose molecules are converted to maltase molecules.
4. Which is an example of enzyme-controlled intracellular digestion? (1) An ameba digests a microorganism within its food vacuole. (2) A human digests food mechanically within its stomach. (3) A grasshopper digests a piece of grass within its intestine. (4) An earthworm grinds food within its gizzard.
5. A fruit fly is classified as a heterotroph, rather than as an autotroph, because it is unable to (1) transport needed materials through the body (2) release energy from organic molecules (3) manufacture its own food (4) divide its cells mitotically
6. What are the end products of carbohydrate hydrolysis? (1) amino acids (2) simple sugars (3) hydrogen ions (4) fatty acids
7. The principal function of mechanical digestion is the (1) hydrolysis of food molecules for storage in the liver (2) production of more surface area for enzyme action (3) synthesis of enzymes necessary for food absorption (4) breakdown of large molecules to smaller ones by the addition of water
8. The process by which digestive enzymes catalyze the breakdown of larger molecules with the addition of water is known as (1) synthesis (2) pinocytosis (3) hydrolysis (4) photosynthesis
9. The end products of protein digestion are (1) amino acids (2) fatty acids (3) simple sugars (4) nucleotides
10. How does mechanical digestion aid the process of chemical digestion?
11. Compare the processes of dehydration synthesis and hydrolysis. What is the function of each process in an organism?

Adaptations for Heterotrophic Nutrition.
Heterotrophs obtain nutrients in various ways.

Fungi. Fungi live in or on their food supply. For example, bread molds live on bread, and mushrooms live on decaying trees. The body of a fungus consists of a mass of threads, or filaments (Figure 2-5). Specialized filaments called *rhizoids* grow into the food, where they secrete hydrolytic enzymes. The end products of digestion are absorbed into the cells of the rhizoids and then diffuse into the other cells of the organism.

Protists. In protists such as the ameba and paramecium, digestion is intracellular. In the ameba, food particles are surrounded and engulfed by extensions of the cell called **pseudopods** (Figure 2-6). This process is known as **phagocytosis.**

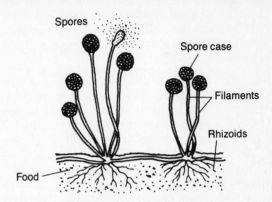

Figure 2-5. Bread mold.

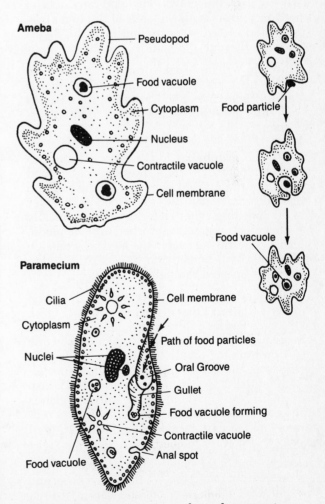

Figure 2-6. Nutrition in ameba and paramecium.

Within the cell, the food particle is enclosed in a **food vacuole**. In the paramecium, food particles are ingested through a fixed opening called the *oral groove*. They are moved into the oral groove by the beating of **cilia**. The food particles are then enclosed in a food vacuole, which circulates in the cytoplasm.

In both the ameba and paramecium, the food vacuole merges with a lysosome, which contains digestive enzymes. The food within the vacuole is digested by these enzymes, and the end products of digestion are then absorbed into the cytoplasm. In the ameba, wastes are expelled from the cell through the cell membrane. In the paramecium, wastes are expelled through a fixed opening called the *anal pore*.

Hydra. The hydra has a saclike digestive cavity with a single opening, the mouth (Figure 2-7). The body of the hydra is only two cell layers thick. Food is pushed into the digestive cavity by the *tentacles* that surround the mouth. Extracellular digestion takes place when cells in the lining of the digestive cavity secrete enzymes directly into the cavity. Phagocytic cells in the lining of the cavity engulf the partially digested food, and digestion is then completed intracellularly (within the cells). The end products of digestion diffuse to all the cells of the organism. Undigested material is expelled from the digestive cavity through the mouth.

Earthworm. The earthworm has a tubelike digestive tract with two openings: the mouth and the anus (Figure 2-8). Food is digested as it passes in one direction through the organs of the digestive tract.

Food is ingested through the **mouth** and passes through the **esophagus** to the **crop**, where it is stored temporarily. From the crop, the food passes into the **gizzard**, where it is crushed and broken down mechanically. The food next passes into the **intestine**, where it is digested chemically and the end products are absorbed into the blood. Because digestion occurs in the food tube outside of the cells, it is considered to be extracellular. Wastes are egested through the **anus**.

Grasshopper. The digestive system of the grasshopper is similar to that of the earthworm (Figure 2-9). There is a food tube with specialized digestive organs and two openings. Food moves in one direction from the mouth to the anus. Unlike the earthworm, the grasshopper has highly specialized mouthparts for cutting and tearing food. Also present in the grasshopper are **salivary glands** and **gastric caeca**, which secrete hydrolytic enzymes into the food tube for chemical digestion.

Human. The human digestive system is essentially like that of the grasshopper and earthworm. Food moves in one direction through a tube, and specialized organs carry out mechanical breakdown and chemical digestion.

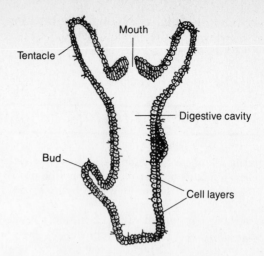

Figure 2-7. Nutrition in hydra.

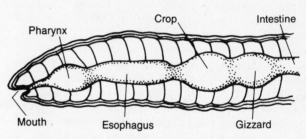

Figure 2-8. Digestive system of the earthworm.

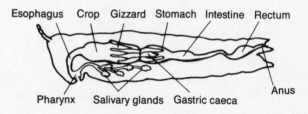

Figure 2-9. Digestive system of the grasshopper.

QUESTIONS

1. An organism with a one-way digestive tube is the (1) paramecium (2) earthworm (3) ameba (4) hydra

2. In paramecia, most intracellular hydrolysis occurs within structures known as (1) ribosomes (2) endoplasmic reticula (3) mitochondria (4) food vacuoles

3. Which organism ingests food by engulfing it with pseudopods? (1) grasshopper (2) paramecium (3) earthworm (4) ameba

4. Which organism *lacks* a one-way (tube-within-a-tube) digestive system? (1) hydra (2) earthworm (3) grasshopper (4) human

5. The grinding action on food that occurs in the gizzard of a grasshopper is an example of which nutritional process? (1) ingestion (2) egestion (3) chemical digestion (4) mechanical digestion

Base your answers to questions 6 through 8 on the diagrams below of an earthworm and a hydra and on your knowledge of biology.

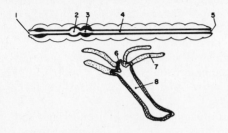

6. Most hydrolysis of foods occurs in structures (1) 1 and 6 (2) 2 and 3 (3) 4 and 6 (4) 4 and 8
7. Ingestion occurs through structures (1) 1 and 6 (2) 2 and 8 (3) 3 and 4 (4) 5 and 7
8. Which structure functions in the mechanical digestion of food? (1) 1 (2) 6 (3) 3 (4) 7
9. Which statement concerning the digestive processes in the ameba and the hydra is true? (1) Digestion does not require water in either organism. (2) Digestion occurs by extracellular methods in both organisms. (3) Digestion occurs by intracellular methods in both organisms. (4) Digestion does not require enzymes in either organism.
10. Distinguish between intracellular and extracellular digestion.
11. How is digestion in the earthworm and the grasshopper similar?

TRANSPORT

Transport involves the absorption of materials through cell membranes and into the body fluids and the circulation of materials throughout an organism.

The Cell Membrane.
The cell membrane surrounds the cell and regulates the passage of materials into and out of the cell.

Structure of the Cell Membrane. A currently accepted model of the structure of the cell membrane is called the *fluid mosaic model*. According to this model, the cell membrane consists of a double layer of lipid in which large protein molecules float (Figure 2-10).

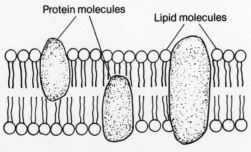

Figure 2-10. The fluid mosaic model of cell membrane structure.

Function of the Cell Membrane. The cell membrane selectively regulates the passage of substances into and out of the cell. Small molecules, including water, carbon dioxide, oxygen, and the soluble end products of digestion, pass easily through the cell membrane. Most larger molecules, such as proteins and starch, cannot pass through the cell membrane. However, molecular size is not the only factor that affects passage through the cell membrane.

Diffusion and Passive Transport.
All ions and molecules are in constant random motion. When such particles collide, they bounce off each other and travel in new directions. As a result of their motion and collisions, the particles tend to spread out from an area of high concentration to an area of low concentration, a process known as **diffusion**. The difference in concentration between two such areas is known as the **concentration gradient**.

Molecules and ions that can pass through the cell membrane tend to move into or out of the cell by diffusion. The direction of diffusion depends on the relative concentration of the substance inside and outside the cell. Diffusion is a type of **passive transport**; it occurs because of the kinetic energy of the molecules and ions, and does not require the use of additional energy by the cell.

The diffusion of water through a membrane is called **osmosis**. In osmosis, water molecules move from a region of higher concentration of water to a region of lower concentration of water.

Active Transport.
Active transport processes involve the movement of particles through a membrane with the use of energy by the cell. In some cases, substances are moved by active transport from a region of lower concentration to a region of higher concentration (against the concentration gradient). In active transport, protein molecules embedded in the cell membrane act as carriers that aid in the transport of materials across the membrane.

Pinocytosis and Phagocytosis.
Large, dissolved molecules can pass through the cell membrane by the process of **pinocytosis** (Figure 2-11). In pinocytosis, the cell membrane folds inward. The outer surface of the cell membrane then closes over, and the large molecule is enclosed within a vacuole inside the cell.

Phagocytosis is a process in which a cell engulfs undissolved, large particles by flowing around them and enclosing them in a vacuole. Amebas engulf food particles by phagocytosis.

Circulation.
Circulation involves the movement of materials both within cells and throughout multicellular organisms. The movement of materials within a cell, *intracellular circulation*, takes place by diffusion and by cyclosis. **Cyclosis** is a natural streaming of the cytoplasm that occurs

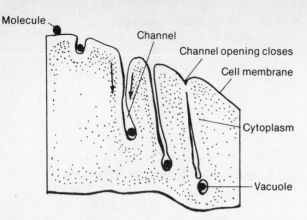

Figure 2-11. Pinocytosis.

within all cells. Intracellular circulation may also involve the movement of materials through the channels of the endoplasmic reticulum. The transport of materials throughout multicellular organisms is called *intercellular circulation*. Depending on the complexity of the organism, intercellular circulation may occur by diffusion or it may involve a specialized circulatory system with conducting, or vascular, tissues.

QUESTIONS

1. Which process would include a net movement of sugar molecules through a membrane from a region of lower concentration to a region of higher concentration? (1) osmosis (2) cyclosis (3) active transport (4) passive transport

2. In the human body, the potassium ion can pass easily through cell membranes, yet the potassium ion concentration is higher inside many cells than it is outside these cells. This condition is mainly a result of the process of (1) passive transport (2) active transport (3) osmosis (4) pinocytosis

3. Chemical analysis indicates that the cell membrane is composed mainly of (1) proteins and starch (2) proteins and cellulose (3) lipids and starch (4) lipids and proteins

4. The net flow of materials through the membrane of a cell against a concentration gradient is known as (1) passive transport (2) active transport (3) osmosis (4) pinocytosis

5. A biologist observed a plant cell in a drop of water and illustrated it as in diagram A. He added a 10% salt solution to the slide, observed the cell, and illustrated it as in diagram B.

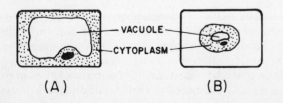

The change in appearance of the cell resulted from more (1) salt flowing out of the cell than into the cell (2) salt flowing into the cell than out of the cell (3) water flowing into the cell than out of the cell (4) water flowing out of the cell than into the cell

6. The natural streaming of the cytoplasm that occurs within all cells is called (1) pinocytosis (2) phagocytosis (3) osmosis (4) cyclosis

7. When a cell uses energy to move materials across a cell membrane, the process is known as (1) osmosis (2) active transport (3) diffusion (4) passive transport

8. The diffusion of water molecules into and out of cells is called (1) cyclosis (2) pinocytosis (3) osmosis (4) homeostasis

9. The net movement of molecules into cells is most dependent upon the (1) selectivity of the plasma membrane (2) selectivity of the cell wall (3) number of nucleoli (4) number of chromosomes

10. A red blood cell placed in distilled water will swell and burst due to the diffusion of (1) salt from the red blood cell into the water (2) water into the red blood cell (3) water from the blood cell into its environment (4) salts from the water into the red blood cell

Base your answers to questions 11 and 12 on your knowledge of biology and on the diagram below, which illustrates a process by which protein molecules may enter a cell.

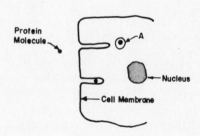

11. Which process is illustrated in this diagram? (1) pinocytosis (2) osmosis (3) diffusion (4) passive transport

12. Structure A is most likely a (1) ribosome (2) mitochondrion (3) nucleolus (4) vacuole

13. The process by which amebas ingest food particles is called (1) pinocytosis (2) osmosis (3) phagocytosis (4) cyclosis

14. Distinguish between active and passive transport.

15. Research and describe the circumstances in which human body cells perform active transport.

Transport in Plants.
The transport of materials in plants involves cyclosis, osmosis, diffusion, and active transport. Some plants contain specialized transport, or vascular, tissues, while others do not.

Bryophytes are simple, multicellular plants that lack vascular tissues. They live in a moist environment, and water and other substances are exchanged between the cells and the external environment by diffusion. Intracellular transport is accomplished by diffusion and cyclosis. Mosses and liverworts are bryophytes.

The **tracheophytes** have specialized vascular tissues for intercellular transport. These tissues are found in the roots, stems, and leaves of the plant. Tracheophytes include ferns, conifers, and flowering plants.

Roots. Roots are structures that are specialized for the absorption of water and minerals from the soil and the conduction of these materials to the stem. Roots also anchor the plant in the soil and may contain stored nutrients in the form of starch.

The surface area of the root for absorption is increased by the presence of **root hairs** just behind the growing tip (Figure 2-12). Water and minerals from the soil are absorbed through the membranes of the root hairs by osmosis, diffusion, and active transport. Materials are transported throughout the plant by two kinds of vascular tissues, **xylem** and **phloem.**

Transport in the Xylem. Water and dissolved materials are carried upward from the roots to the stems and leaves in the xylem. Xylem consists of tubes made up of thickened cell walls of dead, hollow cells. The water in the xylem forms a continuous column that extends from the roots into the stems and leaves. The water molecules in the column are held together by the forces of *cohesion* (the attractive force between like molecules) and *adhesion* (the attractive force between unlike molecules). Water vapor evaporates from the leaves through the stomates, a process called **transpiration.** The evaporation of water from the leaves is thought to pull the column of water in the xylem upward. This upward force, called **transpirational pull,** is thought to be the main mechanism that allows water to move from the roots to the tops of tall trees.

Transport in the Phloem. Dissolved food and other organic substances are transported from the leaves throughout the rest of the plant in the phloem. Food stored in the roots is also transported throughout the plant in the phloem. Phloem tissue is made of living cells that form continuous conducting tubes. Materials can move in either direction in the phloem, and some of the movement involves active transport.

Stems. Although the structure of stems is more complex than that of roots, the xylem and phloem of the stem are continuous with the xylem and phloem of the roots.

Leaves. The xylem and phloem of the leaves, which are in bundles called veins, are continuous with the xylem and phloem of the roots and stem.

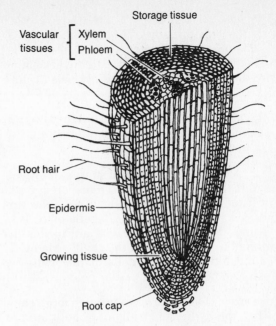

Figure 2-12. Structure of a root tip.

QUESTIONS

1. The primary function of root hairs in a plant is to (1) prevent excessive loss of water (2) provide increased surface area for absorption (3) conduct water and minerals upward (4) conduct organic food materials upward and downward

2. Which structures are found in the veins of a maple leaf? (1) phloem cells (2) guard cells (3) chloroplasts (4) capillaries

3. The mechanism by which water moves from the roots to the leaves of a tall tree is known as (1) evaporation (2) transpiration (3) adhesion (4) transpirational pull

4. The destruction of xylem tissues in a maple tree most directly interferes with the movement of (1) carbon dioxide out of the leaves (2) water to the leaves (3) oxygen out of the leaves (4) nutrients down to the roots

5. The tissue that conducts organic food throughout a vascular plant is composed of (1) cambium cells (2) xylem cells (3) phloem cells (4) epidermal cells

6. The process by which water evaporates from the leaves of a plant is called (1) cohesion (2) respiration (3) active transport (4) transpiration

7. The dissolved sugars produced in the leaves of a maple tree move to the tree's roots through the (1) xylem (2) phloem (3) epidermis (4) guard cells

8. When a living geranium plant is enclosed in a large jar, water droplets appear on the inner surface of the jar. These water droplets are most likely the direct result of (1) hydrolysis and photosynthesis (2) light absorption and reflection (3) transpiration and condensation (4) intracellular and extracellular digestion

Transport in Protists.

Protists and other unicellular organisms have no specialized transport system. Materials enter and leave the cell by diffusion and active transport, and are circulated within the cell by diffusion and cyclosis (Figure 2-13).

Transport in Animals.

All but the simplest animals have a specialized system for the transport of materials.

Hydra. The hydra, which is a simple, multicellular animal, has no specialized transport system. All of its cells are in direct contact with the surrounding water (Figure 2-14). Flagellated cells in the lining of the digestive cavity aid in the circulation of materials within the cavity. Materials are circulated within the cells of the hydra by cyclosis and diffusion.

Earthworm. The earthworm is much more complex than the hydra, and many of its cells are not in direct contact with the external environment. The earthworm has an internal, closed circulatory system that transports materials throughout the animal (Figure 2-15). In a **closed circulatory system**, needed materials and metabolic wastes are dissolved in blood contained within a system of vessels. The blood of the earthworm contains the red pigment **hemoglobin**, which carries respiratory gases between the external environment and the body cells. Blood is moved through the vessels by the pumping of five pairs of *aortic arches*, or "hearts." The exchange of materials between the blood and the body cells takes place through the membranes of the smallest blood vessels, the capillaries.

The digestive tube of the earthworm has an infolding (the *typhlosole*) that increases the surface area for absorption of nutrients into the blood.

Grasshopper. The grasshopper has an internal, open circulatory system (Figure 2-16). In an **open circulatory system**, a pulsating blood vessel acts as a heart and pumps the blood into a blood vessel called the *aorta*. From the aorta, the blood passes into large cavities, or *sinuses*, where it bathes the cells. The exchange of materials between the blood and the body cells takes place while the blood is in the sinuses. Eventually, the blood reenters the pulsating blood vessel through valves. The blood of the grasshopper does not contain hemoglobin, and respiratory gases are not transported in the blood.

The digestive tube of the grasshopper, like that of the earthworm, has an infolding that increases the surface area for the absorption of nutrients from the intestine into the blood.

Human. The human circulatory system is a closed system. Blood is moved through vessels by the pumping action of the heart. Human blood contains hemoglobin, which carries oxygen to the body tissues. As in the earthworm and grasshopper, the human intestine has infoldings that increase the surface area for absorption.

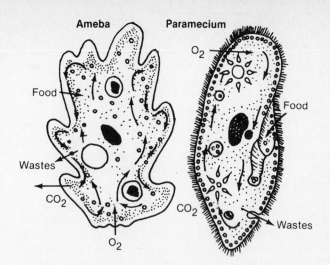

Figure 2-13. Transport in ameba and paramecium.

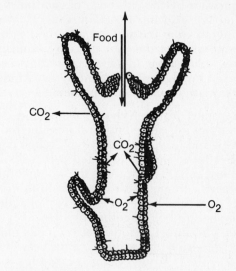

Figure 2-14. Transport in hydra.

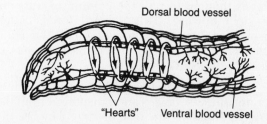

Figure 2-15. Circulatory system of the earthworm.

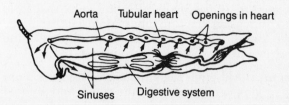

Figure 2-16. Circulatory system of the grasshopper.

1. The circulatory system of the earthworm is most similar in structure and function to that of a (1) hydra (2) protozoan (3) grasshopper (4) human
2. Which organism contains an open circulatory system? (1) earthworm (2) grasshopper (3) hydra (4) ameba
3. How are nutrients transported from the blood of an earthworm to the muscle cells of its body wall? (1) The blood flows directly into the muscle cells. (2) The nutrients diffuse through capillary walls and through the cell membranes. (3) The nutrients pass through pores at the ends of nephridia. (4) The nutrients diffuse through the skin from the outside environment.
4. Which organism has an internal, closed circulatory system that brings materials from the external environment into contact with its cells? (1) ameba (2) paramecium (3) hydra (4) earthworm
5. Materials are circulated within the cells of a hydra by (1) osmosis, only (2) osmosis and diffusion (3) cyclosis and diffusion (4) a transport system
6. Hemoglobin is found in the blood of (1) humans and earthworms (2) earthworms and grasshoppers (3) grasshoppers and humans (4) humans, only
7. A circulatory system in which the blood remains within vessels is called a(n) (1) closed circulatory system (2) open circulatory system (3) internal circulatory system (4) external circulatory system
8. The intestinal fold of the earthworm and the villi of the human small intestine function primarily to (1) increase the surface area for absorption of digested nutrients (2) excrete metabolic wastes (3) circulate blood (4) force the movement of food in one direction through the digestive tract
9. Pairs of aortic arches are found in the circulatory system of the (1) hydra (2) grasshopper (3) earthworm (4) paramecium
10. Compare and contrast the circulatory systems of the earthworm and the human. Why are both referred to as closed systems?

RESPIRATION

The life processes of all organisms require energy. Although there is potential energy in the chemical bonds of organic molecules such as glucose, this energy cannot be used directly in cell metabolism. The only usable form of energy for most living cells is the chemical energy in the bands of the energy-transfer compound **ATP** (*adenosine triphosphate*). Respiration is the process by which chemical bond energy in nutrients is used to synthesize ATP. Respiration occurs continuously in all cells of all organisms.

Cellular Respiration.
Cellular respiration involves a series of enzyme-controlled reactions in which the chemical bond energy released by the breakdown of glucose is transferred to the high-energy bonds of ATP. When ATP is hydrolyzed (broken down by hydrolysis), **ADP** (*adenosine diphosphate*) and phosphate (P) are produced, and energy is released. This energy is used for the reactions of cell metabolism.

The conversion of ATP to ADP is a reversible reaction catalyzed by the enzyme ATP-ase.

$$H_2O + ATP \xrightleftharpoons{ATP\text{-ase}} ADP + P + energy$$

In living organisms, ATP is constantly being converted to ADP, and the energy released is used in metabolism. The ADP is then converted back to ATP by the reactions of cellular respiration.

Anaerobic Respiration. In most organisms, cellular respiration requires the presence of free oxygen, and the process is known as **aerobic respiration.** In a few kinds of organisms, free oxygen is not used, and the process is known as **anaerobic respiration,** or **fermentation.** Some cells, such as muscle cells, that normally carry on aerobic respiration can carry on anaerobic respiration in the absence of oxygen. Other cells, such as yeast and some bacteria, that carry on anaerobic respiration lack the enzymes necessary for aerobic respiration.

During anaerobic respiration, glucose is partially broken down in a series of enzyme-controlled reactions. The end products of these reactions are most commonly either lactic acid or alcohol and carbon dioxide. However, different kinds of organisms produce still other end products. Regardless of the end product, there is a net gain of 2 ATP molecules for each glucose molecule broken down by anaerobic respiration.

$$glucose \xrightarrow{enzymes} 2 \text{ lactic acid} + 2 \text{ ATP}$$

$$glucose \xrightarrow{enzymes} 2 \text{ alcohol} + 2 \text{ CO}_2 + 2 \text{ ATP}$$

Lactic acid fermentation takes place in the skeletal muscles of animals when adequate free oxygen is unavailable, for example, during strenuous exercise. The buildup of lactic acid produces fatigue. Some bacteria also carry on lactic acid fermentation. These bacteria are used to produce cheese, buttermilk, yogurt, and dill pickles. Alcoholic fermentation takes place in some bacteria and in yeast cells. Alcoholic fermentation is used in the production of alcoholic beverages and in baking, where the carbon dioxide released causes the dough to rise.

Because glucose is only partly broken down in anaerobic respiration, the end products, including lactic acid, alcohol, and other organic compounds, still contain much of the potential chemical energy of the original glucose molecule.

✻ Chemistry of Anaerobic Respiration. In the initial reactions of anaerobic respiration, the 6-carbon glucose molecule is converted to two molecules of the 3-carbon compound pyruvic acid.

The first steps of this conversion require the use of 2 ATP. In later steps, 4 ATP are produced. Therefore, the conversion of glucose to pyruvic acid results in a net gain of 2 ATP. Depending on the type of organism in which the reactions occur, pyruvic acid is then converted either to lactic acid or to alcohol and carbon dioxide. These reactions do not yield any additional ATP molecules.

$$\text{glucose} + 2\text{ ATP} \xrightarrow{\text{enzymes}} 2\text{ pyruvic acid} + 4\text{ ATP}$$

or

2 lactic acid   2 alcohol + 2 carbon dioxide

Aerobic Respiration. In aerobic respiration, glucose is broken down completely to carbon dioxide and water by a series of enzyme-controlled reactions. These reactions, which take place mainly in the mitochondria, produce a net gain of 36 ATP molecules.

$$\text{glucose} + \text{oxygen} \xrightarrow{\text{enzymes}} \text{water} + \text{carbon dioxide} + \text{ATP}$$

$$C_6H_{12}O_6 + 6\,O_2 \xrightarrow{\text{enzymes}} 6\,H_2O + 6\,CO_2 + 36\,\text{ATP}$$

✳ Chemistry of Aerobic Respiration. The initial reactions of aerobic respiration are the same as those of anaerobic respiration: one glucose molecule is converted to two molecules of pyruvic acid, and no oxygen is used. This is called the anaerobic phase of aerobic cellular respiration. As in anaerobic respiration, there is a net gain of 2 ATP from these reactions.

✳ In the aerobic phase that follows, the pyruvic acid molecules are completely oxidized to carbon dioxide and water. Energy is released and used to synthesize 34 ATP. Water is formed when hydrogen atoms from the pyruvic acid molecules combine with oxygen. Carbon dioxide molecules are produced as a result of some intermediate reactions in the breakdown of pyruvic acid.

✳ The complete breakdown of glucose by aerobic respiration is much more efficient than the partial breakdown of glucose by anaerobic respiration. Aerobic respiration produces a net gain of 36 ATP molecules from each glucose molecule, while anaerobic respiration produces a net gain of only 2 ATP. The equation below summarizes the relationship between the anaerobic and aerobic phases of aerobic cellular respiration.

QUESTIONS

1. Which compounds are produced in human muscle cells as a result of the oxidation of glucose in the absence of oxygen? (1) lipase and water (2) sucrase and carbon dioxide (3) ethyl alcohol and ATP (4) lactic acid and ATP

2. Most animals make energy available for cell activity by transferring the potential energy of glucose to ATP. This process occurs during (1) aerobic respiration, only (2) anaerobic respiration, only (3) both aerobic and anaerobic respiration (4) neither aerobic nor anaerobic respiration

3. Which of the following processes releases the greatest amount of energy? (1) the oxidation of one glucose molecule to lactic acid molecules (2) the oxidation of one glucose molecule to carbon dioxide and water molecules (3) the conversion of two glucose molecules to a maltose molecule (4) the conversion of one glucose molecule to alcohol and carbon dioxide molecules

4. Alcohol fermentation and aerobic respiration are similar in that both processes (1) utilize light (2) produce ethyl alcohol (3) require free oxygen (4) release carbon dioxide

5. Respiratory enzymes are present in (1) animal cells, but not plant cells (2) plant cells, but not animal cells (3) neither animal nor plant cells (4) both animal and plant cells

6. In animal cells, the energy to convert ADP to ATP comes directly from (1) hormones (2) sunlight (3) organic molecules (4) inorganic molecules

7. Vigorous activity of human voluntary muscle tissues may result in the production of lactic acid. Insufficient amount of which gas would result in the buildup of lactic acid in muscle cells? (1) carbon dioxide (2) nitrogen (3) oxygen (4) hydrogen

8. The organelles in which most of the reactions of aerobic cellular respiration take place are (1) ribosomes (2) chloroplasts (3) lysosomes (4) mitochondria

✳ 9. Anaerobic respiration of glucose is a less efficient energy-releasing system than aerobic respiration of glucose. One of the reasons for this is that in anaerobic respiration (1) lactic acid contains much unreleased potential energy (2) water contains much released potential energy (3) oxygen serves as the final hydrogen acceptor (4) chlorophyll is hydrolyzed into PGAL molecules

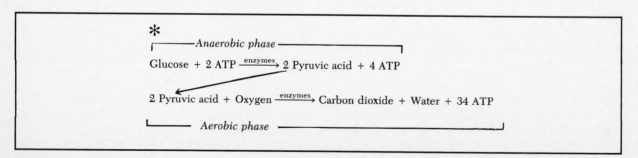

$$2\ ATP + C_6H_{12}O_6 \rightarrow 2\ \text{pyruvic acid} + 4\ ATP$$

2 lactic acid   2 alcohol + 2 CO_2

* **10.** This series of reactions includes the process known as (1) digestion (2) dehydration synthesis (3) fermentation (4) hydrolysis

* **11.** The substances that most directly control the rate of these reactions are known as (1) enzyme molecules (2) oxygen molecules (3) neurotransmitters (4) disaccharides

* **12.** Which organic molecule is represented by $C_6H_{12}O_6$? (1) starch (2) glucose (3) chlorophyll (4) cellulose

* **13.** Which end product is of greatest benefit to the organism in which these reactions occur? (1) lactic acid (2) alcohol (3) pyruvic acid (4) ATP

* Base your answers to questions 14 through 18 on the diagram below, which represents a cellular process in animals, and on your knowledge of biology.

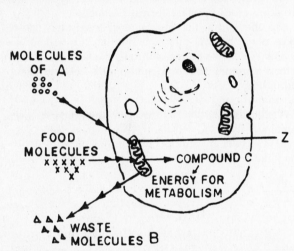

* **14.** The substance labeled "food" is most likely molecules of (1) starch (2) glucose (3) urea (4) chlorophyll

* **15.** Compound *C* most likely represents molecules of (1) oxygen (2) glucose (3) ATP (4) DNA

* **16.** If this cell is carrying on aerobic respiration, *B* represents molecules of a waste product known as (1) carbon dioxide (2) ATP (3) ethyl alcohol (4) pyruvic acid

* **17.** If this represents a kidney cell from the human body, the molecules of *A* are most probably (1) carbon dioxide (2) enzymes (3) lipids (4) oxygen

* **18.** The cell organelle labeled *Z* is known as (1) chloroplast (2) mitochondrion (3) nucleolus (4) vacuole

* **19.** Why must more advanced organisms carry on aerobic respiration?

Adaptations for Respiration.
The oxygen used in aerobic cellular respiration comes from the environment, and the carbon dioxide produced must be excreted into the environment. Although the chemical processes of respiration are similar in most organisms, living things show a variety of adaptations for the exchange of these respiratory gases.

Monera, Protists, and Fungi. In the monera, protists, and fungi, which are very simple organisms, all or most of the cells are in contact with the environment. The exchange of respiratory gases takes place by diffusion through the thin, moist cell membranes (Figure 2-17).

Plants. In plants, respiratory gases are exchanged through the leaves, stems, and roots.

The outer covering of a leaf is dry and impermeable to gases and liquids; it is not a surface for gas exchange. The exchange of respiratory gases occurs by diffusion through the cell membranes of internal cells, which are surrounded by the most intercellular spaces of the spongy layer. The intercellular spaces open to the environment through the stomates, mainly on the undersurface of the leaf. Tiny openings called **lenticels** are found in the stems of woody plants. Respiratory gases are exchanged through the lenticels. In the roots, gas exchange occurs by diffusion through the thin, moist membranes of the cells of the root hairs.

Hydra. The hydra is a simple animal, and all of its cells are in direct contact with the water of its environment. Respiratory gases are exchanged by diffusion between each cell and the environment (Figure 2-18).

Earthworm. In the earthworm, the exchange of respiratory gases takes place by diffusion through the thin skin, which is kept moist by the secretion of mucus (Figure 2-19). The skin contains many capillaries. Blood passing through these capillaries picks up oxygen and gives off carbon dioxide. The presence of hemoglobin increases the capacity of the blood to carry oxygen.

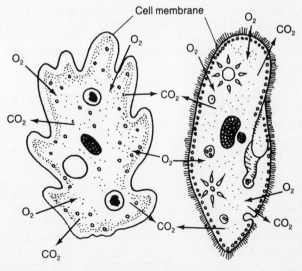

Figure 2-17. Exchange of respiratory gases in protists.

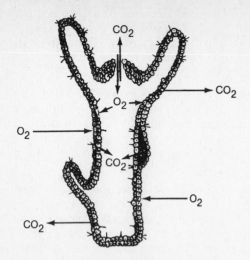

Figure 2-18. Exchange of respiratory gases in hydra.

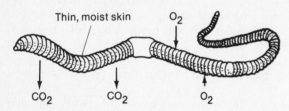

Figure 2-19. Exchange of respiratory gases in the earthworm.

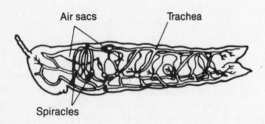

Figure 2-20. Exchange of respiratory gases in the grasshopper.

Grasshopper. In the grasshopper, respiratory gases are not carried in the blood. Instead, they are carried by a system of **tracheal tubes**, or *tracheae*, that open to the environment through small holes in the exoskeleton called **spiracles** (Figure 2-20). Within the grasshopper, the tracheal tubes terminate at the moist membranes of the body cells, where respiratory gases are exchanged. Air sacs help to pump air through the tracheal tubes. Except for the spiracles, the outer body surface of the grasshopper is dry and impermeable to liquids and gases.

Human. In humans, the exchange of respiratory gases takes places at thin, moist membranes within the lungs. Hemoglobin aids in the transport of oxygen in the blood. Carbon dioxide and oxygen are carried between the respiratory surface in the lungs and the environment by a system of air tubes.

QUESTIONS

1. The tracheal tubes of the grasshopper and the air spaces of a geranium leaf are similar in that they both (1) regulate the flow of urea into and out of the organism (2) are the major sites for the ingestion of nutrients (3) contain enzymes that convert light energy to chemical bond energy (4) are surrounded by moist internal surfaces where gas exchange occurs

2. In the earthworm, the exchange of gases with the external environment occurs through the (1) skin (2) lungs (3) nephridia (4) pharynx

3. Protists obtain oxygen from the environment through (1) spiracles (2) cell membranes (3) contractile vacuoles (4) mitochondria

4. Openings in plant tissues that allow the exchange of respiratory gases are (1) tracheae and spiracles (2) spiracles and lenticels (3) lenticels and stomates (4) spiracles and stomates

5. The mucus secreted by cells of the external body wall of the earthworm (1) acts as a stimulus upon the paired nephridia (2) permits transpiration to be accomplished (3) is an excretory waste product (4) provides a moist surface for gas exchange

6. In the hydra, the exchange of respiratory gases takes place by (1) diffusion through the cell membranes (2) active transport through the skin (3) pinocytosis through the cell membranes (4) diffusion through lenticels

7. Identify and describe the respiratory surfaces in the protozoa, hydra, earthworm, grasshopper, and human.

8. How is the grasshopper able to survive without hemoglobin?

EXCRETION

The metabolic activities of living cells produce waste materials. The life process by which the wastes of metabolism are removed from the body is excretion.

Wastes of Metabolism.
The wastes of various metabolic processes are shown in Table 2-1.

Some wastes are toxic, or poisonous, while others are nontoxic. In animals, toxic wastes are excreted from the body; in plants, toxic wastes are sealed off and stored, sometimes in vacuoles. Some nontoxic wastes are excreted, while others are recycled and used in metabolic activities.

Nitrogenous, or nitrogen-containing, wastes are produced by the breakdown of amino acids. Different kinds of organisms produce different kinds of nitrogenous wastes, including **uric acid**, which is nontoxic; **urea**, which is moderately toxic; and **ammonia**, which is highly toxic.

Adaptations for Excretion.
In the simplest organisms, wastes pass from the cells directly into the environment. More complex organisms have a specialized excretory system.

Table 2-1. The Waste Products of Metabolism

Metabolic Activity	Wastes
Respiration	Carbon dioxide and water
Dehydration synthesis	Water
Protein metabolism	Nitrogenous wastes
Certain metabolic processes	Mineral salts

Protists. In general, the excretion of wastes in protists is accomplished by diffusion through the cell membrane (Figure 2-21). In freshwater protozoans, such as the ameba and paramecium, water continuously enters the cell by osmosis. In these organisms, the excess water collects in organelles called **contractile vacuoles**. The contractile vacuoles burst at the surface of the cell, expelling the water back into the environment. This process involves active transport.

In freshwater protozoans, the nitrogenous waste product is ammonia. Although it is very toxic, ammonia is also very soluble in water, and thus it can be easily excreted from the cells of these organisms.

In photosynthetic protists, such as algae, some of the carbon dioxide produced by cellular respiration can be recycled and used in photosynthesis. Some of the oxygen produced by photosynthesis can be used in cellular respiration.

Plants. In plants, as in algae, some of the gases produced by photosynthesis and cellular respiration are recycled. Excess gases diffuse out of the plant through the stomates of the leaves, the lenticels of the stems, and the epidermal cells of the roots.

Hydra. All the cells of the hydra are in contact with the water, and excretion takes place by diffusion through the cell membranes (Figure 2-22). As in freshwater protozoans, the nitrogenous waste product is ammonia.

Earthworm. In the earthworm, carbon dioxide is excreted by diffusion through the thin, moist skin. Water, mineral salts, and urea are excreted by pairs of excretory organs called **nephridia**, which are found in most body segments (Figure 2-23). Wastes are filtered out of the body fluid by the nephridia and excreted through pores into the environment.

Grasshopper. In the grasshopper, carbon dioxide from the body cells diffuses into the body fluids and then into tracheal tubes. It leaves the body through the spiracles. Water, mineral salts, and uric acid crystals accumulate in the **Malpighian tubules**, which are the excretory organs (Figure 2-24). From the Malpighian tubules, the wastes pass into the digestive tube, where most of the water is reabsorbed. Minerals and solid

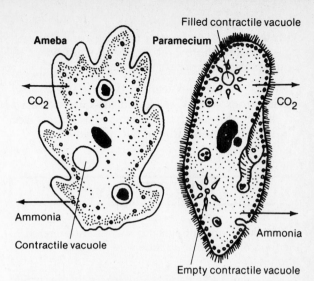

Figure 2-21. Excretion in ameba and paramecium.

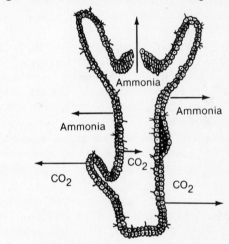

Figure 2-22. Excretion in hydra.

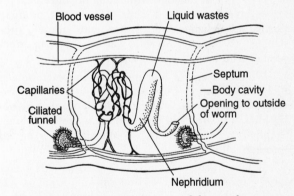

Figure 2-23. Excretory system of the earthworm.

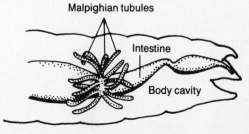

Figure 2-24. Excretory system of the grasshopper.

uric acid crystals are eliminated from the body with the digestive wastes. Uric acid is insoluble in water, and the excretion of the solid waste is an adaptation for conserving water.

Human. In humans, carbon dioxide is excreted by the lungs. Water, salts, and urea are excreted by the nephrons of the kidneys; nephrons are similar to the nephridia of earthworms.

QUESTIONS

1. In the hydra, nitrogenous wastes are excreted in the form of (1) urea (2) uric acid (3) ammonia (4) nitrates

2. An organism containing Malpighian tubules would most likely have (1) a four-chambered heart (2) an endoskeleton (3) an open circulatory system (4) a contractile vacuole

3. Metabolic wastes of animals most likely include (1) water, carbon dioxide, oxygen, and salts (2) carbon dioxide, nitrogenous compounds, water, and salts (3) hormones, water, salts, and carbon dioxide (4) glucose, carbon dioxide, nitrogenous compounds, and water

4. Which activity could produce nitrogenous waste products? (1) protein metabolism (2) glucose metabolism (3) alcoholic fermentation (4) starch hydrolysis

5. The leaf structures closely associated with both transpiration and excretion are (1) lenticels (2) stomates (3) waxy surfaces (4) elongated epidermal cells

6. A hydra can function without an organized excretory system because its cells (1) do not produce wastes (2) change all wastes into useful substances (3) remove only solid wastes (4) are in direct contact with a water environment

7. Which statement best describes the excretion of nitrogenous wastes from paramecia? (1) Urea is excreted by nephrons. (2) Uric acid is excreted by nephridia. (3) Urea and uric acid are excreted through Malpighian tubules. (4) Ammonia is excreted through cell membranes.

8. Which organism is correctly paired with its excretory structure? (1) earthworm—nephridium (2) ameba—skin (3) grasshopper—nephron (4) hydra—Malpighian tubule

9. Most toxic products of plant metabolism are stored in (1) lenticels (2) vacuoles (3) stomates (4) chloroplasts

10. In freshwater protozoans, the organelles involved in the maintenance of water balance in the cell are the (1) food vacuoles (2) ribosomes (3) contractile vacuoles (4) pseudopods

11. In what ways are nephridia similar to nephrons in structure and function?

REGULATION

Regulation involves the control and coordination of life activities. In all organisms, there are chemicals that regulate life activities. In multicellular animals, there is nerve control in addition to chemical control. Both chemical and nerve control aid in the maintenance of homeostasis in living organisms.

Nerve Control. Nerve control depends mainly on the functioning of nerve cells, or **neurons**, which are specialized for the transmission of impulses from one part of the body to another.

Structure of a Neuron. The three parts of a neuron are the **dendrites**; the **cell body**, or *cyton*; and the **axon** (Figure 2-25). Dendrites generally have many branches, but the axon usually branches only at the end farthest from the cell body. Impulses are received by the dendrites and pass to the cell body, which contains the nucleus and other organelles. From the cell body, impulses pass down the axon to its terminal branches.

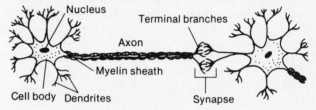

Figure 2-25. Structure of a neuron.

Impulses. An **impulse** is a region of electrical and chemical change that travels over the membrane of a nerve cell. When impulses reach the terminal branches of an axon, they stimulate the release of chemicals called **neurotransmitters**.

Neurotransmitters and Synapses. The junction between adjacent neurons is called a **synapse**. At the synapse, the neurons do not touch; there is a small gap between them (Figure 2-26). When impulses reach the terminal branches of the axon of one neuron, they stimulate the release of chemical neurotransmitters, such as acetylcholine, which diffuse across the gap of the synapse. The neurotransmitter stimulates impulses in the den-

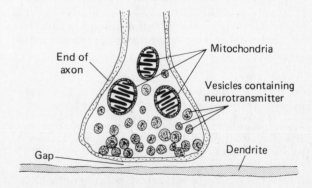

Figure 2-26. Structure of a synapse.

drites of the second neuron. In this way, impulses pass from one neuron to another.

The axons of some neurons have junctions with a muscle or a gland. In such cases, the chemical released by the terminal branches of the axon stimulates contraction of the muscle or secretion by the gland.

Stimulus and Receptors.   Any change in the external or internal environment that initiates impulses is called a **stimulus** (plural, *stimuli*). Stimuli are detected by specialized structures called **receptors**. Each kind of receptor is sensitive to a particular kind of stimulus; for example, eyes are sensitive to light, ears to sound.

Responses and Effectors.   The reaction of an organism to a stimulus is called a **response**. The response itself is carried out by **effectors**, generally muscles or glands.

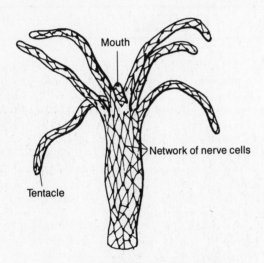

Figure 2-27. Nerve net of a hydra.

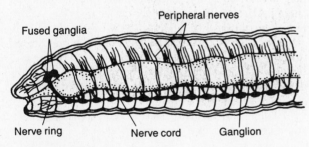

Figure 2-28. Nervous system of the earthworm.

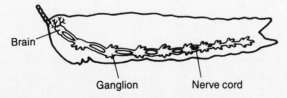

Figure 2-29. Nervous system of the grasshopper.

Adaptations for Nerve Control.   Even the simplest animals have some type of neurons that transmit impulses.

Hydra.   The transmission of impulses in the hydra is carried out by modified neurons that form a **nerve net** throughout the animal (Figure 2-27). There is no brain or control center in this system, and when any neuron is stimulated, impulses travel over the nerve net in all directions.

Earthworm.   The nervous system of the earthworm includes a primitive **brain** and a **nerve cord**, which make up the **central nervous system** (Figure 2-28). The brain is located in the head end of the animal and consists of fused **ganglia** (masses of nerve cells). The nerve cord is connected to the brain and runs along the lower, or *ventral*, side of the worm with a ganglion in each segment. Extending from the brain and nerve cord are **peripheral nerves**, which serve all parts of the body. In the earthworm, impulses travel in one direction over definite pathways.

Grasshopper.   The nervous system of the grasshopper is similar to that of the earthworm; there is a central nervous system and peripheral nerves. Unlike the earthworm, the grasshopper has highly developed sense receptors (Figure 2-29). The receptors include eyes, tympana (for sound), and antennae (for touch).

Human.   Humans have a central nervous system consisting of a highly developed brain and a *dorsal* nerve cord (a nerve cord that runs down the back). There is a peripheral nervous system consisting of an elaborate network of nerves. The central nervous system permits impulses to travel in one direction along definite pathways. There are many highly developed sense organs.

QUESTIONS

1. When a tentacle of a hydra is touched with a needle, the entire body responds as a result of impulses traveling to all cells through the   (1) central nervous system   (2) spinal cord   (3) brain   (4) nerve net

2. Animal cells that are specialized for conducting electrochemical impulses are known as   (1) neurons   (2) synapses   (3) nephrons   (4) neurotransmitters

3. A hawk gliding over a field suddenly dives toward a moving rabbit. The hawk's reaction to the rabbit is known as a   (1) stimulus   (2) synapse   (3) response   (4) tropism

4. Neurotransmitters, such as acetylcholine, are initially detected by which part of a neuron?   (1) dendrite   (2) nucleus   (3) terminal branch   (4) mitochondrion

5. The transmission of nerve impulses at synapses involves chemicals called   (1) auxins   (2) neurotransmitters   (3) enzymes   (4) nucleic acids

6. A central nervous system is present in (1) hydras and humans (2) paramecia and hydras (3) earthworms and grasshoppers (4) amebas and humans

7. Which organism has a nervous system consisting of a simple anterior "brain" and a ventral nerve cord? (1) an earthworm (2) a hydra (3) an ameba (4) a human

8. The central nervous system of a grasshopper is most similar in structure to the central nervous system of (1) a hydra (2) a human (3) an ameba (4) an earthworm

9. Which organism possesses a dorsal nerve cord? (1) hydra (2) human (3) paramecium (4) earthworm

10. The nucleus of a neuron is found in the (1) dendrite (2) axon (3) synapse (4) cell body

11. Structures that detect stimuli are called (1) effectors (2) receptors (3) synapses (4) cell bodies

12. Distinguish between the central nervous system and the peripheral nervous system. What is the function of each?

Chemical Control.

In both plants and animals, various aspects of the life activities are controlled by chemicals called **hormones**.

Plant Hormones. In plants, there are no organs specialized for the production of hormones. Plant hormones are produced in greatest abundance in the cells of actively growing regions, such as the tips of roots and stems and in buds and seeds. The hormones produced in these regions affect the growth and development of cells in other parts of the plant. The effects of hormones vary with their concentration and with the type of tissue being acted on.

Auxins are plant hormones that influence the division, elongation, and differentiation of plant cells. Unequal distribution of auxins in the tissues of the plant result in unequal growth responses called **tropisms**. Unequal auxin distribution can be caused by external stimuli, such as light and gravity, that come primarily from one direction. Tropisms generally increase the plant's chances of survival.

A commonly observed tropism is **phototropism**, the growth of a plant toward a light source (Figure 2-30). In this case, the concentration of auxins in the side of the stem away from the light is higher than in the side nearer the light. The cells of the darker side grow faster than those of the lighter side, causing the stem to bend toward the light.

The growth response of a plant to gravity is called **geotropism**. In most plants, roots tend to grow downward and stems upward in response to the force of gravity.

Other kinds of plant hormones influence flowering, fruit formation, and seed development.

Animal Hormones. Unlike plants, many animals have organs specialized for the synthesis and secretion of hormones. These organs, called **endocrine glands** or **ductless glands**, release their secretions directly into the bloodstream. Hor-

Figure 2-30. Phototropism.

mones are found in a wide variety of animals, both invertebrates and vertebrates. Metabolic activities, including metamorphosis and reproduction, are controlled by hormones.

QUESTIONS

1. The secretions of endocrine glands are known as (1) enzymes (2) hormones (3) neurotransmitters (4) pigments

2. The unequal distribution of auxins in plants results from (1) polyploidy (2) body cell mutations (3) synthesis of chlorophyll molecules (4) stimuli such as light and gravity

3. Geranium leaves grow in positions that permit the optimum use of light as a result of (1) phototropic responses (2) capillary action (3) transpirational pull (4) symbiotic relationships

4. Roots respond to gravity as a result of the unequal distribution of (1) stomates (2) oxygen (3) lenticels (4) auxins

5. A chemical injected into a tadpole caused the tadpole to undergo rapid metamorphosis into a frog. This chemical was most probably (1) an enzyme (2) a neurotransmitter (3) a hormone (4) a blood protein

6. The two systems that directly control homeostasis in most animals are the (1) nervous and endocrine systems (2) endocrine and excretory systems (3) nervous and locomotive systems (4) excretory and locomotive systems

7. Explain the following statement: Tropisms generally increase a plant's chances of survival.

LOCOMOTION

Locomotion is the ability to move from place to place. Among many protists and animals, locomotion increases the organism's chance to survive. It improves chances of finding food and shelter, avoiding predators and other dangers, and finding a mate.

Adaptations for Locomotion.

Many protists and almost all animals are capable of some form of locomotion. Such organisms are said to be *motile*.

Protists. There are three basic forms of locomotion among protists. In the ameba, locomotion is by **ameboid motion**, in which the cell cytoplasm flows into extensions of the cell called pseudopods, causing the organism to move in the direction of the newly formed pseudopod (Figure 2-31). In the paramecium, locomotion involves cilia, which are short, hairlike organelles that cover the outer surface of the cell. The cilia wave back and forth in a coordinated way, moving the cell through the water. Some algae and other protozoans move by means of **flagella**, long, hairlike organelles that can pull the cell through the water.

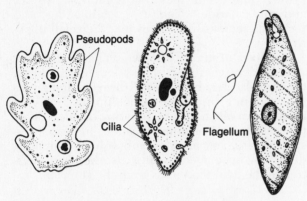

Figure 2-31. Locomotion in protists.

Hydra. The hydra is generally a **sessile** organism—it tends to remain in one place fastened to a plant stem or another structure. However, it does have fibers that have the capacity to contract. These fibers permit some motion, including a type of somersaulting.

Earthworm. Locomotion in the earthworm involves two sets of muscles and **setae**, which are bristles found in pairs on the underside of most segments of the worm (Figure 2-32). The setae anchor the worm in the soil, while the muscles enable the worm to move by lengthening and shortening its body.

Figure 2-32. Locomotion in the earthworm.

Grasshopper. The grasshopper has an external skeleton, or **exoskeleton**, made of *chitin*, a polysaccharide. Locomotion is accomplished by the interactions of muscles with the jointed, chitinous appendages of the exoskeleton. The appendages of a grasshopper include three pairs of legs and two pairs of wings (Figure 2-33).

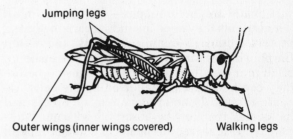

Figure 2-33. Locomotion in the grasshopper.

Human. Humans have an internal skeleton, or **endoskeleton**. Locomotion is accomplished by the interaction of muscles and jointed appendages.

QUESTIONS

1. Which organism is essentially a sessile animal? (1) ameba (2) grasshopper (3) earthworm (4) hydra
2. Which organism moves by the interaction of muscles and chitinous appendages? (1) hydra (2) paramecium (3) grasshopper (4) human
3. Locomotion does *not* increase an animal's opportunity to (1) obtain food (2) reproduce (3) escape from predators (4) transmit impulses
4. Which organism possesses an internal skeleton? (1) earthworm (2) grasshopper (3) human (4) hydra
5. Which two organisms are able to move due to the interaction of muscular and skeletal systems? (1) earthworm and human (2) grasshopper and hydra (3) hydra and earthworm (4) grasshopper and human
6. Setae are structures for locomotion used by the (1) paramecium (2) earthworm (3) ameba (4) hydra
7. Which structures are *not* associated with locomotion in protozoa? (1) flagella (2) pseudopodia (3) cilia (4) tentacles
8. List several advantages of locomotion.
9. Some organisms are sessile, or incapable of movement. How then is their survival insured?

Human Physiology

NUTRITION

Humans are heterotrophs—they must ingest the nutrients they need, including carbohydrates, proteins, lipids, vitamins, minerals, and water. Carbohydrates, lipids, and proteins are made up of large molecules that must be digested before they can be absorbed and used by the cells. Vitamins, minerals, and water are made up of small molecules that can be absorbed without digestion. Nutritional requirements of humans depend on the age, sex, and activity of the individual.

The Human Digestive System.

The human digestive system consists of a one-way digestive tube called the **gastrointestinal,** or GI, **tract** and accessory organs (Figure 3-1). Food is moved through the GI tract by rhythmic, muscular contractions called **peristalsis.** As food moves through the tract, it is broken down mechanically and chemically. The accessory organs, including the liver, gallbladder, and pancreas, secrete enzymes and other substances that aid in digestion into the digestive tract.

Oral Cavity. The mouth, or **oral cavity,** contains the teeth, tongue, and openings from the salivary glands. Food is ingested through the mouth, and digestion begins there.

The teeth function in the mechanical breakdown of food into smaller pieces that provide a larger surface area for the action of digestive enzymes.

The **salivary glands** secrete **saliva,** a fluid that passes into the mouth through ducts. Saliva contains an enzyme, **amylase,** that begins the digestion of starch.

The tongue aids in chewing and in mixing saliva with the food by moving the food around in the mouth. The tongue also moves the food mass to the back of the mouth for swallowing.

Esophagus. When food is swallowed, it passes into the esophagus, and peristalsis of the esophagus wall moves it downward to the stomach. Digestion of starch continues while the food is in the esophagus.

Stomach. Food reaching the lower end of the esophagus enters the stomach, a muscular sac in which it is mixed and liquefied. **Gastric glands** in the stomach lining secrete **hydrochloric acid** and the enzyme **gastric protease.** Hydrochloric acid provides the proper pH (acid medium) required for effective functioning of gastric protease, which begins the digestion of proteins.

Small Intestine. Partially digested food moves from the stomach into the **small intestine,** a long, convoluted tube in which most digestion occurs. The walls of the small intestine are lined with **intestinal glands** that secrete several different enzymes. These enzymes digest proteins, lipids, and disaccharides. The liver, gallbladder, and pancreas secrete substances into the small intestine.

The **liver** produces **bile,** which passes into the **gallbladder,** where it is stored temporarily. From the gallbladder, bile passes through ducts into the small intestine, where it acts on fats, breaking them down mechanically into tiny droplets. This process, known as **emulsification,** increases the surface area of fats for subsequent chemical digestion by enzymes. Bile also helps to neutralize the acid food mass from the stomach.

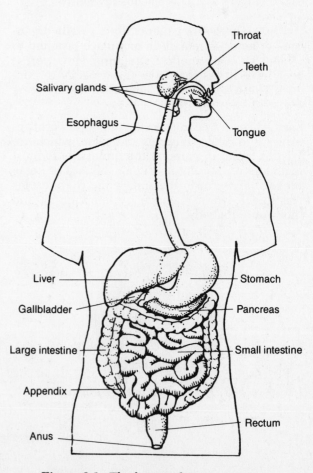

Figure 3-1. The human digestive system.

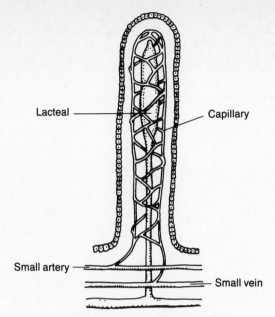

Figure 3-2. Structure of a villus.

The **pancreas** produces and secretes a juice that passes through ducts into the small intestine. Proteases, lipases, and amylase in pancreatic juice, together with the enzymes secreted by the intestinal glands, complete the chemical digestion of proteins, lipids, and carbohydrates in the small intestine.

The end products of digestion, including amino acids, fatty acids, glycerol, and glucose, are absorbed through the lining of the small intestine. The intestinal lining is specially adapted for absorption. Its surface area is greatly increased by many folds and by fingerlike projections called **villi** (singular, *villus*).

Each villus contains a lacteal and capillaries (Figure 3-2). A **lacteal** is a small vessel of the lymphatic system (page 37). Fatty acids and glycerol are absorbed into the lacteals; they are transported in the lymph, which is eventually added to the blood. Glucose and amino acids are absorbed into the blood of the capillaries and transported to the liver for temporary storage. From the liver, glucose and amino acids are distributed by the blood to all the cells as they are needed.

When excess glucose is removed from the blood in the liver, it is converted to glycogen, an insoluble polysaccharide, and stored. When the concentration of glucose in the blood drops below a certain level, the glycogen is broken down to glucose, which is then returned to the blood. The storage of excess glucose as glycogen is an adaptation for the maintenance of a constant blood glucose level and is an example of homeostasis.

Large Intestine. Undigested and indigestible foods and water move from the small intestine into the **large intestine**, which is shorter and wider than the small intestine. In the large intestine, water is reabsorbed from the undigested food into the capillaries in the wall of the large intestine. Reabsorption helps the body to conserve water. The remaining wastes, called **feces**, are moved through the large intestine by strong peristaltic action to the **rectum**, where it is stored temporarily. Feces is periodically egested from the body through the anus.

Mechanism of Chemical Digestion.

In digestion, large, insoluble molecules are broken down into small, soluble molecules by the process of hydrolysis. Each of the many hydrolytic reactions of digestion is regulated by a specific hydrolytic enzyme.

Chemically, hydrolysis is the opposite of dehydration synthesis; large molecules are split with the addition of water. Figure 3-3 shows the hydrolysis of the disaccharide maltose into two glucose molecules. In a series of reactions, polysaccharides, such as starch, are also broken down by hydrolysis to monosaccharides.

In the presence of water and protein-digesting enzymes (proteases), proteins are broken down into their constituent amino acids (Figure 3-4). In the hydrolysis of proteins, peptide bonds are broken.

In the presence of water and lipid-digesting enzymes (lipases), lipid molecules are broken down by hydrolysis into fatty acids and glycerol (Figure 3-5).

Maltose + Water $\xrightarrow{\text{Maltase}}$ Glucose + Glucose

✳Figure 3-3. Hydrolysis of maltose.

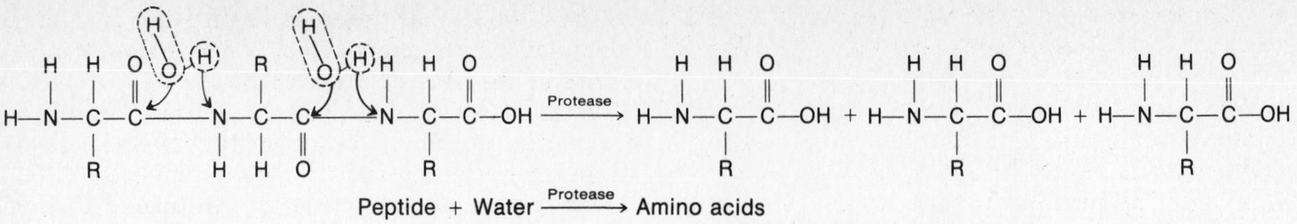

$$\text{Peptide} + \text{Water} \xrightarrow{\text{Protease}} \text{Amino acids}$$

*Figure 3-4. Hydrolysis of a protein.

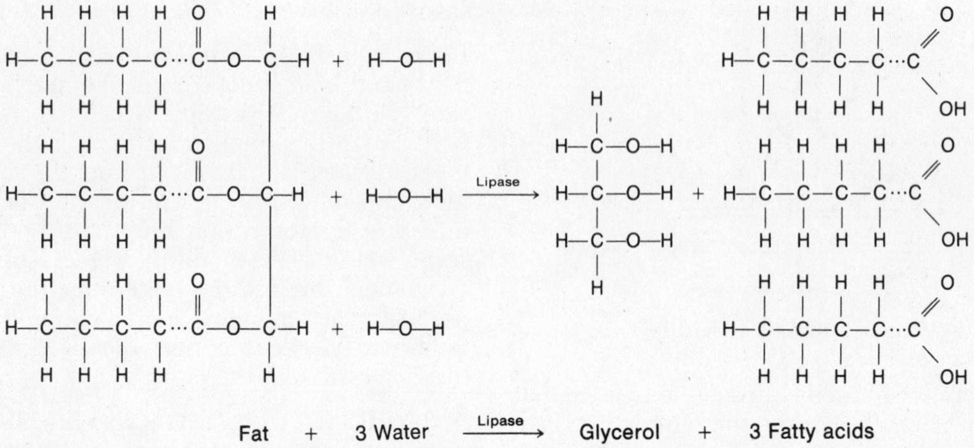

$$\text{Fat} + 3 \text{ Water} \xrightarrow{\text{Lipase}} \text{Glycerol} + 3 \text{ Fatty acids}$$

*Figure 3-5. Hydrolysis of a lipid.

Nutritional Requirements.

A balanced diet must contain carbohydrates, proteins, and fats, as well as vitamins, minerals, and water.

* **Carbohydrates.** Carbohydrates serve as the major source of energy in the body. Excess carbohydrates are converted to glycogen or fat and stored in the body as an energy reserve. Cellulose, a complex carbohydrate found in the cell walls of fruits, vegetables, and whole grains, provides indigestible material that serves as **roughage.** Roughage helps to move the food mass through the intestines.

* **Proteins.** Proteins in food are broken down to their constituent amino acids, which are then used to synthesize human proteins. Twenty different amino acids are needed for the synthesis of human proteins. Twelve of these twenty can be synthesized in the body from other amino acids, but the other eight are **essential amino acids** that must be present in the diet.
* All necessary amino acids must be present at the same time for protein synthesis to occur. An inadequate supply of any essential amino acid limits protein synthesis. Meat proteins generally contain all of the essential amino acids. Such foods are called **complete protein foods.** Vegetable proteins are generally incomplete protein foods—they lack one or more essential amino acids. However, a variety of vegetable proteins, if eaten at the same meal, can complement each other, providing all the essential amino acids.

* **Fats.** Fats contain relatively large amounts of potential energy and serve as an energy-storage compound in organisms. Fats are also a structural component of cell membranes.
* Fats are classified as saturated and unsaturated. **Saturated fats,** which are found in meats, butter, and other animal products, are solid at room temperature. Chemically, saturated fats contain the maximum number of hydrogen atoms and have no double bonds. **Unsaturated fats** contain one or more double bonds and could contain additional hydrogen atoms. An excess of saturated fats in the diet is thought to contribute to cardiovascular disease. Some forms of unsaturated fats are thought to protect against cardiovascular disease.

Disorders of the Digestive System

* An **ulcer** is an open sore in the lining of the stomach or intestines. Ulcers may be caused by the presence of excess amounts of hydrochloric acid, which breaks down, or erodes, the lining of the digestive tract. Ulcers are painful and sometimes cause bleeding.
* **Constipation** is a condition marked by difficulty in eliminating feces from the large intestine. Constipation occurs when too much water is removed from the feces in the large intestine or when there is a reduction in peristaltic activity, slowing down the movement of waste through the large intestine. Insufficient roughage in the diet may also be a cause of constipation.

* **Diarrhea** is a gastrointestinal disturbance characterized by frequent elimination of watery feces. This condition may result from decreased water absorption in the large intestine and increased peristaltic activity. Prolonged diarrhea may result in severe dehydration.

* **Appendicitis** is an inflammation of the **appendix**, a small pouch located at the beginning of the large intestine.

* **Gallstones** are small, hardened cholesterol deposits that sometimes form in the gallbladder. When gallstones enter the bile duct and block the flow of bile, they cause severe pain.

QUESTIONS

1. Into which parts of the human digestive system are digestive enzymes secreted? (1) mouth, esophagus, stomach (2) stomach, small intestine, large intestine (3) mouth, stomach, small intestine (4) esophagus, stomach, large intestine

2. In humans, excess glucose is stored as the polysaccharide known as (1) glycogen (2) glycerol (3) maltose (4) cellulose

3. After a person's stomach was surgically removed, the chemical digestion of ingested protein would probably begin in the (1) mouth (2) small intestine (3) large intestine (4) liver

4. Which organ forms part of the human gastrointestinal tract? (1) trachea (2) esophagus (3) diaphragm (4) aorta

5. The intestinal fold of the earthworm and the villi of the human small intestine function primarily to (1) increase the surface area for absorption of digested nutrients (2) excrete metabolic wastes (3) circulate blood (4) force the movement of food in one direction through the digestive tract

6. Lipase aids in the digestion of (1) fats (2) proteins (3) enzymes (4) salts

7. In humans, which of the following is true of carbohydrate digestion? (1) It begins in the oral cavity and ends in the esophagus. (2) It begins in the oral cavity and ends in the small intestine. (3) It begins in the small intestine and ends in the large intestine. (4) It begins and ends in the small intestine.

8. Organisms are classified as heterotrophs if they derive their metabolic energy from (1) photosynthesis (2) inorganic raw materials (3) lightning (4) preformed organic compounds

9. Glands located within the digestive tube include (1) gastric glands and thyroid glands (2) gastric glands and intestinal glands (3) thyroid glands and intestinal glands (4) adrenal glands and intestinal glands

10. Small lymphatic vessels that extend into the villi are (1) veins (2) lacteals (3) nodes (4) capillaries

11. The principal function of mechanical digestion is the (1) hydrolysis of food molecules for storage in the liver (2) production of more surface area for enzyme action (3) synthesis of enzymes necessary for food absorption (4) breakdown of large molecules to smaller ones by the addition of water

12. In which organ does peristalsis occur? (1) liver (2) pancreas (3) oral cavity (4) esophagus

13. A person who consumes large amounts of saturated fats may increase his or her chances of developing (1) meningitis (2) hemophilia (3) pneumonia (4) cardiovascular disease

14. Distinguish between hydrolysis and dehydration synthesis. Where does each occur in the human body?

Base your answers to questions 15 through 19 on your knowledge of biology and on the graph below, which shows the extent to which carbohydrates, proteins, and fats are chemically digested as food passes through the human digestive tract. The letters represent sequential structures that make up the digestive tract.

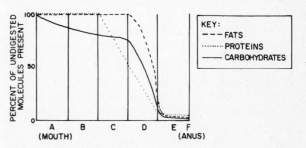

15. Proteins are digested in both (1) A and B (2) B and C (3) C and D (4) A and C

16. The organ represented by letter C is most probably the (1) esophagus (2) stomach (3) small intestine (4) large intestine

17. Enzymes secreted by the pancreas enter the system at (1) E (2) B (3) C (4) D

18. The final products of digestion are absorbed almost entirely in (1) F (2) B (3) C (4) D

19. Water is removed from the undigested material in (1) A (2) B (3) E (4) D

Base your answers to questions 20 and 21 on the equation below and on your knowledge of biology.

$$H-N-C-C-N-C-C-OH + H_2O \longrightarrow$$

$$H-N-C-C-OH + H-N-C-C-OH$$

* 20. Which kind of reaction is represented by the equation below? (1) hydrolysis (2) photosynthesis (3) dehydration synthesis (4) nitrogen fixation

* 21. The class of nutrients represented in the equation is (1) carbohydrates (2) roughage (3) proteins (4) lipids

TRANSPORT

Transport includes the absorption and distribution of materials throughout the body. In humans, dissolved and suspended materials are transported in the blood, which is moved throughout the body by the circulatory system.

Blood.

Blood consists of a fluid called **plasma** in which **red blood cells**, **white blood cells**, and **platelets** are suspended.

Plasma. Blood plasma consists mostly of water. It contains many dissolved materials, including inorganic ions, wastes, nutrients, and a variety of proteins. The proteins include antibodies, enzymes, hormones, and clotting factors.

Red Blood Cells. The most numerous cells in the plasma are the red blood cells, which are produced in the marrow of certain bones. Mature red blood cells do not have a nucleus. Within red blood cells is the red, iron-containing pigment hemoglobin, which carries oxygen between the lungs and the body tissues.

White Blood Cells. White blood cells are larger than red blood cells, and contain one or more nuclei. White blood cells are produced in the bone marrow and in lymph nodes. There are several types of white blood cells, including phagocytes and lymphocytes.

Phagocytes are white blood cells that engulf and destroy bacteria at the site of an infection. By ameboid motion, phagocytes leave the capillaries and enter the body tissues, where they engulf bacteria and other foreign matter in the same way that amebas engulf food.

Lymphocytes are white blood cells that produce special protein molecules called **antibodies**. Antibodies react chemically with foreign substances or microorganisms in the blood and inactivate them.

Any substance that causes antibody production is called an **antigen**. Most antigens are protein in nature. An antigen-antibody reaction is referred to as an **immune response**.

Platelets. The small cell fragments that are involved in the clotting of blood are called platelets. A platelet consists of cytoplasm surrounded by a cell membrane; it has no nucleus.

✻ Blood Clotting. When an injury occurs, blood vessels break and blood is released. To stop the loss of blood, a blood clot forms, blocking the wound. Clotting involves a series of enzyme-controlled reactions. All the substances required for clotting are normally present in the blood. However, the reactions leading to clot formation do not normally take place unless there is a break in a blood vessel. When such an injury occurs, blood platelets are ruptured, and they release an enzyme that initiates the clotting reactions. The plasma protein fibrinogen is converted to fibrin, which forms a meshwork of solid fibers across the wound. Blood cells become trapped in the fibers, forming the clot.

✻ Immunity. The capacity of the body to resist a specific disease is called **immunity**. Immunity, which is a function of antibodies present in the blood, can develop in two ways.

✻ Active immunity results when antibodies are produced in response to a foreign substance (antigen) in the body. When a person develops a disease, for example, chicken pox, antibodies develop against the disease-causing organism. After the illness is over, antibodies against this organism remain in the blood, and protect against reinfection by the same organism.

✻ Active immunity is also produced by vaccination against a particular disease. A **vaccine** contains dead or weakened organisms that can stimulate antibody production, but cannot cause disease.

✻ Passive immunity develops when an individual receives antibodies from the blood of another person or from an animal. These antibodies provide temporary immunity to a particular disease. However, the "borrowed" antibodies are gradually destroyed, and the immunity they provided ends.

✻ Allergies. In some people, exposure to certain common, foreign substances, including dust, pollen, insect bites, foods, and drugs, causes an immune response known as an **allergy**. The antibodies produced may stimulate the release of a substance called **histamine**, which causes the allergic response, such as sneezing, coughing, or a rash.

✻ Blood Typing. Knowledge of immunity has made possible the transplanting of organs and the transfusion of blood from one person to another. In both organ transplants and blood transfusions, an immune response is stimulated if the body of the recipient recognizes foreign antigens in the tissue or blood from the donor. In organ transplants, an antigen-antibody reaction against the transplanted organ is called **rejection**. Donor tissue proteins must be carefully matched to those of the recipient to avoid rejection. Blood typing for transfusions is based on the presence or absence of antigens on the surface of red blood cells. The most important blood group system in blood typing is the ABO blood group system. In this system, two kinds of antigens may be found on the red blood cells: A and B. In addition, the plasma of the blood may contain antibodies: anti-A and anti-B. Table 3-1 shows the antigens and antibodies for each type of blood.

Transport Vessels.

Blood circulates through the human body within blood vessels, including **arteries**, **capillaries**, and **veins**.

✳Table 3-1. Antigens and Antibodies of the ABO Blood Group System

Blood Type	Antigens on Red Cells	Antibodies in Plasma
A	A	Anti-B
B	B	Anti-A
AB	A and B	Neither Anti-A nor Anti-B
O	Neither A nor B	Anti-A and Anti-B

Arteries. Blood is carried from the heart to all parts of the body in arteries, which are thick-walled, muscular vessels that expand and contract to accommodate the forceful flow of blood from the heart. The rhythmic expansion and contraction of the arteries produced by the heartbeat aids the flow of blood to all parts of the body, and is called the **pulse.**

Capillaries. With increasing distance from the heart, arteries branch into smaller and smaller vessels, finally forming capillaries, tiny blood vessels with walls only one cell layer thick. Capillaries are the site of exchange of materials between the blood and the body tissues.

Veins. Blood flows from the capillaries into the veins, thin-walled vessels that carry the blood back to the heart. Veins contain flaps of tissue that act as valves. The valves allow the blood in the veins to flow in only one direction—toward the heart.

Intercellular Fluid and Lymph.
As blood passes through the capillaries of the body, some of the plasma is forced out of the vessels and into the surrounding tissues. This fluid, which bathes all the cells of the body, is called **intercellular fluid,** or **ICF.** Materials diffusing between the blood of the capillaries and the cells are dissolved in the ICF.

Excess intercellular fluid is drained from the tissues by vessels of the **lymphatic system.** Tiny **lymph vessels** are present in all body tissues. Excess intercellular fluid diffuses into the vessels; once inside, the fluid is called **lymph.** The lymph vessels merge, forming progressively larger vessels. Eventually, all lymph flows into two large lymph ducts, which empty into veins near the heart. In this way, the fluid lost from the blood is returned to the blood.

Major lymph vessels have enlarged regions called **lymph nodes** in which phagocytic cells filter bacteria and dead cells from the lymph. Some lymph vessels contain valves that, like valves in veins, keep the lymph flowing toward the heart.

The Heart.
Blood is pumped through the blood vessels of the body by the contractions of the heart.

Structure of the Heart. The heart has four chambers (Figure 3-6). The two upper chambers, the **atria** (singular, *atrium*), receive blood returning to the heart from the rest of the body. The two lower chambers, the **ventricles,** pump blood out of the heart into the arteries. The walls of the ventricles are thicker and more muscular than those of the atria.

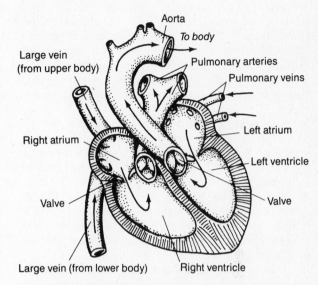

Figure 3-6. Structure of the human heart.

✳ **Circulation Through the Heart.** Deoxygenated (oxygen-poor) blood from the body is returned to the right atrium of the heart through two large veins, the *vena cavae.* This deoxygenated blood flows from the right atrium into the right ventricle; from there it is pumped out of the heart into the pulmonary arteries to the lungs. In the lungs, the blood gives up carbon dioxide and picks up oxygen. The oxygenated (oxygen-rich) blood is then returned through the pulmonary veins to the left atrium of the heart. From the left atrium it passes into the left ventricle, which pumps it into the **aorta,** the largest artery in the body.
✳ The one-way flow of blood through the heart is controlled by valves that prevent backflow of the blood. There are valves between the atria and the ventricles; there is a valve between the right ventricle and the pulmonary artery and between the left ventricle and the aorta.

✳ **Blood Pressure.** The pressure exerted by the blood on the walls of the arteries during the pumping action of the heart is referred to as **blood pressure.** During the contraction phase of the heartbeat cycle, **systole,** arterial blood pressure is highest. During the relaxation phase of the heartbeat cycle, **diastole,** blood pressure is lowest.

✳ **Pathways of Circulation.** The pathway of the blood between the heart and the lungs is called the **pulmonary circulation.** The circulatory pathway between the heart and all other parts of the body except the lungs is called the **systemic circulation**. The system of blood vessels that supplies the heart itself is called the **coronary circulation**.

Disorders of the Transport System

✷ Diseases of the heart and blood vessels are called **cardiovascular diseases**. The most common form of cardiovascular disease is **high blood pressure** or **hypertension**, which is characterized by elevated arterial blood pressure. This condition can be caused by a number of factors, including stress, diet, heredity, cigarette smoking, and aging. High blood pressure can damage the lining of arteries and weaken the muscle of the heart.

✷ A blockage of the coronary artery or its branches is a **coronary thrombosis**, or heart attack. As a result of the blockage, some of the muscle tissue of the heart is deprived of oxygen and is damaged.

✷ A narrowing of the coronary arteries may cause temporary shortages of oxygen to the heart muscle, resulting in intense pain in the chest and sometimes the left shoulder and arm. This condition is called **angina pectoris.**

✷ **Anemia** is a condition in which the blood cannot carry sufficient amounts of oxygen to the body cells. Anemia may be due to inadequate amounts of hemoglobin in the red blood cells or to too few red blood cells. One form of anemia is caused by a shortage of iron in the diet.

✷ **Leukemia** is a form of cancer in which the bone marrow produces abnormally large numbers of white blood cells.

QUESTIONS

1. Which is characteristic of lymph nodes? (1) They carry blood under great pressure. (2) They move fluids by means of a muscular pump. (3) They produce new red blood cells. (4) They contain phagocytic cells.

✷ 2. The accumulation of specific antibodies in the plasma, due to the introduction of an antigen, is characteristic of (1) an immune response (2) angina pectoris (3) a coronary thrombosis (4) cerebral palsy

✷ 3. An organism develops active immunity as a result of (1) manufacturing its own antigens (2) producing antibodies in response to a vaccination (3) receiving an injection of antibodies produced by another organism (4) receiving an injection of a dilute glucose solution

4. In the human body, which blood components engulf foreign bacteria? (1) red blood cells (2) white blood cells (3) antibodies (4) platelets

5. In humans, the exchange of materials between blood and intercellular fluid directly involves blood vessels known as (1) capillaries (2) arterioles (3) venules (4) arteries

6. An injury to a blood vessel may result in the formation of a blood clot when (1) bone marrow cells decrease platelet production (2) kidney tubules synthesize clotting factors (3) ruptured platelets release enzyme molecules (4) white blood cells release antibodies

7. Oxygen carried by the blood in the capillaries normally enters body cells by (1) active transport (2) osmosis (3) diffusion (4) pinocytosis

8. Which type of vessel normally contains valves that prevent the backward flow of materials? (1) artery (2) arteriole (3) capillary (4) vein

9. The blood vessels that transport deoxygenated blood to the heart are known as (1) capillaries (2) lymph vessels (3) veins (4) arteries

Base your answers to questions 10 through 14 on the diagram below, which represents the exchange of materials between capillaries and cells, and on your knowledge of biology.

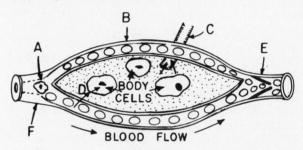

10. Blood vessel *B* has walls that are very thin. This enables this type of vessel to (1) transport hemoglobin to body cells (2) transport red blood cells into the tissue spaces (3) withstand the pressure of the blood coming from veins (4) easily transport substances into and out of the blood

11. A function of cell *A* is to (1) carry oxygen (2) engulf disease-producing organisms (3) transport digested food (4) produce hemoglobin

12. A substance that diffuses in the direction indicated by *D* is most likely (1) fibrin (2) oxygen (3) urea (4) bile

13. Which vessel most likely contains the greatest amount of carbon dioxide? (1) *F* (2) *B* (3) *C* (4) *E*

14. Excess intercellular fluid (ICF) is constantly drained off by lymphatic vessels. Which letter represents such a vessel? (1) *E* (2) *B* (3) *C* (4) *F*

✷ 15. The right ventricle is the chamber of the heart that contains (1) deoxygenated blood and pumps this blood to the lungs (2) deoxygenated blood and pumps this blood to the brain (3) oxygenated blood and pumps this blood to the lungs (4) oxygenated blood and pumps this blood to the brain

✷ 16. What effects would faulty valves have on a human organism? Explain your answer.

17. What relationships exist between the circulatory system and the lymph system?

Base your answers to questions 17 through 20 on the diagram below and on your knowledge of biology. The diagram represents the human heart, and the direction of blood flow is indicated by arrows.

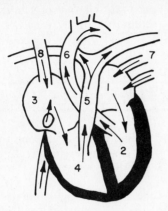

✻ **17.** The aorta is represented by number (1) 1 (2) 6 (3) 8 (4) 4

✻ **18.** Deoxygenated blood returns to the heart through the structure represented by number (1) 8 (2) 7 (3) 3 (4) 5

✻ **19.** The chamber that pumps blood to all parts of the body except the lungs is represented by number (1) 1 (2) 2 (3) 3 (4) 4

✻ **20.** Blood passes from the heart to the lungs through the structure represented by number (1) 5 (2) 6 (3) 7 (4) 8

RESPIRATION

Respiration includes cellular respiration and gas exchange. The process of cellular respiration in humans is basically the same as that in other aerobic organisms (page 23). Glucose is broken down completely to carbon dioxide and water, and ATP is formed from ADP and phosphate.

Anaerobic respiration occurs in human skeletal muscle during prolonged exercise when the amount of oxygen supplied by the circulatory system becomes inadequate for aerobic respiration. Under these circumstances, glucose is broken down in the muscle to lactic acid. The accumulation of lactic acid in skeletal muscle is thought to be responsible for muscle fatigue. When adequate oxygen is again available, the lactic acid is broken down to carbon dioxide and water.

Human Respiratory System.
The human respiratory system moves respiratory gases between the external environment and the internal surfaces for gas exchange within the lungs. The respiratory system consists of a network of passageways that permit air to flow into and out of the lungs (Figure 3-7).

Nasal Cavity. Air generally enters the respiratory system through the **nostrils** and passes into the **nasal cavity**. This cavity is lined with a ciliated mucous membrane that cleans, warms, and moistens the air.

Pharynx. From the nasal cavity, air passes into the **pharynx**, the area where the oral cavity and nasal cavity meet. Air passes through the pharynx on its way to the trachea.

Trachea. The **trachea**, or *windpipe*, is a tube through which air passes from the pharynx to the lungs. The opening of the trachea in the pharynx is protected by a flap of tissue called the **epiglottis**. During swallowing, the epiglottis covers the opening of the trachea so that food and liquids cannot enter the air passages. During breathing, the opening of the trachea is uncovered. In the top of the trachea is the **larynx**, or *voice box*, which functions in speech. The walls of the trachea contain rings of cartilage that keep the trachea open so that the passage of air is unobstructed. The trachea is lined with a ciliated mucous membrane. Microscopic particles in the inhaled air are trapped by mucus, and the beating of the cilia sweeps the mucus upward toward the pharynx.

Bronchi and Bronchioles. The lower end of the trachea splits, forming two tubes called the **bronchi** (singular, *bronchus*). The bronchi, like the trachea, are lined with mucous membrane and ringed with cartilage. Each bronchus extends into a lung, where it branches into smaller and smaller tubes called bronchioles.

The **bronchioles** are lined with mucous membrane, but lack cartilage rings. At the end of each bronchiole is a cluster of tiny, hollow air sacs called **alveoli**.

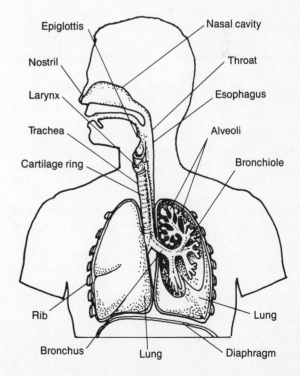

Figure 3-7. Structure of the human respiratory system.

Alveoli. The lungs contain millions of alveoli (singular, *alveolus*). The walls of the alveoli are thin and moist and are surrounded by capillaries. The alveoli are the functional units for gas exchange in the human respiratory system. Oxygen diffuses from the alveoli into the surrounding capillaries, while carbon dioxide and water diffuse from the capillaries into the alveoli.

Lungs. Each bronchus with its bronchioles and alveoli make up a **lung.**

Breathing.
Air moves into and out of the lungs during breathing. The lungs are highly elastic, but contain no muscle tissue. They expand and contract in response to pressure changes in the chest cavity brought about by the actions of the rib cage and diaphragm.

During **inhalation**, the ribs push upward and outward and the diaphragm moves down, enlarging the chest cavity. The enlargement of the chest cavity reduces the pressure around the lungs, which expand, and air flows into the lungs. In **exhalation**, the ribs move inward and downward and the diaphragm moves up. The chest cavity becomes smaller and air is forced out of the lungs.

Gas Exchange. The air that enters the alveoli is rich in oxygen. The blood in the capillaries surrounding the alveoli is oxygen-poor and contains the wastes of cellular respiration—carbon dioxide and water. The oxygen diffuses from the alveoli into the blood, where it enters the red blood cells and becomes loosely bound to the hemoglobin, forming a compound known as *oxyhemoglobin*. In the capillaries of the body tissues, the oxygen and hemoglobin separate. The oxygen diffuses out of the capillary, through the intercellular fluid, and into the body cells. Carbon dioxide and water diffuse from the cells into the blood. Carbon dioxide is carried in the blood mainly in the form of *bicarbonate ions* (HCO_3^-).

When the blood returns to the lungs, these wastes diffuse into the alveoli, and are expelled from the body in the exhaled air.

Breathing Rate. The rate of breathing is controlled by the breathing center in the medulla of the brain. The breathing center is sensitive to the concentration of carbon dioxide in the blood. When the carbon dioxide level is high, nerve impulses from the breathing center to the muscles of the ribs and diaphragm increase the breathing rate, which speeds up the rate of excretion of carbon dioxide from the body. As the carbon dioxide level in the blood drops, the breathing rate decreases.

Respiratory System Disorders

✳ **Bronchitis** is an inflammation of the linings of the bronchial tubes. As a result of swelling, the air passages become narrowed and filled with mucus, causing breathing difficulties and coughing.

✳ **Asthma** is an allergic reaction characterized by a narrowing of the bronchial tubes and results in difficulty in breathing.

✳ **Emphysema** is a disease in which the walls of the alveoli break down, decreasing the surface area for gas exchange. Emphysema is marked by shortness of breath, difficulty in breathing, and decreased lung capacity.

QUESTIONS

1. In humans, alveoli are structures most closely associated with (1) gaseous exchange (2) anaerobic respiration (3) glandular secretion (4) neural transmission

2. In humans, the center for regulating the amount of oxygen in the blood is situated in the (1) cerebrum (2) cerebellum (3) medulla (4) spinal cord

3. The exchange of air between the human body and the environment is a result of the rhythmic contractions of the rib cage muscles and the (1) diaphragm (2) lungs (3) trachea (4) heart

4. The breathing rate of humans is principally regulated by the concentration of (1) carbon dioxide in the blood (2) oxygen in the blood (3) platelets in the blood (4) white blood cells in the blood

Base your answers to questions 5 through 9 on the diagram below, which represents part of the human respiratory system.

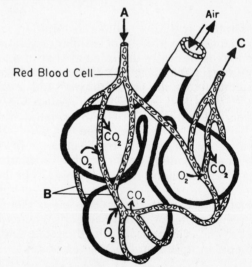

5. The blood vessels (*B*) surrounding these air sacs are known as (1) arteries (2) capillaries (3) veins (4) lymphatic ducts

6. These air sacs are known as (1) alveoli (2) bronchi (3) bronchioles (4) tracheae

7. The heart chamber that most directly pumps blood to the vessel network at *A* is the (1) right atrium (2) left atrium (3) right ventricle (4) left ventricle

8. The process most directly involved with the exchange of gases between these air sacs and blood vessels is (1) active transport (2) pinocytosis (3) hydrolysis (4) diffusion

9. Compared to blood entering at A, blood leaving the vessel network at C has a lower concentration of (1) oxygen (2) hemoglobin and carbon dioxide (3) carbon dioxide (4) oxygen and hemoglobin

10. What properties of the alveoli make them ideal respiratory surfaces?

11. How is the breathing rate in humans controlled?

EXCRETION

The metabolic wastes of humans include carbon dioxide, water, salts, and urea. Excretory wastes pass from the cells into the blood, and are carried to the excretory organs that expel them from the body. The excretory organs include the lungs, liver, sweat glands, and kidneys.

Lungs.
The lungs function in the excretion of carbon dioxide and water vapor, wastes of cellular respiration.

Liver.
The liver is a large organ that performs many functions essential to human survival. One of the excretory functions of the liver is **deamination**, the process by which the amino group (NH_2) is removed from amino acids. Deamination is used to get rid of excess amino acids. The amino groups are converted into urea, which is excreted by the kidneys. The remainder of the amino acid molecule is broken down by cellular respiration. The liver is also responsible for the breakdown of red blood cells.

Sweat Glands.
The **sweat glands** of the skin excrete wastes, including water, salts, and a small amount of urea. These wastes pass by diffusion from capillaries into the sweat glands and then through ducts to pores in the surface of the skin (Figure 3-8). The mixture of wastes and water excreted by the sweat glands is called sweat, or perspiration.

Perspiration functions primarily in the regulation of body temperature. The evaporation of sweat from the surface of the skin occurs when heat is absorbed from skin cells. The absorption of heat lowers body temperature. Temperature regulation is an example of homeostasis.

Urinary System.
The human urinary system consists of the **kidneys**, **ureters**, **urinary bladder**, and **urethra** (Figure 3-9).

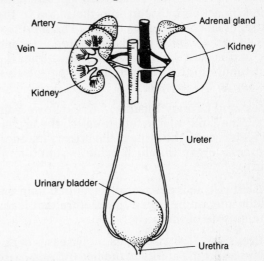

Figure 3-9. Structure of the human urinary system.

Kidneys.
Human kidneys perform two major functions: they remove urea from the blood, and they regulate the concentrations of most of the substances in the body fluids. Blood is carried to each kidney by a large artery. Within the kidney, the artery divides and subdivides into smaller and smaller arteries, and then into balls of capillaries called **glomeruli** (singular, *glomerulus*). Each glomerulus is part of a **nephron**, the functional unit of the kidney (Figure 3-10). There are about one million nephrons in each kidney.

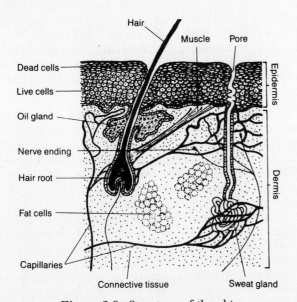

Figure 3-8. Structure of the skin.

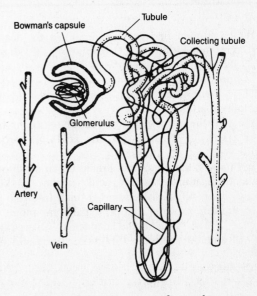

Figure 3-10. Structure of a nephron.

A nephron consists of a glomerulus surrounded by a cup-shaped structure called **Bowman's capsule**. Extending from the capsule is a long, coiled tubule surrounded by capillaries. As blood flows through the glomerulus, water, salts, urea, glucose, and some amino acids diffuse out of the blood into Bowman's capsule. This process is called **filtration**. As these substances pass through the long, coiled tubule of the nephron, glucose, water, amino acids, and some of the salts are reabsorbed by active transport into the blood in the capillaries surrounding the tubule. The fluid that remains in the tubules consists of water, urea, and salts, and is called **urine**. Urine passes from the small tubule of the nephron into larger tubules, and then to the ureter.

Ureters and Urinary Bladder. Urine flows from each kidney into a large tubule called the ureter. The ureters carry the urine to the urinary bladder, a muscular organ in which urine is stored temporarily.

Urethra. Urine is periodically expelled from the bladder into a tube called the **urethra** that leads to the outside of the body.

Diseases of the Kidneys.
Diseases of the kidneys affect the ability of the body to eliminate normal amounts of metabolic wastes.

✻ **Gout** is a condition that produces symptoms similar to arthritis and is caused by the deposition of uric acid in the joints. Victims of gout suffer from severe pain and stiffness in the joints.

✻ Diets that are extremely high in protein result in the production of large amounts of urea, which the kidneys must remove from the blood. The extra strain on the kidneys in eliminating these wastes may result in kidney malfunctions.

QUESTIONS

1. Which human body system includes the lungs, liver, skin, and kidneys? (1) respiratory (2) digestive (3) transport (4) excretory
2. In humans, the filtrate of the nephrons is stored in the (1) glomerulus (2) alveolus (3) gallbladder (4) urinary bladder
3. What is the principal nitrogenous waste in humans? (1) salt (2) urea (3) uric acid (4) carbon dioxide
4. In humans, the organ that breaks down red blood cells and deaminates amino acids is the (1) kidney (2) liver (3) gallbladder (4) small intestine
5. In addition to water, the principal components of urine are (1) amino acids and fatty acids (2) urea and salts (3) ammonia and bile (4) hydrochloric acid and bases
6. Nitrogenous wastes are produced as a result of the metabolism of (1) glucose (2) glycogen (3) fatty acids (4) amino acids

7. In humans, urine is eliminated from the bladder through the (1) urethra (2) ureter (3) nephron (4) collecting tubule
8. The basic structural and functional excretory units of the human kidney are known as (1) nephridia (2) nephrons (3) alveoli (4) ureters
9. The excretory organ associated with the storage of glycogen is the (1) stomach (2) lung (3) kidney (4) liver
10. Compare the structure of a sweat gland and a nephron. Note similarities and differences.

Base your answers to questions 11 through 13 on the diagram below of a nephron and its capillaries and on your knowledge of biology.

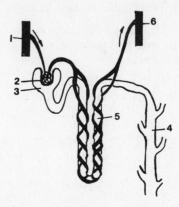

11. Into which structure does the filtrate first pass? (1) 5 (2) 6 (3) 3 (4) 4
12. In which area is water being reabsorbed? (1) 5 (2) 2 (3) 3 (4) 4
13. In which area does urine collect? (1) 1 (2) 2 (3) 6 (4) 4

HUMAN NERVOUS SYSTEM

Regulation in humans involves the interaction of the nervous and endocrine systems. The two systems are similar in that they both secrete chemicals and both play a major role in the maintenance of homeostasis. In general, they differ in that the responses of the nervous system are more rapid and of shorter duration than those of the endocrine system.

Neurons.
The nervous system is made up of nerve cells, or neurons, which are adapted for the transmission of impulses. The nervous system contains three different types of neurons, which differ both in structure and function; these are sensory neurons, motor neurons, and interneurons.

Sensory neurons transmit impulses from sense organs, or receptors, to the brain and the spinal cord. Sense organs include the eyes, ears, tongue, nose, and skin.

Motor neurons transmit impulses from the brain and spinal cord to effectors—muscles and glands.

Interneurons are found in the spinal cord and brain; they transmit nerve impulses from sensory neurons to motor neurons.

Nerves.

Neurons or parts of neurons are bound together in bundles called **nerves**. There are three kinds of nerves: **sensory nerves**, which contain only sensory neurons; **motor nerves**, which contain only motor neurons; and **mixed nerves**, which contain both sensory and motor neurons.

Central Nervous System.

The two main divisions of the human nervous system are the **central nervous system**, which includes the brain and **spinal cord**, and the **peripheral nervous system**, which includes all the nerves outside the central nervous system.

The Brain. The brain is a large mass of neurons located in the cranial cavity. It is surrounded and protected by the bones of the skull. The three major parts of the brain are the **cerebrum**, the **cerebellum**, and the **medulla** (Figure 3-11). Each controls different functions of the body.

In humans, the cerebrum is the largest part of the brain. It is the center for thought, memory, and learning; it receives and interprets messages from the sense organs; and it initiates all voluntary, or conscious, movements.

The cerebellum is located below and behind the cerebrum. It coordinates all motor activities and is involved in maintaining the body's balance.

The medulla is located at the base of the brain and connects the brain and spinal cord. The medulla controls many important involuntary activities in the body, including breathing, heartbeat, blood pressure, and peristalsis.

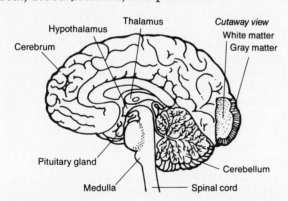

Figure 3-11. Structure of the human brain.

The Spinal Cord. The medulla of the brain is continuous with the spinal cord, which is surrounded and protected by the vertebrae of the backbone, or spinal column. The spinal cord coordinates activities between the brain and other body structures. Impulses from sense receptors throughout the body are transmitted by sensory neurons to the spinal cord. In the spinal cord, impulses are transmitted by interneurons to the

brain. Impulses from the brain are carried by motor neurons through the spinal cord and then to the appropriate effectors.

Peripheral Nervous System.

The peripheral nervous system includes all neurons, both sensory and motor, outside the central nervous system; these neurons carry impulses between the central nervous system and the rest of the body.

✳ The two divisions of the peripheral nervous system are the somatic nervous system and the autonomic nervous system. The **somatic nervous system** includes all the nerves that control the movements of the voluntary muscles of the body, as well as the sensory neurons that transmit impulses from sense receptors to the central nervous system.

✳ The **autonomic nervous system** consists of the nerves that control the activities of smooth muscle, cardiac muscle, and glands. The activities of this system, which are not under voluntary control, include regulation of the heartbeat and circulation, respiration, and peristalsis.

Habits.

A **habit** is a kind of learned behavior that becomes automatic through repetition. The repetition establishes pathways for nerve impulse transmission that permit a rapid, automatic response to a particular stimulus.

Reflexes.

An automatic, inborn response to a particular stimulus is called a **reflex**. In a reflex response, impulses follow a set pathway called a **reflex arc** (Figure 3-12). In this pathway, impulses pass from a *receptor* to a *sensory neuron* to an *interneuron* in the spinal cord to a *motor neuron* to an *effector*. Although impulses may also pass from the interneuron to the brain, the reflex response is controlled by the spinal cord and occurs without the involvement of the brain. Reflexes are generally protective in nature, allowing a rapid response to a potentially dangerous stimulus.

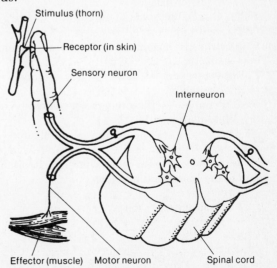

Figure 3-12. A reflex arc.

Disorders of the Nervous System

✱ **Cerebral palsy** is a group of diseases caused by damage to the parts of the brain that control voluntary movement. This damage occurs during embryonic development.

✱ **Meningitis** is an inflammation of the membranes that surround the brain and spinal cord. Meningitis may be caused by viral or bacterial infections, and symptoms include headache, muscle stiffness, fever, and chills.

✱ **A stroke** is a disorder in which the brain is damaged as a result of a *cerebral hemorrhage* (a broken blood vessel in the brain) or a blood clot in a blood vessel in the brain.

✱ **Polio** is a disease caused by a virus that affects the central nervous system and may result in paralysis. Polio can be prevented by immunization.

QUESTIONS

1. The major function of a motor neuron is to (1) transmit impulses from the spinal cord to the brain (2) act as a receptor for environment stimuli (3) transmit impulses from sense organs to the central nervous system (4) transmit impulses from the central nervous system to muscles or glands

2. Ganglia are composed of clusters of (1) smooth muscle cells (2) neurons (3) phagocytes (4) striated muscle cells

3. Which part of the human central nervous system is involved primarily with sensory interpretation and thinking? (1) spinal cord (2) medulla (3) cerebrum (4) cerebellum

✱ 4. The somatic nervous system contains nerves that run from the central nervous system to the (1) muscles of the skeleton (2) heart (3) smooth muscles of the gastrointestinal tract (4) endocrine glands

5. If the cerebellum of a human were damaged, which of the following would probably result? (1) inability to reason (2) difficulty in breathing (3) loss of sight (4) loss of balance

6. Which is a correct route of an impulse in a reflex arc?

(1) receptor → sensory neuron → interneuron → motor neuron → effector

(2) effector → receptor → motor neuron → sensory neuron → interneuron

(3) sensory neuron → effector → motor neuron → receptor → interneuron

(4) motor neuron → sensory neuron → interneuron → effector

Base your answers to questions 7 through 10 on the diagram of the human brain below.

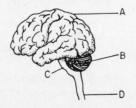

7. Injury to which part would most likely result in loss of memory? (1) A (2) B (3) C (4) D

8. Which part of the brain controls the involuntary movements of the digestive system? (1) A (2) B (3) C (4) D

9. Which part of the brain is involved with balance and the coordination of body movements? (1) A (2) B (3) C (4) D

10. Sight and hearing are functions of the structure labeled (1) A (2) B (3) C (4) D

11. The brain and spinal cord make up the (1) autonomic nervous system (2) peripheral nervous system (3) central nervous system (4) somatic nervous system

12. Impulses are transmitted from receptors to the central nervous system by (1) receptor neurons (2) sensory neurons (3) interneurons (4) motor neurons

13. Explain how a reflex arc works to protect the human body from a potentially dangerous stimulus.

HUMAN ENDOCRINE SYSTEM

The human endocrine system is made up of the endocrine glands, which secrete hormones directly into the blood. The hormones are transported by the circulatory system to the organs and tissues on which they act.

✱ **Endocrine Glands.** The glands of the human endocrine system include the **hypothalamus, pituitary, thyroid, parathyroids, adrenals, islets of Langerhans,** and **gonads (ovaries** and **testes)** (Figure 3-13).

✱ **Hypothalamus.** Hormone-secreting cells are present in a small part of the brain called the hypothalamus. The hormones of the hypothalamus influence the activities of the pituitary gland.

✱ **Pituitary Gland.** Many hormones are secreted by the pituitary gland, which is located at the base of the brain. Some pituitary hormones regulate the activities of other endocrine glands.

✱ **Growth-stimulating hormone** is a pituitary hormone that has widespread effects in the body in addition to stimulating the growth of long bones.

✱ **Thyroid-stimulating hormone** (TSH) is a pituitary hormone that stimulates the secretion of the thyroid hormone thyroxin.

✱ **Follicle-stimulating hormone** (FSH) is a pituitary hormone that stimulates the development of follicles in the ovaries of females. In males, it influences sperm production.

✱ **Thyroid Gland.** The iodine-containing hormone **thyroxin** is produced by the thyroid gland, which is located in the neck. Thyroxin regulates the rate of metabolism in the body cells and is essential for normal physical and mental development.

✱ **Parathyroid Glands.** Embedded in the back of the thyroid are the parathyroid glands, which secrete the hormone **parathormone**. Parathor-

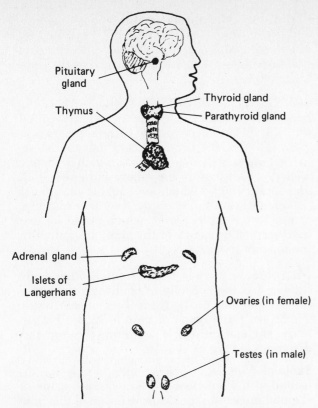

Figure 3-13. Structure of the human endocrine system.

mone controls calcium metabolism. Calcium is required for normal nerve function, blood clotting, and growth of teeth and bones.

＊ **Adrenal Glands.** An adrenal gland is located on the top of each kidney. The outer layer of the adrenal glands is the **adrenal cortex**; the inner layer is the **adrenal medulla**.

＊ The adrenal cortex secretes two types of steroid hormones. One type stimulates the conversion of fats and proteins to glucose, thereby increasing the level of glucose in the blood. The other type stimulates the reabsorption of sodium from the kidney tubules into the bloodstream. The concentration of sodium in the blood affects blood pressure and water balance.

＊ The adrenal medulla secretes the hormone **adrenaline**, which increases the blood glucose level and accelerates the rates of the heartbeat and breathing. Adrenaline is released in times of stress and heavy exercise.

＊ **Islets of Langerhans.** The small groups of endocrine cells found throughout the pancreas are called the islets of Langerhans. These endocrine cells secrete the hormones insulin and glucagon.

＊ **Insulin** promotes the absorption of glucose from the blood into the body cells, thereby lowering the blood glucose level. It also stimulates the conversion of glucose to glycogen in the liver and in skeletal muscle.

＊ **Glucagon** increases the blood glucose level by promoting the conversion of glycogen to glucose in the liver and skeletal muscle. The glucose then passes from the organs into the blood. Through their opposite effects, insulin and glucagon function to keep the blood glucose level within certain limits.

＊ **The Gonads.** The gonads—the testes and ovaries—both function as endocrine glands. The testes secrete the male sex hormone **testosterone**, which stimulates the development of male reproductive organs and secondary sex characteristics; it also stimulates sperm production. The ovaries secrete the female sex hormones **estrogen** and **progesterone**. Estrogen stimulates the production of egg cells and influences the development of female secondary sex characteristics. Progesterone stimulates the thickening of the uterine lining in preparation for the implantation of the embryo.

＊ **Negative Feedback.** The secretion of hormones by the endocrine glands is regulated by a mechanism known as **negative feedback**. In many cases, the level of one hormone in the blood stimulates or inhibits the production of a second hormone. The blood level of the second hormone in turn stimulates or inhibits the production of the first hormone. The relationship between thyroid-stimulating hormone (TSH) produced by the pituitary and the thyroid hormone thyroxin is an example of the negative feedback mechanism.

＊ When the concentration of thyroxin in the blood drops below a certain level, the pituitary is stimulated to secrete TSH. TSH then stimulates the secretion of thyroxin by the thyroid. When the blood thyroxin concentration reaches a certain level, the further secretion of TSH by the pituitary is inhibited.

Disorders of the Endocrine System

＊ A **goiter** is an enlargement of the thyroid gland that is most commonly caused by a lack of iodine in the diet.

＊ **Diabetes** is a disorder in which the islets of Langerhans do not secrete adequate amounts of insulin and the blood glucose level is elevated.

QUESTIONS

＊ **1.** Which of the following is *not* an endocrine gland? (1) thyroid (2) salivary gland (3) pancreas (4) testis

＊ **2.** The part of the brain that is most directly related to the endocrine system is the (1) cerebrum (2) medulla (3) hypothalamus (4) cerebellum

＊ **3.** Which structure secretes the substance that it produces directly into the bloodstream? (1) gallbladder (2) salivary gland (3) adrenal gland (4) skin

✳ **4.** The hormones insulin and glucagon are produced by the (1) thyroid (2) pituitary (3) pancreas (4) liver

✳ **5.** Which hormone lowers blood sugar levels by increasing the rate of entry of glucose into the cells? (1) follicle-stimulating hormone (2) insulin (3) parathormone (4) adrenalin

✳ **6.** A person was admitted to the hospital with abnormally high blood sugar and an abnormally high sugar content in his urine. Which gland most likely caused this condition by secreting lower than normal amounts of its hormone? (1) pancreas (2) parathyroid (3) salivary (4) thyroid

✳ **7.** Which hormone stimulates activity in the ovaries? (1) testosterone (2) ACTH (3) insulin (4) FSH

✳ **8.** The rate of metabolism is regulated by a hormone secreted by the (1) parathyroids (2) thyroid (3) pancreas (4) adrenals

✳ **9.** Estrogen, which influences the development of secondary sex characteristics, is produced by the (1) pituitary (2) adrenals (3) parathyroids (4) ovaries

✳ **10.** In humans, the level of calcium in the blood is regulated by the (1) pancreas (2) thyroid (3) adrenals (4) parathyroids

✳ **11.** The mechanism that regulates the secretion of hormones by endocrine glands is called (1) peristalsis (2) active transport (3) negative feedback (4) filtration

✳ **12.** Insufficient iodine in the diet may cause goiter, a disorder of the (1) adrenal glands (2) pancreas (3) pituitary (4) thyroid

✳ **13.** What is negative feedback? Give one example to show how the endocrine system uses negative feedback to coordinate activity.

LOCOMOTION

Locomotion in humans involves the interaction of bones, cartilage, muscles, tendons, and ligaments.

Bones. The human endoskeleton is made up mainly of bones of various shapes and sizes. All bones are made of bone tissue, which is quite hard and rigid. Bones provide support and protection for the soft parts of the body; they are the sites of attachment for muscles; and at joints, bones act as levers, enabling the body to move when the attached muscles contract. The production of new red blood cells and white blood cells occurs in the marrow of certain bones.

Cartilage. In addition to bone, the human skeleton contains **cartilage**, a type of flexible, fibrous, elastic connective tissue. In embryos, most of the skeleton is made of cartilage. After birth, the cartilage is gradually replaced by bone, so that in adults, almost all of the cartilage has been replaced. In adults, cartilage is found at the ends of ribs, between vertebrae, at the ends of bones, and in the nose, ears, and trachea. Cartilage provides cushioning and flexibility at joints and support and pliability in structures such as the nose and ears.

Joints. The places in the skeleton where the bones are connected to each other are called **joints**. Joints make movement of the skeleton possible. There are several kinds of movable joints in the human body. *Hinge joints*, which can move back and forth, are in the elbow and knee. *Ball-and-socket joints*, which are capable of circular movements, are found in the shoulder and hip. The neck has a *pivot joint*, which can move in a half circle. The bones of the skull are joined in *immovable joints*.

Muscles. Muscle tissue, unlike other body tissues, has the capacity to contract, or shorten. All movement in the body involves muscle tissue. There are three types of muscle in the human body: **skeletal muscle**, **smooth muscle**, and **cardiac muscle** (Figure 3-14).

Skeletal Muscle. The voluntary muscles attached to the bones of the skeleton are made of skeletal muscle tissue. Muscle tissue of this type appears striated, or striped, when viewed with a microscope, and is also known as **striated muscle**. The contraction of skeletal muscle is controlled by the nervous system, which makes coordinated movements possible.

Skeletal muscles generally operate in antagonistic pairs; the contraction of one muscle of the pair extends the limb, while contraction of the

Smooth muscle

Cardiac muscle

Skeletal muscle

Figure 3-14. Skeletal, smooth, and cardiac muscle.

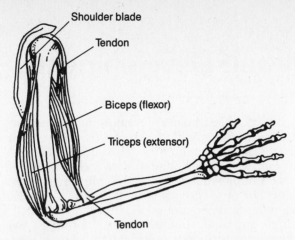

Shoulder blade

Tendon

Biceps (flexor)

Triceps (extensor)

Tendon

Figure 3-15. Muscles and bones of the upper arm.

other muscle flexes the limb. Figure 3-15 shows the muscles of the upper arm. The triceps is the extensor, while the biceps is the flexor. When the biceps contracts, the triceps relaxes, and the arm flexes, bending at the elbow. When the triceps contracts, the biceps relaxes, and the arm is extended.

Smooth Muscle. When viewed with a microscope, smooth muscle tissue does not appear striated. This type of muscle, which is also called *visceral muscle*, is found in the walls of the digestive organs and arteries, as well as in other internal organs. Smooth muscles are not under voluntary control.

Cardiac Muscle. Cardiac muscle is found only in the heart. Although it appears striated when viewed with a microscope, it is not under voluntary control, and its structure is different from skeletal muscle tissue.

Tendons and Ligaments.
Muscles are attached to bones by tough, inelastic, fibrous cords of connective tissue called **tendons**. Bones are connected together at movable joints by **ligaments**, which are composed of tough, elastic connective tissue.

Disorders of Locomotion
✻ **Arthritis** is an inflammation of the joints, which can be very painful.
✻ **Tendonitis** is an inflammation of a tendon, usually where it is attached to a bone. This condition occurs most commonly in athletes.

1. Which type of muscle tissue found in the walls of the human stomach is most closely associated with the process of peristalsis? (1) striated (2) cardiac (3) voluntary (4) smooth
2. At movable joints, bones are attached to each other by (1) elastic ligaments (2) cartilaginous tissues (3) smooth muscles (4) skeletal muscles
3. Which is *not* a major function of cartilage tissues in a human adult? (1) giving pliable support to body structures (2) cushioning joint areas (3) adding flexibility to joints (4) providing skeletal levers
4. Which type of connective tissue makes up the greatest proportion of the skeleton of a human embryo? (1) ligaments (2) cartilage (3) tendons (4) bone
5. Which structure contains pairs of opposing skeletal muscles? (1) stomach (2) small intestine (3) heart (4) hand
6. Which statement most accurately describes human skeletal muscle tissue? (1) It is involuntary and striated. (2) It is involuntary and lacks striations. (3) It is voluntary and striated. (4) It is voluntary and lacks striations.
7. In the human elbow joint, the bone of the upper arm is connected to the bones of the lower arm by flexible connective tissue known as (1) tendons (2) ligaments (3) muscles (4) neurons

For each phrase in questions 8 through 12, select the human structure, chosen from the list below, that is best described by that phrase.

Human Structures
A. Bones
B. Cartilage tissues
C. Ligaments
D. Smooth muscles
E. Tendons
F. Voluntary muscles

8. Cause peristalsis in the alimentary canal (1) B (2) C (3) D (4) F
9. Serve as extensors and flexors (1) A (2) D (3) E (4) F
10. Serve as levers for body movements (1) A (2) B (3) C (4) E
11. Bind the ends of bones together (1) B (2) C (3) D (4) E
12. Attach the muscles to bones (1) B (2) C (3) D (4) E
13. What role do muscles, tendons, bones, and joints play in locomotion?
14. State one example to show how skeletal muscles operate in antagonistic pairs.

UNIT 4 Reproduction and Development

The survival of a species depends on reproduction, the production of new individuals. There are two types of reproduction: asexual and sexual. **Asexual reproduction** involves only one parent, and the new organism develops from a cell or cells of the parent organism. In **sexual reproduction** there are usually two parents, and each contributes a specialized sex cell to the new generation. The two sex cells, one from each parent, fuse to form the first cell of the new generation.

MITOSIS

All cells arise from other cells by cell division, during which the nucleus duplicates, or replicates, and the cytoplasm divides in two, forming two cells. **Mitosis** is the orderly series of changes that results in the duplication of the complete set of chromosomes and the formation of two new nuclei that are identical to each other and to the nucleus of the parent cell. The division of the cytoplasm occurs either during or after mitosis, and results in the formation of two identical daughter cells.

Events of Mitosis.
During the period between cell divisions, the chromosome material is dispersed in the nucleus in the form of **chromatin**. At the beginning of mitosis, before the chromosomes become visible as distinct units, the chromatin replicates. It then contracts, forming a visible set of double-stranded chromosomes. Each double-stranded chromosome consists of two identical strands, or **chromatids**, that are joined together at a region called the **centromere** (Figure 4-1).

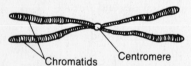

Chromatids   Centromere

Figure 4-1. A double-stranded chromosome.

During the early stages of mitosis, the nuclear membrane disintegrates and disappears, while a network of fibers called the **spindle apparatus** forms (Figure 4-2). In animal cells, two small organelles called **centrioles** move to the opposite ends, or *poles*, of the cell, where they are involved in the formation of the spindle apparatus. Plant cells generally lack centrioles, but the spindle apparatus forms without them, and the movement of chromosomes is similar to that in animal cells.

The double-stranded chromosomes become attached to the spindle apparatus by their centromeres and line up along the cell's equator. The centromeres replicate, and the two chromatids of each double-stranded chromosome separate and move to opposite poles of the cell. A nuclear membrane forms around each of the two sets of single-stranded chromosomes, forming two daughter nuclei that are identical to each other and to the original nucleus.

Division of the Cytoplasm.
In animal cells, the cytoplasm is divided when the cell membrane "pinches in," separating the two nuclei and dividing the cytoplasm into approximately equal halves.

In plant cells, the cytoplasm is divided when a **cell plate** forms across the center of the cell. The cell plate forms new cell walls.

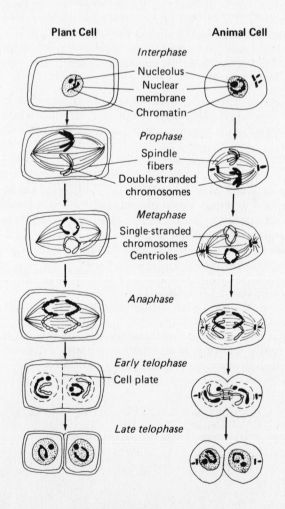

Figure 4-2. Stages of mitosis.

Uncontrolled Cell Division. In some multicellular organisms, cells sometimes undergo abnormal and rapid divisions, resulting in growths called *tumors*, which invade surrounding tissues and organs and interfere with their normal activities. Tumors are linked to a group of diseases called **cancers**.

QUESTIONS

1. Structures that hold chromatids together in double-stranded chromosomes are known as (1) centrioles (2) polar bodies (3) centromeres (4) spindle fibers

2. Each of the two daughter cells that result from the normal mitotic division of the original parent cell contains (1) the same number of chromosomes, but has genes different from those of the parent cell (2) the same number of chromosomes and has genes identical to those of the parent cell (3) one-half the number of chromosomes, but has genes different from those of the parent cell (4) one-half the number of chromosomes and has genes identical to those of the parent cell

3. The following list describes some of the events associated with normal cell division.

A. Nuclear membrane formation around each set of newly formed chromosomes

B. Separation of centromeres

C. Replication of each chromosome

D. Movement of single-stranded chromosomes to opposite ends of the spindle

What is the normal sequence in which these events occur? (1) $A \to B \to C \to D$ (2) $C \to B \to D \to A$ (3) $C \to D \to B \to A$ (4) $D \to C \to A \to B$

4. What is the result of normal chromosome replication? (1) Lost or wornout chromosomes are replaced. (2) Each daughter cell is provided with twice as many chromosomes as the parent cell. (3) The exact number of centrioles is provided for spindle fiber attachment. (4) Two identical sets of chromosomes are produced.

5. Normally, a complete set of chromosomes is passed on to each daughter cell as a result of (1) reduction division (2) mitotic cell division (3) meiotic cell division (4) nondisjunction

6. In nondividing cells, the chromosome material is in the form of (1) chromatids (2) centrioles (3) centromeres (4) chromatin

7. Organelles that play a role in mitotic division in animal cells but not in plant cells are (1) centrioles (2) chromatids (3) centromeres (4) chromosomes

8. Compare the process of mitosis in a plant and an animal cell.

9. Research how a tumor forms. What role does mitosis play in the formation of a tumor?

TYPES OF ASEXUAL REPRODUCTION

Asexual reproduction is the production of new organisms without the fusion of nuclei of two specialized sex cells. In asexual reproduction, the new organism develops by mitotic cell divisions, and the offspring are genetically identical to the parent.

Binary Fission. The form of asexual reproduction that occurs most commonly in one-celled organisms, such as the ameba and paramecium, is **binary fission**. (Figure 4-3). In this type of reproduction, the nucleus divides by mitosis, and the cytoplasm divides, forming two daughter cells of equal size. These newly formed cells are smaller than the parent cell, but contain the same number of chromosomes.

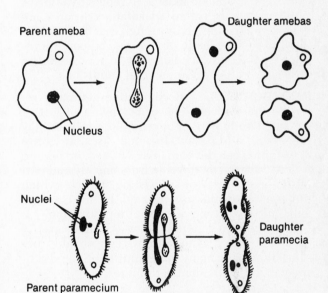

Figure 4-3. Binary fission in ameba and paramecium.

Budding. Yeasts and some other simple organisms carry on a form of asexual reproduction called budding, which is basically similar to binary fission. However, in budding, the division of the cytoplasm is unequal, so that one of the daughter cells is larger than the other. The daughter cells may separate or they may remain attached, forming a colony (Figure 4-4).

In multicellular organisms such as hydra, budding refers to the production of a multicellular growth, or bud, from the body of the parent (Fig-

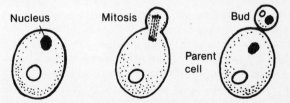

Figure 4-4. Budding in yeast.

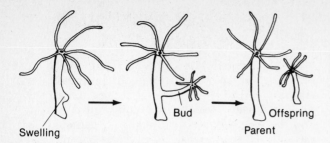

Figure 4-5. Budding in hydra.

ure 4-5). The bud is produced by mitotic cell division, and it develops into a new organism. The new organism may detach from the parent, or it may remain attached, forming a colony.

Sporulation.
In some multicellular organisms, such as bread mold, specialized cells called **spores** are produced in large numbers by mitosis. This process is called **sporulation**. Spores are generally surrounded by a tough coat that enables them to survive harsh environmental conditions. Each spore may develop into a new organism under favorable environmental conditions.

Regeneration.
Regeneration generally refers to the replacement, or regrowth, of lost or damaged body parts. For example, a lobster may regenerate a lost claw. In some cases, an entire new animal can develop from a part of the parent. A new starfish can develop from one ray and part of the central disc of an existing starfish (which then generates the missing ray). In this case, regeneration is a type of asexual reproduction.

Invertebrates generally show a greater capacity for regeneration than vertebrates, probably because they have many more undifferentiated (unspecialized) cells than vertebrates.

Vegetative Propagation.
Vegetative propagation involves various forms of asexual reproduction in plants in which new plants develop from the roots, stems, or leaves of the parent plant (Figure 4-6).

1. A **cutting** is a piece of a plant stem with leaves. When a cutting is placed in water or soil, roots may form at the cut end, and a new plant will develop. Coleus and geranium plants may develop from cuttings.

2. A **bulb** is an underground stem that is surrounded by fleshy leaves. Small bulbs arise from the existing bulb, and each new bulb may develop into a new plant. Onions and tulips grow from bulbs.

3. A **tuber** is an enlarged underground stem containing stored food. New plants develop from buds on the tuber. White potatoes are tubers, and new plants grow from the buds, or "eyes."

4. A **runner** is a horizontal stem that grows close to the ground. New plants arise at points where buds on the runner touch the ground. Strawberry plants reproduce from runners.

5. **Grafting** is a technique in which a cut twig from one tree is attached to the trunk or a branch of another tree. The rooted plant is called the **stock**, while the grafted twig is called the **scion**. The scion maintains the characteristics of the plant from which it originally came. Grafting is used to propagate selected varieties of flowers and seedless fruits, such as seedless oranges.

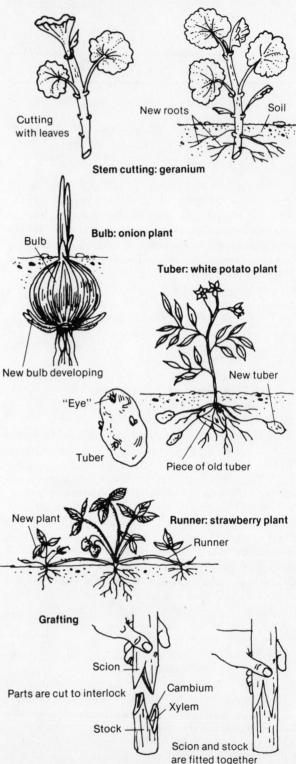

Figure 4-6. Forms of vegetative propagation.

MEIOSIS AND SEXUAL REPRODUCTION

1. Compared to the parent cell, a daughter cell produced as a result of binary fission (1) has one-half as many chromosomes (2) has twice as many chromosomes (3) is the same size, but has fewer chromosomes (4) is smaller, but contains the same number of chromosomes

2. A form of asexual reproduction that occurs in hydras is (1) binary fission (2) budding (3) vegetative propagation (4) spore formation

3. What is a type of asexual reproduction that commonly occurs in many species of unicellular protists? (1) external fertilization (2) tissue regeneration (3) binary fission (4) vegetative propagation

4. The rooted plant onto which a twig is grafted is the (1) scion (2) spore (3) cutting (4) stock

5. An enlarged, underground stem that gives rise to new plants from buds, or "eyes," is a (1) bulb (2) tuber (3) runner (4) cutting

6. A type of asexual reproduction in which new plants develop from the roots, stems, or leaves of an existing plant is called (1) binary fission (2) budding (3) regeneration (4) vegetative propagation

7. A form of asexual reproduction found in bread mold involves the production of large numbers of specialized cells, each surrounded by a tough coat. This process is called (1) binary fission (2) budding (3) sporulation (4) regeneration

8. Compared to vertebrates, invertebrate animals exhibit a higher degree of regenerative ability because they (1) produce larger numbers of gametes (2) produce larger numbers of spindle fibers (3) possess more chromosomes in their nuclei (4) possess more undifferentiated cells

9. One apple tree can bear such varieties as Delicious, McIntosh, and Cortland apples on its branches. These three varieties of apples grow on the same tree as a result of a type of vegetative propagation known as (1) cross-pollination (2) fertilization (3) grafting (4) binary fission

10. What specific type of reproduction is shown in the diagrams below of an ameba? (1) vegetative propagation (2) binary fission (3) budding (4) meiosis

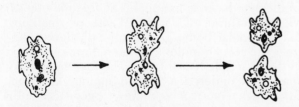

11. What role does mitosis play in asexual reproduction?

12. In what ways are regeneration and vegetative propagation similar? Why are the offspring identical to the parent in both processes?

In organisms that reproduce sexually, specialized sex cells, or **gametes**, are produced by meiosis, a special kind of cell division. One type of gamete, the **sperm cell**, is produced by the male parent, while another type of gamete, the **egg cell**, is produced by the female parent. The fusion of the nuclei of the sperm cell and egg cell is called **fertilization**. The resulting cell, which is called the **zygote**, undergoes repeated mitotic cell divisions to form the embryo.

Chromosome Number. All members of a given species have a characteristic number of chromosomes in each of their body cells. This **diploid**, or $2n$, **chromosome number** remains constant from generation to generation. The body cells of humans have 46 chromosomes, fruit flies have 8, while garden peas have 14.

The chromosomes of a body cell are actually in the form of *homologous pairs*. The two chromosomes of each homologous pair are similar in size and shape, and control the same traits. Thus, in humans there are 23 pairs of homologous chromosomes, in fruit flies there are 4 pairs, and in garden peas there are 7 pairs.

Mature sperm and egg cells contain half the diploid number of chromosomes—they contain one member of each homologous pair. Half the diploid chromosome number is called the **monoploid chromosome number**. Mature sex cells contain the monoploid number of chromosomes; every other cell in the body contains the diploid number.

In sexually mature individuals, monoploid eggs and sperm are formed in the gonads (ovaries and testes) by the process of **meiosis**, or *reduction division*.

Meiosis. Meiosis occurs only in maturing sex cells and consists of two nuclear and cytoplasmic divisions, but only one chromosome replication. The first meiotic division produces two cells containing the monoploid number of double-stranded chromosomes. The second meiotic division results in the formation of four cells, each containing the monoploid number of single-stranded chromosomes.

First Meiotic Division. The first meiotic division begins in a nondividing cell with the replication of the single-stranded chromosomes to form double-stranded chromosomes (Figure 4-7). Pairs of homologous chromosomes, consisting of four strands, become aligned side-by-side and attached together at their centromeres. This pairing of homologous chromosomes is called **synapsis**, and the grouping of the two double-stranded chromosomes is called a *tetrad*.

As in mitosis, the nuclear membrane disappears, and a spindle apparatus forms. The chromosomes, in tetrads, become attached to the spindle by their centromeres and move to the cell equator.

The double-stranded chromosomes of each homologous pair then separate and move along the spindle toward opposite poles of the cell, a process called **disjunction**. A nuclear membrane forms around each set of chromosomes. Each daughter nucleus contains *one* of each homologous pair of double-stranded chromosomes, and thus has the monoploid number of chromosomes. The cytoplasm divides, forming two daughter cells with the monoploid number of double-stranded chromosomes. Both daughter cells undergo the second meiotic division.

Second Meiotic Division. There is no replication of the chromosomes before the second meiotic division, which often follows immediately after the first division. In the second meiotic division, the double-stranded chromosomes be-

come attached to the spindle by their centromeres and move to the cell's equator. The centromeres divide, and each of the double-stranded chromosomes separates into two single-stranded chromosomes. The two single-stranded chromosomes separate and move toward opposite poles of the cell. Two nuclei form and the cytoplasm divides, forming daughter cells containing the monoploid number of single-stranded chromosomes.

As a result of meiosis, a single primary sex cell with the diploid chromosome number gives rise to four cells, each with the monoploid (*n*) chromosome number. These cells mature into gametes—sperm or eggs.

Meiosis is a source of genetic variations because it provides new combinations of chromosomes for the resulting gametes. A gamete receives only one member of each pair of homologous chromosomes from the 2*n* primary sex cells. The sorting of these chromosomes during disjunction is random.

Gametogenesis.

Gametogenesis is the process in which sperm and eggs are produced. It involves meiotic cell division and cell maturation. Gametogenesis occurs in specialized paired sex organs, or gonads. The male gonads are the testes (singular, *testis*); the female gonads are the ovaries. In most animals, the sexes are separate—that is, each individual has either testes or ovaries. However, some animals, such as the hydra and the earthworm, have both male and female gonads. Such animals are called **hermaphrodites**.

Spermatogenesis. The development of sperm in the testes of the male is called **spermatogenesis** (Figure 4-8). The process begins with meiosis in primary sperm cells, which are diploid. As a result of meiosis, each primary sperm cell develops into four monoploid cells of equal size. As they mature, these cells lose most of their cytoplasm and develop a long, tail-like flagellum that is used in locomotion.

Oogenesis. Egg cells are produced by **oogenesis** (Figure 4-9). In oogenesis, a primary egg cell undergoes meiosis. The chromosomal changes are identical to those occurring in spermatogenesis (2*n* to *n*). However, in oogenesis, division of the cytoplasm is unequal. The first meiotic division produces one large cell and one small one called a **polar body**. The larger cell then undergoes the second meiotic division, forming an egg cell and another polar body. The first polar body may also undergo a second meiotic division, forming two more polar bodies. Oogenesis results in the production of one large, monoploid egg cell and three small polar bodies. The polar bodies disintegrate. The advantage of the unequal cytoplasmic division is that the egg cell is provided with a large supply of stored nutrients in the form of **yolk**.

First meiotic division   Second meiotic division

Cell with 2*n* number of double-stranded chromosomes

Two cells from first meiotic division

Centrioles
Homologous chromosomes
Spindle fibers

Double-stranded chromosomes

Centromeres replicate

Homologous chromosomes separate

Sister chromatids separate

Cell membrane pinches in

Cell division

Cell division

Two daughter cells with *n* number of double-stranded chromosomes

Four daughter cells with *n* number of single-stranded chromosomes

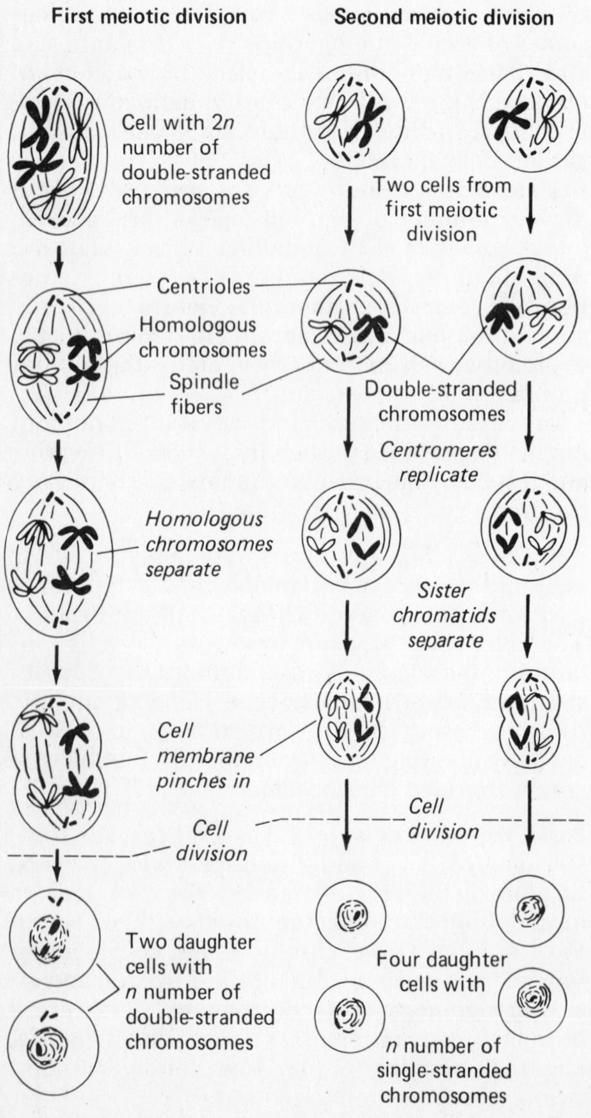

Figure 4-7. Stages of meiosis.

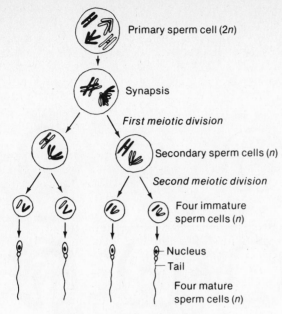

Figure 4-8. Spermatogenesis.

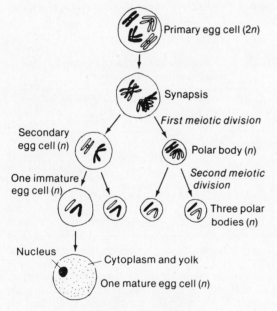

Figure 4-9. Oogenesis.

Comparison of Mitosis and Meiosis.

The daughter cells produced by mitotic cell division have the same number and kinds of chromosomes as the original parent cell. (A cell with the 2n chromosome number produces daughter cells with the 2n chromosome number.) Mitosis produces extra body cells for growth and repair of tissues. It is also associated with asexual reproduction.

As a result of meiotic cell division, the daughter cells have one-half the number of chromosomes of the original cell. (A cell with the 2n chromosome number produces daughter cells with the n chromosome number.) Meiosis occurs only in the gonads during the production of gametes.

QUESTIONS

1. Monoploid gametes are produced in animals as a result of (1) meiosis (2) mitosis (3) fertilization (4) fission

2. In human males, the maximum number of functional sperm cells that is normally produced from each primary sex cell is (1) one (2) two (3) three (4) four

3. Sexually reproducing species show greater variation than asexually reproducing species due to (1) lower rates of mutation (2) the occurrence of polyploidy (3) environmental changes (4) the recombination of alleles

4. In animals, polar bodies are formed as a result of (1) meiotic cell division in females (2) meiotic cell division in males (3) mitotic cell division in females (4) mitotic cell division in males

5. During the normal meiotic division of a diploid cell, the change in chromosome number that occurs is represented as (1) $4n \rightarrow n$ (2) $2n \rightarrow 4n$ (3) $2n \rightarrow n$ (4) $n \rightarrow \frac{1}{2}n$

6. In a species of corn, the diploid number of chromosomes is 20. What is the number of chromosomes found in each of the normal egg cells produced by this species? (1) 5 (2) 10 (3) 20 (4) 40

7. A human zygote is produced from two gametes that are identical in (1) size (2) method of locomotion (3) genetic composition (4) chromosome number

8. The pairing of homologous chromosomes during the first meiotic division is called (1) synapsis (2) crossing-over (3) disjunction (4) polyploidy

9. Organisms that contain both functional male and female gonads are known as (1) hybrids (2) hermaphrodites (3) phagocytes (4) parasites

10. Compare the processes of mitosis and meiosis. What is the function of each process?

11. The diagrams below represent the sequence of events in a cell undergoing normal meiotic cell division.

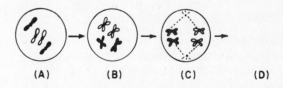

Which diagram most likely represents stage *D* of this sequence? (1) 1 (2) 2 (3) 3 (4) 4

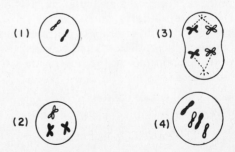

FERTILIZATION AND DEVELOPMENT

Fertilization is the union of a monoploid (*n*) sperm nucleus with a monoploid (*n*) egg nucleus to form a diploid (2*n*) cell, the **zygote**, which is the first cell of the new organism. Fertilization restores the diploid species number of chromosomes.

External Fertilization.

The union of a sperm and egg outside the body of the female is called **external fertilization**. External fertilization generally occurs in a watery environment, and is characteristic of reproduction in fish, frogs, and many other aquatic vertebrates.

In external fertilization, large numbers of eggs and sperm are released into the water at the same time to increase the chances that fertilization will take place and to help ensure that at least some of the fertilized eggs will develop and survive to adulthood.

Internal Fertilization.

The union of a sperm and egg in the moist reproductive tract of a female is called **internal fertilization**. Reproduction in most terrestrial, or land-dwelling, vertebrates, including birds and mammals, is characterized by internal fertilization.

With internal fertilization, relatively few eggs are produced at one time. The chances that fertilization will occur are much greater with internal fertilization than with external fertilization.

Stages of Development.

The early stages of embryonic development are similar in all animals. Development begins when the zygote undergoes a rapid series of mitotic cell divisions called **cleavage**.

✻ Cleavage. During cleavage, there is no increase in the size of the embryo—just an increase in the number of cells (Figure 4-10). Cell growth and specialization begin after cleavage.

✻ Blastula Formation. The mitotic divisions of cleavage result in the formation of the **blastula**, a hollow ball made up of a single layer of cells.

✻ Gastrulation. As mitotic divisions continue, one side of the blastula pushes inward, or indents, a process called **gastrulation**. The resulting embryonic stage, called a **gastrula**, consists of an inner layer, or **endoderm**, and an outer layer, or **ectoderm**. A third layer, called the **mesoderm**, forms between the endoderm and ectoderm. The endoderm, mesoderm, and ectoderm are called the **germ layers**.

✻ Differentiation and Growth. The germ layers differentiate to form the various tissues, organs, and organ systems of the developing animal (Table 4-1).

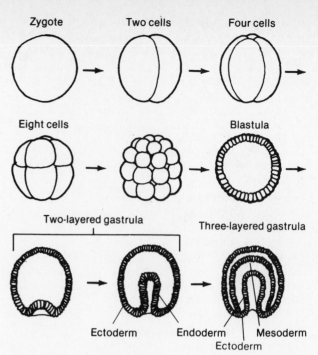

✻Figure 4-10. Early stages of embryonic development.

✻Table 4-1. Tissues and Organs Formed From Embryonic Germ Layers

Embryonic Layer	Organs and Organ Systems
Ectoderm	Nervous system; skin
Mesoderm	Muscles; circulatory, skeletal, excretory, and reproductive systems
Endoderm	Lining of digestive and respiratory tracts; liver; pancreas

✻ Embryonic development involves growth, as well as differentiation. Growth includes both an increase in the size of the embryonic cells and an increase in the number of cells.

✻ External Development. Embryonic development may occur outside or inside the body of the female. **External development** of the embryo occurs outside the female's body. **Internal development** involves the growth of the embryo within the body of the female.

The eggs of many fish and amphibians are fertilized externally and develop externally in an aquatic environment. In eggs that develop externally, the embryo obtains food in the form of yolk, which is part of the egg. In general, the parents provide little or no care for eggs that develop externally in water.

✻ The eggs of birds, many reptiles, and a few mammals, such as the platypus, develop externally on land. The eggs of these animals are enclosed in tough shells that protect the developing embryo and prevent it from drying out. Tiny pores in the shell allow the exchange of respiratory gases.

✷ In addition to the shell, the eggs of these animals are enclosed by several membranes, each of which serves a specific function (Figure 4-11).

✷ The **yolk sac** surrounds the yolk, which is the embryo's source of food. Blood vessels that penetrate the yolk sac transport food to the embryo.

✷ The **amnion** is a sac that surrounds the embryo. The sac is filled with **amniotic fluid**, which provides a watery environment, protects the embryo from shock, and prevents adhesion of embryonic tissue to the shell.

✷ The **allantois** is a membrane that provides a storage site for uric acid, a nitrogenous waste. Blood vessels that penetrate the allantois transport nitrogenous wastes from the embryo to the allantois, where they are stored. The allantois also functions in the exchange of respiratory gases.

✷ The **chorion** is a membrane that lines the inside of the shell, and together with the allantois, functions in the exchange of respiratory gases.

Internal Development.

In most mammals, both fertilization and development are internal. The eggs of mammals have little yolk and are very small compared with the eggs of reptiles and birds. In all mammals, the young are nourished after birth by milk from the mother's mammary glands.

Placental Mammals. Most mammals are placental mammals in which the embryo develops in the uterus of the female, and receives food and oxygen and gets rid of wastes through the placenta.

The **placenta** is a temporary organ that forms within the uterus from embryonic and maternal tissues and is rich in both embryonic and maternal blood vessels. The embryo is connected to the placenta by the **umbilical cord**, which contains blood vessels that carry dissolved materials between the mother and the embryo. In the placenta, the exchange of materials between mother and embryo occurs by diffusion and active transport. Food and oxygen pass from the mother's blood into the blood of the embryo, while wastes pass from the embryo's blood into the blood of the mother. The blood of the mother and the embryo never mix.

Marsupials. Pouched mammals, or **marsupials**, are nonplacental mammals. In this group, which includes kangaroos and opossums, fertilization is internal, but no placenta or umbilical cord forms. Marsupial embryos obtain nourishment from yolk in the egg for a relatively short time; they are then born at a very immature stage of development. After birth, they crawl into an external pouch on the mother's abdomen, where they feed on milk from mammary glands. The young marsupial remains in the pouch until development is complete.

QUESTIONS

1. The embryos of marsupials, such as the kangaroo and opossum, complete their development externally. What is the source of nutrition for the last stages of a marsupial embryo's development? (1) milk from maternal mammary glands (2) diffusion of nutrients through the uterine wall (3) concentrated food in the yolk stored in the egg (4) food gathered from the environment and fed to the embryo

2. In mammals, the placenta is essential to the embryo for (1) nutrition, reproduction, and growth (2) nutrition, respiration, and excretion (3) locomotion, respiration, and excretion (4) nutrition, reproduction, and excretion

3. Which characteristic of sexual reproduction has specifically favored the survival of terrestrial animals? (1) fertilization within the body of the female (2) male gametes that may be carried by the wind (3) gametic fusion in the outside environment (4) female gametes that develop within gonads

4. Which structure allows animal embryos to receive nourishment directly from the mother? (1) amnion (2) shell (3) placenta (4) ovary

✷ **5.** In a developing embryo, the process most closely associated with the differentiation of cells is (1) gastrulation (2) menstruation (3) ovulation (4) fertilization

✷ **6.** In most species of fish, a female produces large numbers of eggs during a reproductive cycle. This would indicate that reproduction in fish is most probably characterized by (1) internal fertilization and internal embryonic development (2) internal fertilization and external embryonic development (3) external fertilization and internal embryonic development (4) external fertilization and external embryonic development

✷ **7.** In the early development of a zygote, the number of cells increases without an increase in mass by a process known as (1) ovulation (2) cleavage (3) germination (4) metamorphosis

✷ **8.** Distinguish between internal and external fertilization and development. What adaptations in each insure the survival of the species?

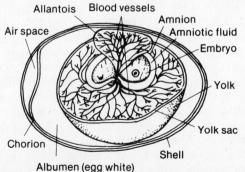

Allantois   Blood vessels
Air space   Amnion
             Amniotic fluid
             Embryo
             Yolk
             Yolk sac
Chorion
        Shell
Albumen (egg white)

✷**Figure 4-11.** Structure of a bird's egg.

✱ 9. Which type of fertilization and development is exhibited by birds and many reptiles?
(1) external fertilization and external development
(2) internal fertilization and internal development
(3) external fertilization and internal development
(4) internal fertilization and external development

✱ 10. Which structure is a source of food for embryos that develop externally? (1) yolk (2) placenta (3) chorion (4) amnion

✱ 11. If an allantois failed to develop in a bird egg, the most likely result would be that (1) the embryo would not be protected from its environment (2) a placenta could not develop (3) the processes of gas exchange and excretion would be affected (4) food could not be transported to the developing embryo

✱ 12. The structure in a bird egg that absorbs shock and provides a watery environment for an embryo is known as the (1) placenta (2) yolk sac (3) chorion (4) amniotic sac

Base your answers to questions 13 through 16 on the diagram below, which represents some stages in the embryonic development of a specific vertebrate.

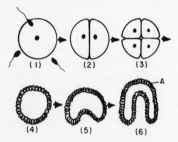

✱ 13. Structures 2 and 3 are formed as a direct result of (1) meiosis (2) gastrulation (3) cleavage (4) differentiation

✱ 14. The structure in stage 4 represents a (1) zygote (2) blastula (3) gastrula (4) follicle

✱ 15. The cells of layer A give rise to the (1) digestive system and liver (2) excretory system and muscles (3) circulatory system and gonads (4) nervous system and skin

✱ 16. Which cells are *not* represented in the diagrams? (1) endoderm cells (2) mesoderm cells (3) diploid cells (4) monoploid cells

HUMAN REPRODUCTION AND DEVELOPMENT

✱ **Male Reproductive System.** The male reproductive system functions in the production of sperm and the placement of sperm in the female reproductive system. The reproductive system is also responsible for production of male sex hormones.

✱ **Sperm Production.** The sperm-producing organs, the testes, are located in an outpocketing of the body wall called the **scrotum** (Figure 4-12). The temperature in the scrotum, which is 1° to 2°C cooler than normal body temperature, is best suited for the production and storage of sperm.

✱ From the testes, the sperm pass through a series of ducts into which liquid is secreted by various glands. The liquid serves as a transport medium for the sperm cells, and is an adaptation for life on land. The liquid and sperm together are called **semen**.

✱ Semen passes to the outside of the body through the urethra, a tube through the penis. The **penis** is used to deposit the semen in the female reproductive tract.

✱ **Hormone Production.** The testes produce the male sex hormone testosterone, which regulates the maturation of sperm cells. Testosterone also regulates the development of male secondary sex characteristics, including body form, beard development, and deepening of the voice.

✱ **Female Reproductive System.** The female reproductive system functions in the production of egg cells and the female sex hormones.

✱ **Egg Production.** The female reproductive organs, the ovaries, are located within the lower portion of the body cavity (Figure 4-13). In the ovaries, each egg cell is present in a tiny sac called a **follicle**. About once a month, a follicle matures and bursts, and the egg within it is released from the surface of the ovary, a process called **ovulation**. The egg cell then passes into the **oviduct**, or **Fallopian tube**, which leads to the **uterus**. If sperm are present, fertilization may occur in the oviduct. If the egg is fertilized, it passes into the uterus, where embryonic development may occur. If the egg is not fertilized, it degenerates.

✱ The lower end of the uterus, the **cervix**, opens to a muscular tube called the **vagina**, or **birth canal**. When embryonic development is complete, the baby leaves the body of the mother through the vagina.

✱ **Hormone Production.** The ovaries produce the female sex hormones estrogen and progesterone. These hormones regulate the maturation of egg cells, as well as the development of secondary sex characteristics, including the development of the mammary glands and the broadening of the pelvis. Estrogen and progesterone are also involved in the menstrual cycle and pregnancy.

✱ **The Menstrual Cycle.** The series of events that prepares the uterus for pregnancy is called the **menstrual cycle**. The cycle begins with the thickening of the lining of the uterine wall. The lining also becomes vascularized (filled with blood vessels). If fertilization does not occur, the thickened uterine lining breaks down and the material is expelled from the body during menstruation. The cycle then begins again.

✱ The menstrual cycle begins at **puberty**, the stage at which the individual becomes capable of reproducing. It is temporarily interrupted by

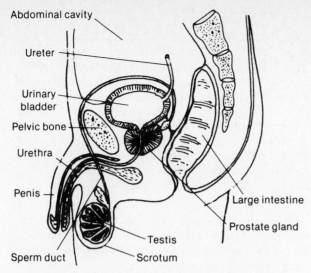

∗Figure 4-12. The male reproductive system.

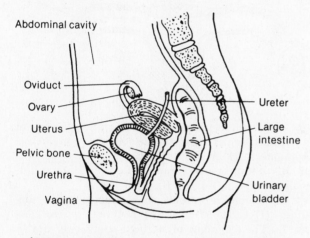

∗Figure 4-13. The female reproductive system.

pregnancy and sometimes by illness, and ceases permanently at **menopause.** The cycle is regulated by the interaction of hormones, and lasts approximately 28 days.

∗ The menstrual cycle consists of four stages (Figure 4-14).

1. During the follicle stage, an egg matures and the follicle secretes estrogen, which stimulates the thickening of the uterine lining. This stage lasts about 14 days.

2. About midway in the cycle, **ovulation** occurs. The egg is released from the ovary and enters the oviduct.

3. Following ovulation, the **corpus luteum** forms from the ruptured follicle. The corpus luteum secretes progesterone, which continues the vascularization of the uterine lining started by estrogen. This state lasts about 12 days.

4. If fertilization does not occur, the thickened uterine lining breaks down, and the extra tissue, together with some blood and mucus, pass out of the body through the vagina. The shedding of the uterine lining is called **menstruation.** This stage lasts from 2 to 4 days.

∗ Hormones of the Menstrual Cycle.

The menstrual cycle is controlled by hormones from the hypothalamus, pituitary gland, and the ovaries.

∗ During the follicle stage, the pituitary gland, under the influence of hormones from the hypothalamus, secretes FSH (follicle-stimulating hormone), which in turn stimulates the follicle to secrete estrogen. Estrogen stimulates ovulation and initiates vascularization of the uterine lining.

∗ Increased blood estrogen levels inhibit the production of FSH by the pituitary, and the secretion of LH (luteinizing hormone) by the pituitary increases. Ovulation occurs at about this time in the cycle. After ovulation, LH stimulates the formation of the corpus luteum from the ruptured follicle. The corpus luteum secretes progesterone, which enhances the vascularization of the uterine lining.

∗ If fertilization does not occur, the high levels of progesterone in the blood inhibit the production of LH by the pituitary. The drop in LH level causes a drop in the progesterone level. The lining of the uterus thins out, and at about the twenty-eighth day of the cycle, the shedding of the uterine lining, or menstruation, begins. The blood flow of menstruation is caused by the breakage of many small blood vessels.

∗ The relationship between the ovarian hormones estrogen and progesterone and the pituitary hormones FSH and LH is an example of negative feedback.

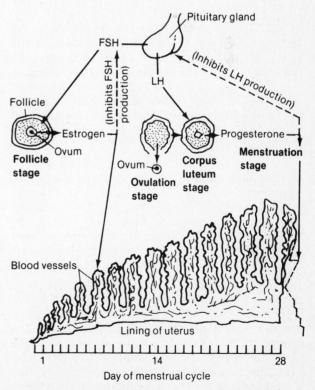

∗Figure 4-14. Stages of the menstrual cycle.

✻ Fertilization and Development.

If fertilization does occur in the oviduct, the zygote undergoes cleavage to form a blastula. Six to ten days later, the blastula becomes implanted in the uterine lining. Gastrulation usually occurs after implantation. The germ layers of the gastrula begin to differentiate and grow, resulting in the formation of specialized tissues and organs. The placenta and umbilical cord form, enabling the embryo to obtain nutrients and oxygen and dispose of metabolic wastes. An amnion filled with fluid provides a watery environment for the embryo and protects it from shocks.

✻ In Vitro Fertilization.

Fertilization that occurs outside the body of the female is known as *in vitro* fertilization. After fertilization, the early embryo is implanted into the uterus, where development is completed.

✻ Multiple Births.

Sometimes two or more embryos may develop in the uterus simultaneously. **Fraternal twins** develop when two eggs are released from the ovary at the same time and both are fertilized. The two eggs are fertilized by two different sperm cells. Fraternal twins may be of the same sex or of opposite sexes. **Identical twins** develop when a zygote separates into two equal halves early in cleavage. Each half develops into an offspring. Since identical twins develop from the same zygote, they have identical genetic makeups, and are always of the same sex.

✻ Birth.

The time between fertilization and birth is referred to as the **gestation period**. In humans, the gestation period is about 9 months. At the end of the gestation period, the secretion of progesterone decreases and another hormone from the pituitary causes strong muscular contractions of the uterus. The amnion bursts, and the baby is expelled from the mother's body through the vagina.

✻ During *postnatal development* (development after birth), humans pass through different stages, including childhood, puberty, adulthood, and old age. Puberty begins at early adolescence. In males, puberty usually occurs between the ages of 12 and 18; in females, it occurs from 9 to 14.

✻ **Aging** is a series of complex structural and functional changes in the body that occur naturally with the passage of time. The causes of aging are not fully understood. However, it now appears that aging may result from an interaction of both hereditary and environmental factors. The aging process ends in death, which may be described as an irreversible cessation of brain function.

QUESTIONS

✻ **1.** Which of the following organs *least* affects the human female menstrual cycle? (1) pituitary (2) ovary (3) pancreas (4) corpus luteum

✻ **2.** A woman gave birth to triplets, two identical girls and one boy. The number of egg cells involved would be (1) 1 (2) 2 (3) 3 (4) 4

✻ **3.** Which membrane is both a protective sac and a container for the fluid in which an embryo is suspended? (1) chorion (2) placenta (3) allantois (4) amnion

Base your answers to questions 4 through 6 on the diagram below, which represents a cross section of a part of the human female reproductive system, and on your knowledge of biology.

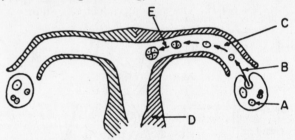

✻ **4.** Which structure is prepared for implantation of a fertilized egg as a result of the action of reproductive hormones? (1) A (2) B (3) C (4) D

✻ **5.** Within which structure does fertilization normally occur? (1) A (2) B (3) C (4) D

✻ **6.** Which represents the process of ovulation? (1) A (2) B (3) C (4) D

✻ **7.** The technique of uniting a sperm cell with an egg cell in a test tube is an example of (1) in vitro fertilization (2) internal fertilization (3) gametogenesis (4) artificial ovulation

Base your answers to questions 8 through 10 on the diagram below, which represents a stage in human development.

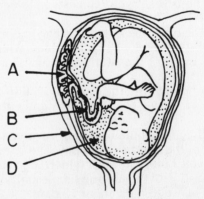

✻ **8.** The exchange of oxygen, food, and wastes between mother and fetus occurs at (1) A (2) B (3) C (4) D

✻ **9.** What is the function of the fluid labeled D? (1) nourishment (2) protection (3) excretion (4) respiration

10. The structure labeled *C*, within which development occurs, is known as the (1) oviduct (2) birth canal (3) uterus (4) placenta

For each of the processes in questions 11 through 13 choose the stage of the human menstrual cycle, chosen from the list below, during which that process occurs.

Human Menstrual Cycle Stages
A. Ovulation
B. Follicle stage
C. Menstruation
D. Corpus luteum stage

11. The lining of the uterus is shed. (1) *A* (2) *B* (3) *C* (4) *D*

12. An egg is released from an ovary. (1) *A* (2) *B* (3) *C* (4) *D*

13. An egg matures in an ovary. (1) *A* (2) *B* (3) *C* (4) *D*

14. Which of the following hormones is *not* involved in the regulation of the human menstrual cycle? (1) progesterone (2) estrogen (3) FSH (4) testosterone

15. Fraternal twins develop from (1) one egg and two sperm (2) two eggs and one sperm (3) two eggs and two sperm (4) one egg and one sperm

16. Identical twins develop from (1) one egg and two sperm (2) two eggs and one sperm (3) two eggs and two sperm (4) one egg and one sperm

17. List the four major hormones which play a role in the menstrual cycle and discuss how they interact during the cycle.

SEXUAL REPRODUCTION IN FLOWERING PLANTS

Flowers are the reproductive organs of **angiosperms**, or flowering plants.

Structure of Flowers.
Flowers may contain the following structures: sepals, petals, stamens, and pistils (Figure 4-15).

Sepals are leaflike structures at the base of a flower that enclose and protect the flower bud. In some species, the sepals are green, while in others, the sepals are white or brightly colored.

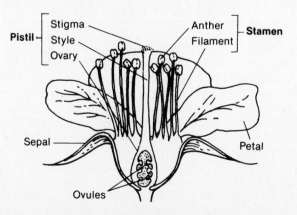

Figure 4-15. Structure of a flower.

Petals are leaflike structures inside the sepals that surround the reproductive organs of the flower. Petals may be brightly colored or white, and often have a sweet fragrance.

Stamens are the male reproductive organs of a flower. Each stamen consists of an oval-shaped **anther** supported by a stalk, or **filament**. **Pollen grains** containing monoploid sperm nuclei are produced by meiosis by the diploid cells of the anther. The thick wall that encloses the pollen grain prevents the contents from drying out. This is an adaptation for life on land.

Pistils are the female reproductive organs of a flower. A pistil consists of a stigma, style, and ovary. The **stigma**, which is a knoblike, sticky structure, is adapted for receiving pollen grains. The stigma is supported by the **style**, a slender stalk that connects the stigma to the **ovary**, which is at the base of the pistil. In the ovary, monoploid egg cells are produced by meiosis in structures called **ovules**.

The flowers of some species contain both stamens and pistils. In other species, some flowers contain only stamens, while others contain only pistils. The flowers of some species have both sepals and petals, while the flowers of other species lack one or the other.

Pollination and Fertilization.
The transfer of pollen grains from an anther to a stigma is called **pollination**. The transfer of pollen from an anther to a stigma of the same flower or to a stigma of another flower on the same plant is called **self-pollination**. The transfer of pollen from an anther of one flower to a stigma of a flower on another plant is **cross-pollination**. Cross-pollination increases the chances of genetic variation in the offspring.

Pollination may be carried out by wind, insects, or birds. Brightly colored petals and the odor of nectar attract insects and birds. Pollen grains adhere to their bodies and are carried to another flower, where they rub off on the sticky surface of a stigma.

When a pollen grain reaches a stigma, it germinates, or sprouts (Figure 4-16). A **pollen tube** grows from the pollen grain down through the stigma and style to an ovule within the ovary. The growth of the pollen tube is controlled by the **tube nucleus**. Two sperm nuclei and the tube nucleus pass down through the pollen tube. The sperm nuclei enter an ovule, where one sperm nucleus fertilizes the egg nucleus to form a diploid (2*n*) zygote. The other sperm nucleus fuses with two *polar nuclei* in the ovule to form a triploid (3*n*) *endosperm nucleus*, which divides to form a food storage tissue. The zygote undergoes repeated mitotic division to form a multicellular plant embryo. After fertilization, the ovule ripens to form a **seed**, while the ovary develops into a **fruit**. The seeds of flowering plants are found inside the fruits.

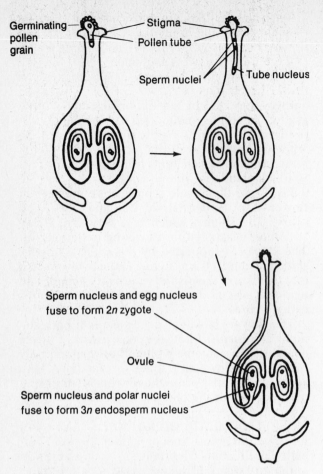

Germinating pollen grain — Stigma — Pollen tube

Sperm nuclei — Tube nucleus

Sperm nucleus and egg nucleus fuse to form 2n zygote

Ovule

Sperm nucleus and polar nuclei fuse to form 3n endosperm nucleus

Figure 4-16. Fertilization in flowering plants.

Structure of a Seed.
A seed consists of a seed coat and a plant embryo with one or two cotyledons (Figure 4-17).

The **seed coat**, which develops from the outer coverings of the ovule, surrounds and protects the embryo.

The plant embryo consists of the epicotyl, hypocotyl, and cotyledon. The **epicotyl** is the

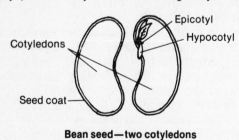

Cotyledons — Epicotyl — Hypocotyl

Seed coat

Bean seed—two cotyledons

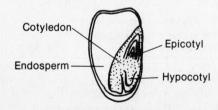

Cotyledon — Epicotyl

Endosperm — Hypocotyl

Corn seed—one cotyledon

Figure 4-17. Structure of a seed.

upper portion of the embryo; it develops into the leaves and upper portion of the stem. The **cotyledons** contain endosperm, the stored food that provides nutrients for the developing plant.

The **hypocotyl** is the lower portion of the embryo, which develops into the roots and, in some species, the lower portion of the stem.

Fruits.
The fruits of flowering plants are structures specialized for seed dispersal; they carry the seed away from the parent plant, and thereby prevent overcrowding. The fruits of dandelions and maples, for example, are dispersed by wind; coconuts are dispersed by water; and cockleburs are fruits that become attached to the fur of animals and are carried away from the parent plant by the animal. Fleshy fruits are often eaten by animals or birds, and the seeds later deposited with the animal's wastes.

Seed Germination.
Under conditions of sufficient moisture and oxygen and proper temperature, seeds germinate. The embryo plant develops leaves and roots, and begins to produce its own food by photosynthesis. The development of a mature plant from an embryo involves cell division, differentiation, and growth.

Plant Growth.
In flowering plants, only certain regions called **meristems** have the capacity to undergo cell division. There are two types of meristem regions: *apical meristems* are found in the tips of roots and stems, and cell division in these regions bring about an increase in length; *lateral meristems*, or **cambiums**, are found between the xylem and phloem and bring about an increase in diameter of roots and stems. The undifferentiated cells of the meristem regions divide actively and then undergo elongation and differentiation, forming the different kinds of plant tissues.

QUESTIONS

1. Which reproductive structures are produced within the ovaries of plants? (1) pollen grains (2) sperm nuclei (3) egg nuclei (4) pollen tubes
2. In a flowering plant, the ovule develops within a part of the (1) style (2) anther (3) pistil (4) stigma
3. Which embryonic structure supplies nutrients to a germinating bean plant? (1) pollen tube (2) hypocotyl (3) epicotyl (4) cotyledon
4. Heavy use of insecticides in springtime may lead to a decrease in apple production. This decreased apple production is most probably due to interference with the process of (1) pollination (2) cleavage (3) absorption (4) transpiration

Base your answers to questions 5 through 7 on the diagram below and on your knowledge of biology.

5. In this diagram, the stigma and anther are (1) 1 and 2 (2) 1 and 4 (3) 2 and 4 (4) 2 and 3
6. Which process has occurred in this flower? (1) pollen germination (2) seed formation (3) zygote formation (4) fruit production
7. Where would fertilization occur? (1) 1 (2) 2 (3) 3 (4) 4
8. In a bean seed, the part of the embryo that develops into the leaves and upper portion of the stem is known as the (1) seed coat (2) epicotyl (3) hypocotyl (4) cotyledon
9. A condition necessary for the germination of most seeds is favorable (1) light (2) chlorophyll concentration (3) temperature (4) nitrate concentration
10. In flowering plants, the female reproductive organs are called (1) filaments (2) anthers (3) styles (4) pistils
11. In flowering plants, pollen grains are formed in the (1) styles (2) anthers (3) sepals (4) stigmas
12. The seeds of flowering plants develop from the ripened (1) fruits (2) cotyledons (3) ovules (4) endosperm

13. The seeds of flowering plants are enclosed in (1) cotyledons (2) ovules (3) endosperm (4) fruits
14. The fruits of flowering plants develop from the ripened (1) seeds (2) ovules (3) ovaries (4) pollen tubes
15. Which of the following is *not* part of a plant embryo? (1) epicotyl (2) seed coat (3) hypocotyl (4) cotyledon
16. Explain why cross-pollination increases the chances of genetic variation in the offspring.
17. Compare sexual reproduction in mammals and flowering plants. How is the process similar in both mammals and flowering plants?
18. Which portion of a bean seed contains the greatest percentage of starch? (1) seed coat (2) epicotyl (3) cotyledon (4) hypocotyl

Base your answers to questions 19 and 20 on the diagram of the internal structure of a bean seed and on your knowledge of biology.

19. In which structure would most of the stored food for the embryo be found? (1) A (2) B (3) C (4) D
20. The epicotyl and the hypocotyl are represented by (1) A and C (2) B and D (3) C and D (4) A and B

UNIT 5 Transmission of Traits from Generation to Generation

FOUNDATIONS OF GENETICS

Genetics is the branch of biology that deals with inheritance. The science of genetics originated with the work of an Austrian monk, **Gregor Mendel**, who performed a series of experiments with sweet pea plants between 1856 and 1868.

Principles of Mendelian Genetics.

In his breeding experiments, Mendel, who had no knowledge of chromosomes or genes, made careful observations of the patterns of inheritance of specific contrasting traits found in pea plants. Through a mathematical analysis of the traits found in the large numbers of offspring of his experimental crosses, Mendel developed his principles of **dominance**, **segregation**, and **independent assortment**. Mendel also concluded that the traits he observed were controlled by pairs of inherited "factors," with one member of each pair coming from each parent organism.

Gene-Chromosome Theory.

The importance of Mendel's work was not recognized until the early 1900s, when the development of better microscopes had enabled biologists to observe chromosome behavior during meiotic cell division. Biologists then linked the separation of homologous chromosome pairs during meiosis and their recombination at fertilization with the inheritance of Mendel's "factors." Breeding experiments carried out by **T. H. Morgan** with the fruit fly, *Drosophila*, provided supporting evidence for Mendel's principles of inheritance.

Mendel's hereditary factors, now called **genes**, are arranged in a linear fashion on the chromosomes. Each gene has a definite position, or *locus* (plural, *loci*), on the chromosome. The two genes that control each trait are called **alleles**, and they are located in the same position on homologous chromosomes. The **gene-chromosome theory** explains the hereditary patterns observed by Mendel.

SOME MAJOR CONCEPTS IN GENETICS

Dominance.

In Mendel's experiments, he crossed plants that were pure for contrasting traits. For example, he crossed pure tall plants with pure short plants. All the offspring of such crosses showed only one of the two contrasting traits. In the cross of tall plants and short plants, all the offspring were tall. In this type of inheritance, the allele that is expressed in the offspring is said to be **dominant**; the allele that is present but is not expressed is said to be **recessive**.

By convention, the dominant allele is represented by a capital letter, while the recessive allele is represented by the lowercase form of the same letter. For example, the allele for tallness, which is dominant, is shown as T, while the allele for shortness, which is recessive, is shown as t.

If, in an organism, the two genes of a pair of alleles are the same, for example, TT or tt, the organism is said to be **homozygous** for that trait. The genetic makeup of the organism, which is its **genotype**, is either homozygous dominant (TT) or homozygous recessive (tt). If the two genes of a pair of alleles are different, for example, Tt, the organism is said to be **heterozygous**, or **hybrid**, for that trait.

The physical appearance of an organism resulting from its genetic makeup is called its **phenotype**. For example, a pea plant that is heterozygous for height has a genotype Tt. Its appearance, or phenotype, is tall. When an organism that is homozygous for the dominant trait is crossed with an organism homozygous for the recessive trait ($TT \times tt$), the appearance, or phenotype, of the offspring is like that of the dominant parent. The genotype of the offspring is heterozygous.

In studies involving genetic crosses, the organisms used to begin the studies are called the *parent generation*. The offspring produced by crossing members of the parent generation are called the *first filial*, or F_1, *generation*. The offspring of a cross between members of the F_1 generation make up the *second filial*, or F_2, *generation*.

QUESTIONS

1. When a strain of fruit flies homozygous for light body color is crossed with a strain of fruit flies homozygous for dark body color, all of the offspring have light body color. This illustrates the principle of (1) segregation (2) dominance (3) incomplete dominance (4) independent assortment

2. For a given trait, the two genes of an allelic pair are not alike. An individual possessing this gene combination is said to be (1) homozygous for that trait (2) heterozygous for that trait (3) recessive for that trait (4) pure for that trait

3. In peas, flowers located along the stem (*axial*) are dominant to flowers located at the end of the stem (*terminal*). Let *A* represent the allele for axial flowers and *a* represent the allele for terminal flowers. When plants with axial flowers are crossed with plants having terminal flowers, all of the offspring have axial flowers. The genotypes of the parent plants are most likely   (1) *aa* × *aa*   (2) *Aa* × *Aa*   (3) *aa* × *Aa*   (4) *AA* × *aa*

4. Two genes located in corresponding positions on a pair of homologous chromosomes and associated with the same characteristic are known as   (1) gametes   (2) zygotes   (3) chromatids   (4) alleles

5. Curly hair in humans, white fur in guinea pigs, and needlelike spines in cacti all partly describe each organism's   (1) alleles   (2) autosomes   (3) chromosomes   (4) phenotype

6. The appearance of a recessive trait in offspring of animals most probably indicates that   (1) both parents carried at least one recessive gene for that trait   (2) one parent was homozygous dominant and the other parent was homozygous recessive for that trait   (3) neither parent carried a recessive gene for that trait   (4) one parent was homozygous dominant and the other parent was hybrid for that trait

7. Which statement describes how two organisms may show the same trait, yet have different genotypes for that phenotype?   (1) One is homozygous dominant and the other is heterozygous.   (2) Both are heterozygous for the dominant trait.   (3) One is homozygous dominant and the other is homozygous recessive.   (4) Both are homozygous for the dominant trait.

8. In cabbage butterflies, white color (*W*) is dominant and yellow color (*w*) is recessive. If a pure white cabbage butterfly mates with a yellow cabbage butterfly, all the resulting (*F₁*) butterflies are heterozygous white. Which cross represents the genotypes of the parent generation?   (1) *Ww* × *ww*   (2) *WW* × *Ww*   (3) *WW* × *ww*   (4) *Ww* × *Ww*

9. Explain how organisms can have the same phenotypes and different genotypes.

Segregation and Recombination.

When gametes are formed during meiosis, the two chromosomes of each homologous pair separate, or *segregate*, randomly. Each gamete contains only one allele for each trait. After the gametes fuse during fertilization, the resulting cell contains pairs of homologous chromosomes, but new combinations of alleles may be present.

Figure 5-1 illustrates segregation and recombination in a cross between two individuals that are

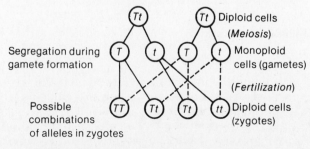

Figure 5-1. Segregation and recombination.

heterozygous for tallness. In a large number of such crosses with a large number of offspring, two types of numerical ratios can be observed. In terms of genotype, the ratio is 1 homozygous dominant (*TT*):2 heterozygous (*Tt*):1 homozygous recessive (*tt*). In terms of phenotype, the ratio is 3 tall:1 short. These genotype and phenotype ratios are typical for all crosses between organisms hybrid for one trait.

Test Cross.

To determine the genotype of an organism showing the dominant phenotype, a test cross is performed. In a **test cross,** the organism in question is crossed with a homozygous recessive organism (Figure 5-2). If the test organism is homozygous dominant, all offspring will be heterozygous and show the dominant phenotype. If any offspring show the recessive phenotype, the individual being tested is heterozygous.

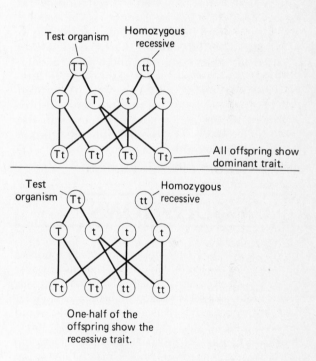

Figure 5-2. A test cross.

Punnett Squares.

The possible offspring of a genetic cross are often shown with diagrams called **Punnett squares.** We can use a Punnett square to show the possible offspring of a cross between a heterozygous tall pea plant (*Tt*) and a homozygous short pea plant (*tt*).

The first step in using a Punnett square is to determine the possible genotypes of the gametes of each parent. In this example, the heterozygous tall plant (*Tt*) produces two types of gametes: half will contain the dominant gene for height, *T*, and half will contain the recessive gene, *t*. The gametes of the homozygous short plant (*tt*) will each contain a recessive gene for height, *t*.

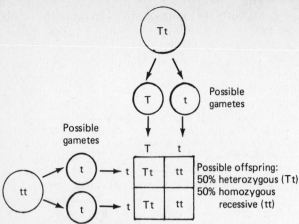

Figure 5-3. Use of a Punnett square.

As shown in Figure 5-3, the letters representing the trait carried by the gametes of one parent are written next to the boxes on the left side of the square; the letters for the gametes of the second parent are written next to the boxes at the top of the square. The letters from the top and side of the square are then combined and written in each of the boxes below and to the right of the letters. The dominant gene, when present, is written first. The pairs of letters in the four boxes represent the possible combinations of genes in the offspring of the cross. Of the possible offspring of this cross, half would be heterozygous tall (*Tt*) and half would be homozygous recessive (*tt*).

QUESTIONS

1. Polydactyly is a characteristic in which a person has six fingers per hand. Polydactyly is dominant over the trait for five fingers. If a man who is heterozygous for this trait marries a woman with the normal number of fingers, what are the chances that their child would be polydactyl? (1) 0% (2) 50% (3) 75% (4) 100%

2. A cross between two pea plants hybrid for a single trait produces 60 offspring. Approximately how many of the offspring would be expected to exhibit the recessive trait? (1) 15 (2) 45 (3) 30 (4) 60

3. Which concept states that chromosomes are distributed to gametes in a random fashion? (1) dominance (2) linkage (3) segregation (4) mutation

4. In guinea pigs, black coat color is dominant over white coat color. The offspring of a mating between two heterozygous black guinea pigs would probably show a phenotype ratio of (1) two black to two white (2) one black to three white (3) one white to three black (4) four black to zero white

5. The offspring of a mating between two heterozygous black guinea pigs would probably show a genotype ratio of (1) 1 *BB*:2 *Bb*:1 *bb* (2) 3 *Bb*:1 *bb* (3) 2 *BB*:2 *bb* (4) 2 *BB*:1 *Bb*:1 *bb*

6. If a breeder wanted to discover whether a black guinea pig was homozygous (*BB*) or heterozygous (*Bb*) for coat color, the animal in question would be crossed with an individual with the genotype (1) *BB* (2) *bb* (3) *Bb* (4) *BbBb*

7. In horses, black color is dominant over chestnut color. Two black horses produce both a black and a chestnut-colored offspring. If coat color is controlled by a single pair of genes, it can best be assumed that (1) in horses, genes for hair color frequently mutate (2) one of the parent horses is homozygous dominant and the other is heterozygous for hair color (3) both parent horses are homozygous for hair color (4) both parent horses are heterozygous for hair color

8. When is a test-cross used? Explain how it works.

Intermediate Inheritance.
The traits that Mendel studied had two clearly contrasting forms, one dominant and the other recessive. However, because of the complex nature of gene action, some traits are not clearly dominant or recessive. Some traits show a pattern of **intermediate inheritance** in which the heterozygous individual is different from both the homozygous dominant and homozygous recessive.

One type of intermediate inheritance is called **codominance.** In this type of inheritance, both alleles are expressed in the phenotype of the heterozygous offspring—both alleles are dominant. Roan coat color in cattle is the result of codominance. The coat of a roan animal contains both red hairs and white hairs, and is produced by crossing an animal with a pure red coat with one with a pure white coat. The genotype of the pure red animal is represented as $C^R C^R$, while the pure white animal is $C^W C^W$. The heterozygous roan coat is represented by $C^R C^W$. In humans, codominance occurs in the inheritance of blood type (page 66) and sickle-cell anemia.

Another type of intermediate inheritance is called **incomplete dominance.** In this type of inheritance, the phenotype of the heterozygous individual is intermediate between the contrasting homozygous parents. For example, when a pure red snapdragon (*RR*) is crossed with a pure white snapdragon (*WW*), the heterozygous offspring are pink (*RW*) (Figure 5-4).

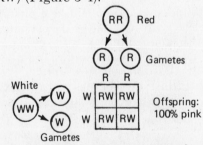

Figure 5-4. A cross between contrasting homozygous organisms for a trait that shows incomplete dominance.

In all kinds of intermediate inheritance, the offspring of a cross between two heterozygous individuals show a phenotype ratio of 1:2:1. For example, a cross between two pink snapdragons would produce 1 red:2 pink:1 white offspring (Figure 5-5).

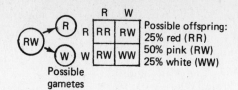

		R	W
	R	RR	RW
	W	RW	WW

Possible offspring:
25% red (RR)
50% pink (RW)
25% white (WW)

Possible gametes

Figure 5-5. A cross between organisms heterozygous for a trait that shows incomplete dominance.

Independent Assortment.

In Mendel's experiments, he performed crosses in which he studied the inheritance of two separate traits; for example, he crossed pure tall plants with yellow seeds (*TTYY*) with pure short plants with green seeds (*ttyy*) (Figure 5-6). All members of the F_1 generation were tall with yellow seeds (*TtYy*). Organisms hybrid for two traits are called **dihybrids**. Crosses between the dihybrid members of the F_1 generation produced an F_2 generation in which individuals showed four different phenotypes: tall with yellow seeds, tall with green seeds, short with yellow seeds, and short with green seeds. The ratio of these phenotypes was 9:3:3:1.

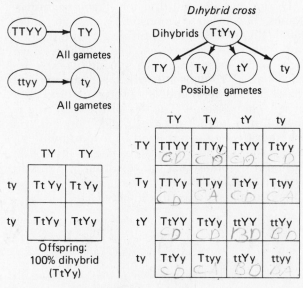

Figure 5-6. A dihybrid cross illustrating independent assortment.

Because members of the F_2 generation showed combinations of alleles different from those of the parent generation, Mendel concluded that the two traits he had studied were inherited independently of one another. This was the basis for his law of independent assortment, which stated that different traits are inherited independently of one another.

Linkage.

When the events of meiosis were discovered, it became clear that traits are inherited independently of one another only when their genes are on nonhomologous chromosomes. When the genes for two different traits are located on the same pair of homologous chromosomes, they tend to be inherited together. Such genes are said to be **linked**. The patterns of inheritance and phenotype ratios for linked traits are different from those observed by Mendel with nonlinked traits.

Crossing-over.

During synapsis in the first meiotic division, the chromatids of a pair of homologous chromosomes often twist around each other, break, exchange segments, and rejoin (Figure 5-7). This exchange of segments, called **crossing-over**, results in a rearrangement of linked genes and produces variations in offspring. Crossing-over is a source of genetic variation in sexual reproduction.

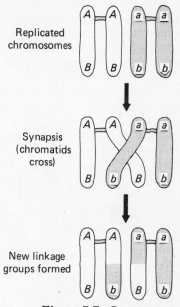

Figure 5-7. Crossing-over.

QUESTIONS

1. When pure white and pure red four-o'clocks are crossed, all the offspring are pink. The phenotype of the offspring illustrates the pattern of inheritance known as (1) dominance (2) segregation (3) incomplete dominance (4) multiple alleles

2. A number of matings of roan-coated cows with roan-coated bulls resulted in the following offspring:

75 red-coated
150 roan-coated
75 white-coated

The pattern of inheritance of coat color in these cattle is known as (1) dominance (2) codominance (3) crossing-over (4) sex-linkage

3. When a mouse with black fur is crossed with a mouse with white fur, all F_1 generation offspring have gray fur. Which phenotypic results can be expected in the F_2 generation? (1) 100% gray (2) 25% black, 75% white (3) 50% black, 50% white (4) 25% black, 50% gray, 25% white

4. Mendel's principle of independent assortment applies to traits whose genes are found on (1) homologous chromosomes (2) sex chromosomes (3) the same chromosome (4) nonhomologous chromosomes

5. The process in which the chromatids of pairs of homologous chromosomes exchange segments is called (1) linkage (2) crossing-over (3) independent assortment (4) intermediate inheritance

6. When a roan-coated cow (C^{RCW}) is mated with a red-coated bull, ($C^R C^R$), the probable percentage of roan-coated offspring would be (1) 25% (2) 50% (3) 75% (4) 100%

7. Explain the following statement: Traits are inherited independently of one another only if their genes are on nonhomologous chromosomes. You may use diagrams to support your explanation.

Multiple Alleles.

In the inheritance of some traits there are more than two different alleles for the trait—there are **multiple alleles**. However, no more than two alleles for a trait can be present in a cell. This means that while there may be three or more different forms of a gene for a particular trait, any given organism can have only two of them.

Blood type in humans is a trait involving multiple alleles. There are three possible alleles, which are written as I^A, I^B, and i. I^A and I^B are codominant (both are expressed when they are present) and i is recessive to both I^A and I^B. The possible blood types produced by these alleles are A, B, AB, and O. The genotypes associated with these blood types are shown in Table 5-1.

Table 5-1. Blood Types and Genotypes in the ABO Blood Group System

Blood Type	Genotype
A	$I^A I^A$ or $I^A i$
B	$I^B I^B$ or $I^B i$
AB	$I^A I^B$
O	ii

QUESTIONS

1. A man of blood type AB marries a woman of blood type A. What are the possible blood types of their offspring if the woman's mother was blood type O? (1) AB, only (2) A and B (3) A, B, and O (4) A, B, and AB

2. Two parents, both heterozygous for blood type A, produce a child. What are the chances that the child has blood type A? (1) 1 out of 4 (2) 1 out of 2 (3) 3 out of 4 (4) 1 out of 1

3. Three brothers have blood types A, B, and O. What are the chances that a fourth child of the same parents will have blood type AB? (1) 0% (2) 25% (3) 50% (4) 100%

4. A child with blood type O has a mother with blood type A and a father with blood type B. The parental genotypes for blood types must be (1) $I^A I^A$ and $I^B I^B$ (2) $I^A i$ and $I^B I^B$ (3) $I^A I^B$ and $I^B i$ (4) $I^A i$ and $I^B i$

5. There are multiple alleles for the ABO blood group. Why are there only two of these alleles normally present in any one individual? (1) There are not enough nucleotides in a red blood cell to produce a third allele. (2) Each parent contributes only one allele for the ABO blood group to the offspring. (3) Each allele in the ABO group must be either dominant or recessive. (4) Blood group alleles are not segregated during meiosis.

6. Why is blood type considered to be a type of codominance?

Sex Determination.

The diploid cells of many organisms contain two types of chromosomes: **autosomes** and **sex chromosomes**. There is generally one pair of sex chromosomes, and all the other chromosomes are autosomes. In human body cells there are twenty-two pairs of autosomes and one pair of sex chromosomes. The sex chromosomes are called X and Y chromosomes. Females have two X chromosomes and males have one X and one Y chromosome.

During meiotic cell division, the sex chromosomes, like other chromosome pairs, are separated (Figure 5-8). The resulting gametes contain only one sex chromosome. Since females have two X chromosomes, each female gamete receives an X chromosome. Since the genotype of males is XY, sperm cells may receive either an X or a Y chromosome. The sex of the offspring is determined at fertilization and depends on whether the egg is fertilized by a sperm with an X or a sperm with a Y chromosome. If the sperm has an X chromosome, the resulting zygote will be female (XX). If the sperm has a Y chromosome, the resulting zygote will be male (XY).

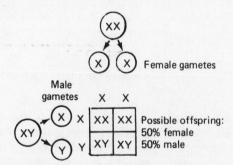

Figure 5-8. Sex determination.

Sex-Linked Traits.

T. H. Morgan, in his experiments with fruit flies, found that some rare, abnormal recessive traits appear with greater frequency in males than in females. From his observations, Morgan concluded that the genes for these traits are present on the X chromosome and

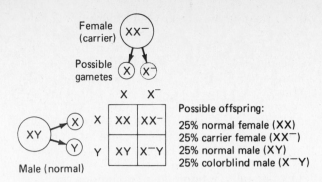

Figure 5-9. Inheritance of color blindness.

that there are no corresponding alleles for these traits on the *Y* chromosome. Genes found on the *X* chromosome are called **sex-linked genes**. Recessive sex-linked traits appear more frequently in males than in females because in females there is usually a normal, dominant allele on the other *X* chromosome, so that the phenotype is normal. In males, there is no second allele, so the presence of one recessive gene produces a recessive phenotype.

Hemophilia and **color blindness** are sex-linked disorders; they occur more frequently in males than in females. Hemophilia is a condition in which the blood does not clot properly, while color blindness is an inability to see certain colors. The genes for normal blood clotting and normal color vision are dominant; the genes for hemophilia and color blindness are recessive. For a female to show either of these disorders, she must have recessive genes on both of her *X* chromosomes. Females with one normal dominant and one recessive gene for these disorders are called "carriers." They can pass the disorder to their offspring, but do not themselves show symptoms of the disorder.

Figure 5-9 shows the possible genotypes of children of a normal male and a female carrier of color blindness.

QUESTIONS

1. If a color-blind man marries a woman who is a carrier for color blindness, it is most probable that (1) all of their sons will have normal color vision (2) half of their sons will be color-blind (3) all of their sons will be color-blind (4) none of their children will have normal color vision
2. A color-blind man marries a woman with normal vision. Her mother was color-blind. They have one child. What is the chance that this child is color-blind? (1) 0% (2) 25% (3) 50% (4) 100%
3. A color-blind woman marries a man who has normal color vision. What are their chances of having a color-blind daughter? (1) 0% (2) 25% (3) 75% (4) 100%
4. Which parental pair could produce a color-blind female? (1) homozygous normal-vision mother and color-blind father (2) color-blind mother and normal-vision father (3) heterozygous normal-vision mother and normal-vision father (4) heterozygous normal-vision mother and color-blind father
5. Which statement correctly describes the normal number and type of chromosomes present in human body cells of a particular sex? (1) Males have 22 pairs of autosomes and 1 pair of sex chromosomes known as *XX*. (2) Females have 23 pairs of autosomes. (3) Males have 22 pairs of autosomes and 1 pair of sex chromosomes known as *XY*. (4) Males have 23 pairs of autosomes.
6. Based on the pattern of inheritance known as sex linkage, if a male is a hemophiliac, how many genes for this trait are present on the sex chromosomes in each of his diploid cells? (1) 1 (2) 2 (3) 3 (4) 4
7. Traits controlled by genes on the *X* chromosome are said to be (1) sex-linked (2) incompletely dominant (3) homozygous (4) mutagenic
8. Use a diagram to show why, for each pregnancy, the chances of giving birth to a boy or girl is 50-50.
9. Explain why more males than females are hemophiliacs. Use a diagram.

MUTATIONS

Changes in the genetic material are called **mutations**. Mutations in sex cells may be transmitted to the next generation. Mutations in body cells may be passed on to new cells of the individual as a result of mitosis, but will not be transmitted to the offspring by sexual reproduction.

Mutations may involve alterations in chromosomes or alterations in the chemical makeup of genes.

Chromosomal Alterations. Chromosomal alterations involve a change in the structure or number of chromosomes. The effects of chromosomal alterations are often seen in the phenotype of an organism because each chromosome contains many genes.

Nondisjunction. During meiosis, the two chromosomes of each homologous pair separate from each other; each gamete produced by the division receives only one member of each homologous pair. The separation of homologous chromosomes is called *disjunction*. **Nondisjunction** is a type of chromosomal alteration in which one or more pairs of homologous chromosomes fail to separate normally during meiotic cell division (Figure 5-10) (page 68).

As a result of nondisjunction, one of the gametes produced contains both members of the homologous pair, while another gamete contains neither. Nondisjunction results in the production of some gametes with more chromosomes than normal and some gametes with fewer chromosomes than normal. If one of these abnormal gametes is involved in fertilization, the resulting zygote will have either more than or less than the normal (2*n*) number of chromosomes.

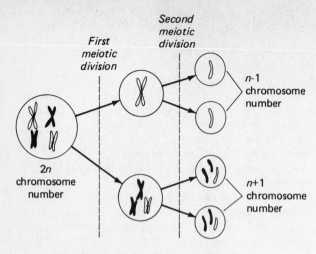

First meiotic division

Second meiotic division

n-1 chromosome number

2*n* chromosome number

n+1 chromosome number

Figure 5-10. Nondisjunction.

Down syndrome in humans is caused by the presence of an extra chromosome number 21. Nondisjunction during gamete production in one of the parents produces a gamete with an extra chromosome. As a result of fertilization, the extra chromosome is transmitted to the offspring.

Polyploidy. Occasionally during gamete formation a complete set of chromosomes fails to undergo disjunction, and a gamete is produced that contains the diploid (2*n*) chromosome number. If a diploid gamete unites with a normal (*n*) gamete during fertilization, the resulting zygote will have a 3*n* chromosome number. If two 2*n* gametes fuse, a 4*n* zygote results. The inheritance of one or more complete extra sets of chromosomes is called **polyploidy**. This condition is common in plants, but rare in animals. In plants, polyploid individuals are usually larger or more vigorous than diploid varieties. Certain strains of wheat, potatoes, alfalfa, apples, tobacco, and zinnias are polyploid. Some polyploid plants produce seedless fruit and are sterile.

Changes in Chromosome Structure. Changes in the makeup of chromosomes may result from random breakage and recombination of chromosome parts.

✳ **Translocation** is a chromosomal rearrangement in which a section of a chromosome breaks off one chromosome and becomes reattached to a nonhomologous chromosome.

✳ **Addition** of a chromosome segment occurs when a segment breaks off one chromosome and becomes reattached to the homologous chromosome.

✳ **Deletion** of a chromosome segment occurs when a portion of a chromosome breaks off and does not become attached to any other chromosome.

Gene Mutations.

A random change in the chemical makeup of the DNA (genetic material) is a **gene mutation**. The effects of some gene mutations, such as albinism, are noticeable, but other gene mutations may not produce noticeable effects.

Inheritable gene mutations tend to be harmful to the individual, rather than helpful. Sickle-cell anemia and Tay-Sachs disease are caused by gene mutations. Fortunately, most gene mutations are recessive and are hidden by the normal, dominant allele. However, if both parents carry the same recessive mutant gene, there is a chance that their offspring will be homozygous recessive and show the harmful trait.

Occasionally, random gene mutations produce changes that make the individual better adapted to the environment. Such mutant genes tend to increase in frequency within a population.

Mutagenic Agents. Although mutations occur spontaneously, the rate of mutation can be increased by exposure to certain chemicals and forms of radiation. Agents that increase the incidence of mutation are called **mutagenic agents**. X rays, ultraviolet rays, radioactive substances, and cosmic rays are mutagenic agents. Mutagenic chemicals include formaldehyde, benzene, and asbestos fibers.

QUESTIONS

1. Which terms best describe most mutations? (1) dominant and disadvantageous to the organism (2) recessive and disadvantageous to the organism (3) recessive and advantageous to the organism (4) dominant and advantageous to the organism
2. The failure of a pair of homologous chromosomes to separate during meiotic cell division is called (1) nondisjunction (2) translocation (3) addition (4) deletion
3. The condition in which a gamete contains the 2*n*, 3*n*, or 4*n* number of chromosomes is called (1) translocation (2) a gene mutation (3) polydactyly (4) polyploidy
4. The presence of only one *X* chromosome in each body cell of a human female produces a condition known as Turner's syndrome. This condition most probably results from the process known as (1) polyploidy (2) crossing-over (3) nondisjunction (4) hybridization
5. A random change in the chemical structure of DNA produces (1) polyploidy (2) a translocation (3) nondisjunction (4) a gene mutation
6. Down syndrome in humans is characterized by the presence of an extra chromosome 21 in the cells of the body. The number of chromosomes present in the body cells of individuals with this condition is (1) *n* + 1 (2) 3*n* (3) 2*n* + 1 (4) 4*n*
7. Ultraviolet rays, X rays, and certain other forms of radiation can increase the rate of mutation. These forms of radiation are said to act as (1) mutagenic agents (2) catalysts (3) enzymes (4) indicators
8. The large size and exceptional vigor of certain varieties of wheat, alfalfa, apples, and zinnias result from

the possession of extra sets of chromosomes. The extra sets of chromosomes result from (1) incomplete dominance (2) gene mutations (3) nondisjunction of complete sets of chromosomes (4) nondisjunction of chromosome number 21, only

9. The graph below shows the relationship between the number of cases of children with Down syndrome per 1,000 births and maternal age.

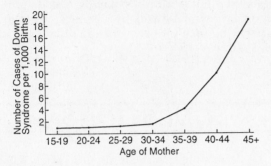

According to the graph, the incidence of Down syndrome (1) generally decreases as maternal age increases (2) is about nine times greater at age 45 than at age 30 (3) stabilized at 2 per 1,000 births after age 35 (4) is greater at age 15 than at age 35

10. A type of chromosomal alteration in which a piece of chromosome breaks off and is lost is called (1) addition (2) polyploidy (3) deletion (4) translocation

11. Explain how it is possible for an individual to inherit an extra chromosome. List some human genetic diseases caused by the inheritance of an abnormal number of chromosomes.

HEREDITY AND THE ENVIRONMENT

The development and expression of inherited traits are influenced by genes in combination with environmental factors. The relationship between gene action and environmental influence can be seen in the following examples.

1. Temperature affects fur color in the Himalayan rabbit. Under normal circumstances, these rabbits are white with black ears, nose, tail, and feet. However, when part of the white fur of the back is shaved off and the area kept covered with an ice pack, the new hairs grow in black. The artificial change in temperature produces a change of fur color.

2. Experiments in which parts of leaves are covered have shown that the production of chlorophyll requires exposure to sunlight. In the covered parts of the leaves, chlorophyll production stops.

3. Studies of human identical twins separated at birth and raised in different homes have shown that environment can influence both physical and mental development.

QUESTIONS

1. If bean plant seedlings are germinated in the dark, the seedlings will lack green color. The best explanation for this condition is that (1) bean plants are heterotrophic organisms (2) bean seedlings lack nitrogen compounds in their cotyledons (3) the absence of an environmental factor limits the expression of a genotype (4) bean plants cannot break down carbon dioxide to produce oxygen in the dark

2. In many humans, exposing the skin to sunlight over prolonged periods of time results in the production of more pigment by the skin cells (tanning). This change in skin color provides evidence that (1) ultraviolet light can cause mutations (2) gene action can be influenced by the environment (3) the inheritance of skin color is an acquired characteristic (4) albinism is a recessive characteristic

3. Identical twins were separated at birth and brought together aftern thirteen years. They varied in height by 2 inches and in weight by 20 pounds. The most probable explanation for these differences is that (1) their environments affected the expression of their traits (2) their cells did not divide by mitotic cell division (3) they developed from two different zygotes (4) they differed in their genotypes

4. A normal bean seedling which had the ability to synthesize chlorophyll did not produce any chlorophyll when grown in soil totally deficient in magnesium salts. Which statement concerning this plant's inability to produce chlorophyll is true? (1) The lack of magnesium prevented the plant's roots from absorbing water. (2) The production of chlorophyll was controlled solely by heredity. (3) The lack of magnesium caused by mutation of the gene controlling chlorophyll production. (4) The production of chlorophyll was influenced by environmental conditions.

5. Identify and discuss three environmental factors that influence phenotype.

HUMAN HEREDITY

The principles of genetics apply to all organisms. However, specific studies of human genetics are limited because humans are not suitable subjects for experimentation: human generation time is too long; there are only a small number of offspring per generation in a human family; scientists cannot perform controlled experiments in human heredity. Knowledge of human heredity has been gathered indirectly through studies of human pedigree charts and materials obtained in the course of genetic counseling.

✱ **Human Pedigree Charts.** The patterns of inheritance of certain traits can be traced in families for a number of generations. These patterns can be illustrated in **pedigree charts** that show the presence or absence of certain genetic traits in each generation. The use of a pedigree chart may also make it possible to identify carriers of recessive genes.

* Human Genetic Disorders.
Some diseases caused by genetic abnormalities are sickle-cell anemia, Tay-Sachs disease, and phenylketonuria. These disorders are caused by gene mutations.

* **Sickle-cell anemia** is a blood disorder found most commonly in individuals of African descent. The disorder is caused by a gene mutation that results in the production of abnormal hemoglobin molecules and red blood cells. The abnormal hemoglobin and sickle-shaped cells do not carry oxygen efficiently, resulting in anemia. The sickle-shaped red cells also tend to obstruct blood vessels, causing severe pain. Sickle-cell anemia occurs in individuals homozygous for the trait. Both homozygous and heterozygous individuals can be detected by blood tests.

* **Tay-Sachs disease** is a recessive genetic disorder in which nerve tissue in the brain deteriorates because of an accumulation of fatty material. The disorder is a result of the body's inability to synthesize a particular enzyme. Tay-Sachs disease, which is fatal, occurs most commonly among Jewish people of Central European descent.

* **Phenylketonuria** (PKU) is a disorder in which the body cannot synthesize an enzyme necessary for the normal metabolism of the amino acid phenylalanine. The disease, which occurs in homozygous recessive individuals, is characterized by the development of mental retardation. Analysis of the urine of newborn infants can detect PKU. Mental retardation can be avoided by a diet free of phenylalanine.

* Detection of Genetic Disorders.
Some human genetic disorders can be detected either before or after birth by the use of one or more of the following techniques.

1. Advances in genetic research have resulted in the development of simple blood and urine tests to identify individuals with certain genetic disorders. Carriers of sickle-cell anemia and Tay-Sachs disease can be identified by these **screening** techniques.

2. **Karyotyping** is a technique in which a greatly enlarged photograph of the chromosomes of a cell is prepared. The homologous pairs of chromosomes are matched together, and the chromosomes examined for abnormalities in number and structure.

3. **Amniocentesis** is a technique in which a small sample of amniotic fluid is withdrawn from the amniotic sac of a pregnant woman. The fluid contains fetal cells, which can be used for karyotyping or for chemical analysis. Amniocentesis is used in the identification of sickle-cell anemia, Tay-Sachs disease, and Down syndrome in fetuses.

* Genetic Counseling.
The various techniques described above are used by **genetic counselors** to inform concerned parents about the possible occurrence of genetic defects in their children. For couples whose families show the presence of a particular genetic disorder, a pedigree chart may be developed to predict the probability of their children's having the disorder. Amniocentesis followed by chemical tests and karyotyping may be used once pregnancy is established.

QUESTIONS

* **1.** An inherited metabolic disorder known as phenylketonuria (PKU) is characterized by severe mental retardation. This condition results from the inability to synthesize a single (1) enzyme (2) hormone (3) vitamin (4) carbohydrate

* **2.** Which statement best describes amniocentesis? (1) Blood cells of an adult are checked for fragility. (2) Saliva of a child is analyzed for amino acids. (3) Urine of a newborn baby is analyzed for the amino acid phenylalanine. (4) Fluid surrounding an embryo is removed for cellular analysis.

* **3.** Which is a genetic disorder in which abnormal hemoglobin leads to fragile red blood cells and obstructed blood vessels? (1) phenylketonuria (2) sickle-cell anemia (3) leukemia (4) Down's syndrome

* **4.** Human disorders such as PKU and sickle-cell anemia, which are defects in the synthesis of individual proteins, are most likely the result of (1) gene mutations (2) nondisjunction (3) crossing-over (4) polyploidy

* **5.** Which technique can be used to examine the chromosomes of a fetus for possible genetic defects? (1) pedigree analysis (2) analysis of fetal urine (3) karyotyping (4) cleavage

6. List three reasons why a study of the inheritance of human traits is difficult. How is information concerning patterns of human genetics obtained?

PLANT AND ANIMAL BREEDING

Using the principles of genetics, plant and animal breeders have been able to produce, improve, and maintain new varieties of plants and animals. Methods used by breeders include artificial selection, inbreeding, and hybridization.

In **artificial selection**, individuals with the most desirable traits are crossed or allowed to mate with the hopes that their offspring will show the desired traits.

The offspring of selected organisms may be mated with one another to produce more individuals with the desirable traits. This technique, called **inbreeding**, involves the mating of closely related organisms.

Two varieties of a species may have different desirable traits. In a technique called **hybridization**, breeders cross two such varieties with the hope of producing hybrid offspring that show the desirable traits of both varieties.

QUESTIONS

1. To insure the maintenance of a desirable trait in a particular species of plant, a farmer would use (1) binary fission (2) mutagenic agents (3) vegetative propagation (4) natural selection
2. The mating of closely related organisms is called (1) inbreeding (2) hybridization (3) artificial selection (4) genetic engineering
3. Plant and animal breeders usually sell or destroy undesirable specimens and use only desirable ones for breeding. This practice is referred to as (1) vegetative propagation (2) artificial selection (3) natural breeding (4) random mating
4. Describe some steps a breeder would take to produce an organism with desirable traits.

MODERN GENETICS

Biochemists have learned that the DNA of the chromosomes is the genetic material that is passed from generation to generation. Genes are sections of **DNA (deoxyribonucleic acid)** molecules. DNA controls cellular activities by controlling the production of enzymes

DNA Structure.
DNA molecules are very large; each is made up of thousands of repeating units called **nucleotides**. A DNA nucleotide is composed of three parts: a **phosphate group**; a molecule of the 5-carbon sugar **deoxyribose**; and a **nitrogenous base** (Figure 5-11).

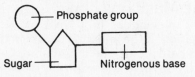

Figure 5-11. Structure of a DNA nucleotide.

There are four different nitrogenous bases found in DNA nucleotides—**adenine, cytosine, guanine**, and **thymine**. Therefore, there are four different kinds of nucleotides, depending on which base is present.

Watson-Crick Model. In the model of DNA developed by James Watson and Francis Crick, the DNA molecule consists of two connected chains of nucleotides forming a ladderlike structure (Figure 5-12). The sides of the "ladder" are composed of alternating phosphate and deoxyribose molecules. Each rung of the ladder consists of a pair of nitrogenous bases bonded together by hy-

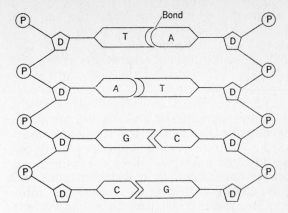

Figure 5-12. Structure of DNA.

drogen bonds. The two chains of the DNA molecule are twisted to form a spiral, or **double helix**.

The four nitrogenous bases of DNA nucleotides bond together in only one way: adenine (A) pairs with thymine (T), and cytosine (C) pairs with guanine (G). Because the bases pair together in only one way, the two strands of a DNA molecule are *complementary*. Where there is an adenine nucleotide on one strand, there is always a thymine nucleotide on the other; where there is a cytosine on one strand, there is a guanine on the other. If you know the order of bases in one strand, you also know the order in the second.

✱ DNA Replication. DNA, unlike any other chemical compound, can make exact copies of itself, a process called **replication**. DNA replication is a necessary part of the chromosome replication that occurs in mitosis and meiosis.
✱ In replication, the double-stranded DNA helix unwinds; the two strands then separate, or unzip, by the breaking of the hydrogen bonds between pairs of bases (Figure 5-13). Free nucleo-

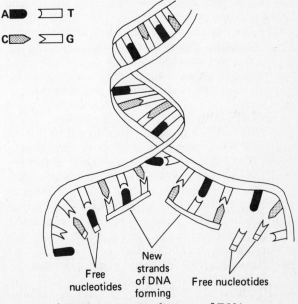

✱Figure 5-13. Replication of DNA.

tides from the cytoplasm enter the nucleus, where they bond to complementary bases on the DNA strands. Replication produces two identical DNA molecules that are exact copies of the original molecule.

* Gene Control of Cellular Activities.
The unique qualities of an organism are determined by the DNA of its genes. The genes control enzyme synthesis, and the enzymes control cell activities. For example, brown eye color in humans is determined by a dominant gene that causes the production of an enzyme that influences the synthesis of melanin, a brown pigment.
* The hereditary information is in the sequence of the nucleotides in DNA molecules. The DNA nucleotide sequence determines the sequence of amino acids in enzymes and other proteins. The genetic control of protein synthesis involves RNA as well as DNA.

* RNA.
Molecules of **ribonucleic acid**, or **RNA**, are similar to DNA in that they are also made up of nucleotides. However, in RNA nucleotides, the 5-carbon sugar **ribose** is substituted for deoxyribose, and **uracil** (U) is substituted for thymine. RNA molecules consist of one strand of nucleotides, while DNA molecules have two. There are three kinds of RNA molecules in cells: **messenger RNA** (mRNA) **transfer RNA** (tRNA), and **ribosomal RNA** (rRNA).
* Messenger RNA is synthesized in the cell nucleus. Portions of a DNA molecule unwind, and the two strands separate. RNA nucleotides pair with complementary bases on a DNA strand, forming a strand of messenger RNA that is complementary to the DNA strand. (The DNA serves as a *template*, or pattern, for the synthesis of messenger RNA.) In this way, the hereditary information in the nucleotide sequence of DNA is copied in complementary form into the nucleotide sequence of messenger RNA.

The sequence of nucleotides in messenger RNA contains the genetic code, which determines the amino acid sequence of proteins. The genetic code for each amino acid is a specific sequence of three nucleotides. The three-nucleotide sequence in messenger RNA that specifies a particular amino acid is called a **codon**.
* Transfer RNA molecules are found in the cytoplasm. Their function is to carry amino acid molecules to the ribosomes, the sites of protein synthesis. There are 20 different kinds of amino acids in cells, and there is a different form of transfer RNA for each amino acid. Each kind of transfer RNA has a three-nucleotide sequence, called an **anticodon**, that is complementary to a codon on the messenger RNA.
* Ribosomal RNA is found in the ribosomes.

* Protein Synthesis.
Protein synthesis begins with the synthesis of messenger RNA molecules, which then move from the nucleus into the cytoplasm. In the cytoplasm, the strand of messenger RNA becomes associated with ribosomes (Figure 5-14). Amino acids are carried to the ribosomes and messenger RNA by transfer RNAs. The anticodons of the transfer RNAs align with the codons of the messenger RNA. The amino acids carried by the transfer RNAs bond together in a sequence determined by the base sequence of the messenger RNA. The resulting chain of amino acids is a polypeptide. Some proteins consist of a single polypeptide chain, while others include two or more.

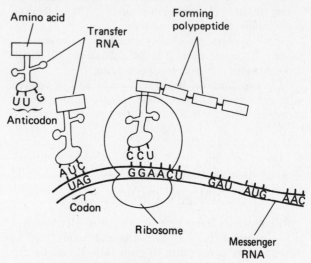

*Figure 5-14. Protein synthesis.

* One Gene–One Polypeptide Hypothesis.
According to the **one gene–one polypeptide hypothesis**, each gene controls the synthesis of a single polypeptide. A modern definition of the gene is the sequence of nucleotides in a DNA molecule necessary to synthesize a polypeptide.

* Gene Mutations.
Any change in the sequence of nucleotides in a DNA molecule is a gene mutation. If the mutation occurs in the DNA of the sex cells, it may be inheritable. Gene mutations may involve the *addition* or *deletion* of bases, or the *substitution* of one base for another. Sickle-cell anemia is caused by the substitution of one incorrect nitrogenous base in a gene that controls hemoglobin synthesis. The incorrect base results in the insertion of one incorrect amino acid, which in turn affects the structure and function of the hemoglobin protein.

* Cloning.
The process by which a group of genetically identical offspring are produced from the cells of an organism is called **cloning**. The cloning of plants shows great promise for agriculture, where plants with desirable qualities can be produced rapidly from the cells of a single plant. The cloning of animals has been achieved in frogs, mice, and sheep.

✻ Genetic Engineering.

"Gene splicing," or **genetic engineering**, involves the transfer of genetic material from one organism to another, resulting in the formation of **recombinant DNA**. Using gene splicing techniques, genes from one organism can be inserted into the DNA of another organism. Human genes that control the synthesis of insulin, interferon, and growth hormone have been introduced into bacterial cells, where they function as part of the bacterial DNA. In this way, bacterial cells are being used to synthesize substances needed by humans. Genetic engineering may eventually be able to correct genetic defects and produce agriculturally desirable plants and animals.

QUESTIONS

1. Which diagram best illustrates the structure of a portion of a DNA molecule? (1) 1 (2) 2 (3) 3 (4) 4

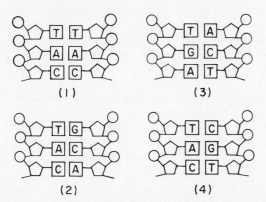

✻ 2. DNA and RNA molecules are similar in that they both contain (1) nucleotides (2) a double helix (3) deoxyribose sugars (4) thymine

3. Which series is arranged in correct order according to *decreasing* size of structures? (1) DNA, nucleus, chromosome, nucleotide, nitrogenous base (2) nucleotide, chromosome, nitrogenous base, nucleus, DNA (3) nucleus, chromosome, DNA, nucleotide, nitrogenous base (4) chromosome, nucleus, nitrogenous base, nucleotide, DNA

4. Which substances are components of a DNA nucleotide? (1) phosphate, deoxyribose, and uracil (2) phosphate, ribose, and adenine (3) thymine, deoxyribose, and phosphate (4) ribose, phosphate, and uracil

5. Which two bases are present in equal amounts in a double-stranded DNA molecule? (1) cytosine and thymine (2) adenine and thymine (3) adenine and uracil (4) cytosine and uracil

✻ 6. By which process can a group of genetically identical plants be rapidly produced from the cells of a single plant? (1) screening (2) chromosomal karyotyping (3) genetic engineering (4) cloning

For each phrase in questions 7 through 10, select the type of nucleic acid, *chosen from the list below*, that is best described by the phrase. (Note that there are only three choices.)

Types of Nucleic Acid
(1) DNA
(2) Messenger RNA
(3) Transfer RNA

✻ 7. Genetic material responsible for the individuality of an organism, that is passed from parent to offspring (1) 1 (2) 2 (3) 3

✻ 8. Carries genetic information from the cell nucleus to the ribosomes (1) 1 (2) 2 (3) 3

✻ 9. Contains thymine instead of uracil (1) 1 (2) 2 (3) 3

✻ 10. Carries amino acid molecules to the ribosomes (1) 1 (2) 2 (3) 3

✻ 11. In humans, a gene mutation results from a change in the (1) sequence of the nitrogenous bases in DNA (2) chromosome number in a sperm (3) chromosome number in an egg (4) sequence of the sugars and phosphates in DNA

✻ 12. The genetic code for one amino acid molecule consists of (1) five sugar molecules (2) two phosphates (3) three nucleotides (4) four hydrogen bonds

✻ 13. During the replication of a DNA molecule, separation or "unzipping" of the DNA molecule will normally occur when hydrogen bonds are broken between (1) thymine and thymine (2) guanine and uracil (3) adenine and cytosine (4) cytosine and guanine

✻ 14. In the diagram, what is represented by the letter x? (1) ribose (2) deoxyribose (3) phosphate (4) adenine

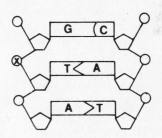

✻ 15. Which principal actions of genes insure homeostatic control of life processes and continuity of hereditary material? (1) oxidation and hydrolysis (2) enzyme synthesis and replication (3) oxygen transport and cyclosis (4) pinocytosis and dehydration synthesis

✻ 16. The formation of recombinant DNA results from the (1) addition of messenger RNA molecules to an organism (2) transfer of genes from one organism to another (3) substitution of a ribose sugar for a deoxyribose sugar (4) production of a polyploid condition by a mutagenic agent

✻ 17. The replication of a double-stranded DNA molecule begins when the strands separate at the (1) phosphate bonds (2) ribose molecules (3) deoxyribose molecules (4) hydrogen bonds

Base your answers to questions 18 through 22 on the diagram below, which represents the biochemical process of protein formation in a typical cell.

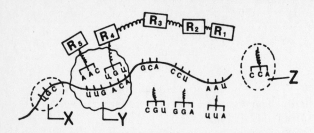

✳ 18. The original template for this process is known as   (1) DNA   (2) messenger RNA   (3) transfer RNA   (4) ribosomal RNA

✳ 19. The units labeled R_1, R_2, and R_3 represent   (1) nucleotides   (2) RNA molecules   (3) DNA molecules   (4) amino acids

✳ 20. The organelle labeled Y on which this process occurs is the   (1) nucleus   (2) ribosome   (3) chloroplast   (4) mitochondria

✳ 21. The circled portion labeled X is known as   (1) an amino acid   (2) a codon   (3) a polypeptide   (4) a single nucleotide

✳ 22. The circled portion labeled Z represents a molecule of   (1) DNA   (2) messenger RNA   (3) transfer RNA   (4) ribosomal RNA

Base your answers to questions 23 through 27 on the passage below.

Gene Splicing

Recent advances in cell technology and gene transplanting have allowed scientists to perform some interesting experiments. Some of these experiments have included splicing a human gene into the genetic material of bacteria. The altered bacteria express the added genetic material.

Bacteria reproduce rapidly under certain conditions. This means that bacteria with the gene for human insulin could multiply rapidly, resulting in a large bacterial population which could produce large quantities of human insulin.

The traditional source of insulin has been the pancreases of slaughtered animals. Continued use of this insulin can trigger allergic reactions in some humans. The new bacteria-produced insulin does not appear to produce these side effects.

The bacteria used for these experiments are *E. coli*, bacteria common to the digestive systems of many humans. Some scientists question these experiments and are concerned that the altered *E. coli* may accidentally get into water supplies.

Directions (23–27): For each of the following statements, write the number 1 if the statement is true according to the paragraph, the number 2 if the statement is false, or the number 3 if not enough information is given in the paragraph.

✳ 23. Transplanting genetic material into bacteria is a simple task.   (1) 1   (2) 2   (3) 3

✳ 24. Under certain conditions bacteria reproduce at a rapid rate.   (1) 1   (2) 2   (3) 3

✳ 25. Continued use of insulin from other animals may cause harmful side effects in some people.   (1) 1   (2) 2   (3) 3

✳ 26. The bacteria used in these experiments are normally found only in the nerve tissue of humans.   (1) 1   (2) 2   (3) 3

✳ 27. Bacteria other than *E. coli* are unable to produce insulin.   (1) 1   (2) 2   (3) 3

Base your answers to questions 28 through 31 on the passage below and on your knowledge of biology.

Today some plants are cloned to produce millions of offspring from a small piece of the original plant. Plant cloning is possible because the plant's diploid cells have the same genetic potential as the zygote that originally produced the plant and because of the action of the plant hormones auxin and cytokinin. These hormones are combined with other organic and inorganic substances in a growth medium that stimulates the production of new plants. The cloning process occurs in a sterile environment. The new plants produced are genetically identical to the original plant and to each other.

The process and equipment for cloning are more expensive than for other forms of vegetative propagation. The advantage of cloning is that large numbers of desirable plants can be produced in a short period of time. For example, a million plants of a new variety can be cloned in about six months.

✳ 28. For which reason is cloning used to reproduce plants?   (1) Plants with a large degree of genetic variability are produced.   (2) Plants are produced more cheaply than by other vegetative methods.   (3) Plants are produced by the sexual process, resulting in seeds.   (4) A large number of plants are produced in a short period of time.

✳ 29. If the diploid chromosome number of a cloned plant is 12, the chromosome number of the plant cell used to produce the cloned plant is   (1) 3   (2) 6   (3) 12   (4) 24

✳ 30. Which statement describes the hormones auxin and cytokinin?   (1) They are forms of vegetative propagation.   (2) They can develop into a zygote.   (3) They stimulate the production of new plants.   (4) They inhibit the production of new plants.

✳ 31. Cloning is defined as   (1) a form of sexual reproduction   (2) a form of vegetative propagation   (3) an inorganic hormone   (4) an inorganic component of the growing medium

✳ 32. Describe two important functions of DNA.

✳ 33. Why is DNA replication critical to the survival of organisms?

✱ Population Genetics.
The study of factors that affect gene frequencies in populations of sexually reproducing organisms is known as **population genetics**. A **population** includes all members of a species living in a given area.

✱ The **gene pool** of a population is the sum total of all inheritable genes in a given population.

✱ **Gene frequency** is the percentage of each allele for a particular trait in a population. For example, in the gene pool of a hypothetical population, the frequency of the allele for brown eyes may be 70 percent, while the frequency of the allele for blue eyes is 30 percent.

✱ Hardy-Weinberg Principle.
In 1908, G. H. Hardy and W. Weinberg stated that the gene frequencies in a population of sexually reproducing individuals will remain stable from generation to generation under certain conditions:
1. The population must be large.
2. Mating must be random within the population.
3. There must be no migration of organisms into or out of the population.
4. There must be no mutations.

✱ The conditions for gene-pool stability described in the **Hardy-Weinberg principle** seldom, if ever, exist. Thus the gene pool of a population tends to change from generation to generation.

QUESTIONS

✱ **1.** The gene frequency of which trait could be studied by means of the Hardy-Weinberg principle? (1) chloroplast shape in mitotically dividing algae (2) feather color in sexually reproducing fowl (3) leg number in bees reproducing parthenogenetically (4) cilia length in fissioning paramecia

✱ **2.** According to the Hardy-Weinberg principle, which would most likely upset the stability of the gene pool of a population? (1) maintaining a large population (2) geographic isolation of part of the population (3) a lack of mutations (4) random mating

✱ **3.** Which level of biological organization is studied in the Hardy-Weinberg principle? (1) population (2) community (3) ecosystem (4) organism

✱ **4.** All the heritable genes found in a population constitute the population's (1) recessive alleles (2) chromosome mutations (3) homologous structures (4) gene pool

✱ **5.** The gene pool in a population of *Rana pipiens* in a pond remained constant for many generations. The most probable reason for this stable gene pool is that (1) it was a small population with nonrandom mating and many mutations (2) random mating occurred in a small population with many mutations (3) no mutations occurred in a large, migrating population (4) no migration occurred in a large population with random mating

Base your answers to questions 6 and 7 on the graph below and on your knowledge of biology. The graph illustrates changes in the percentages of two varieties of a certain species.

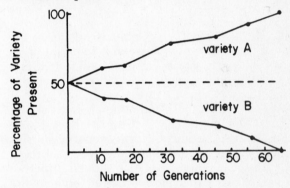

✱ **6.** Which variety will contribute significantly to the future of the species gene pool? (1) variety A, only (2) variety B, only (3) both variety A and variety B (4) neither variety A nor variety B

✱ **7.** What is the most probable reason that the percentage of variety A is increasing in the population of this species? (1) There is no chance for variety A to mate with variety B. (2) There is no genetic difference between variety A and variety B. (3) Variety A has some adaptive advantage that variety B does not. (4) Variety A is somehow less fit to survive than variety B.

UNIT 6 Evolution

Evolution is a process of change through time. The theory of evolution suggests that existing forms of life on earth have evolved from earlier forms over long periods of time. Evolution accounts for the differences in structure, function, and behavior among life forms, as well as the changes that occur in populations over many generations.

EVIDENCE OF EVOLUTION

Observations supporting the theory of evolution have been obtained from the study of the geologic record and from studies of comparative anatomy, embryology, cytology, and biochemistry.

Geologic Record.

Geologists estimate the age of the earth to be between 4.5 and 5 billion years. This estimate is based on radioactive dating of the oldest known rocks from the earth's crust. (It is assumed that the earth is at least as old as the oldest rocks and minerals in its crust.)

In studying the earth, scientists have found many **fossils**, the remains or traces of organisms that no longer exist. From their studies of rocks and fossils, scientists have developed a picture of the changes that have occurred both in the earth itself and in living things on the earth.

Fossils.

The earliest fossils known are traces of bacteria-like organisms that are about 3.5 billion years old. (The age of these fossils was determined by radioactive dating of the rocks in which they were found.)

Fossils of relatively intact organisms have been found preserved in ice, in tar, and in amber, a sticky plant resin that hardens. Mineralized bones, shells, and other hard parts of ancient organisms are sometimes found intact. (The soft parts generally decay in a short time.)

Other fossils have been formed by **petrifaction**, a process in which the tissues are gradually replaced by minerals that produce a stone replica of the original material.

Imprints, casts, and **molds** of organisms or parts of organisms are frequently found in **sedimentary rock.** This type of rock is formed from the deposition of thick layers of soft sediments that eventually harden and turn to rock from the weight of overlying sediments and water. The fossils form when the remains of dead organisms settle to the bottom of a body of water and are quickly covered by sediment. The overlying sediment slows or halts decay. When the layers of sediment harden, traces of the buried organisms are preserved in the rock.

In studying undisturbed sedimentary rock, scientists assume that each layer is older than all the layers, or *strata*, above it. Thus, fossils in the lower strata are older than fossils in overlying strata. It has been found that fossils in the upper strata of a sedimentary rock sample are generally more complex than fossils in the lower strata, which contain simpler life forms. Fossils in the upper strata are different from those in the lower strata, but there is often a resemblance between them. This suggests a link between modern forms and older forms. The fossil record may also provide evidence of divergent evolutionary pathways of some organisms from a common ancestor.

Some fossils in older strata are unlike any modern, living things. This suggests that some organisms have died out, or become extinct. On the other hand, some fossils are very similar to modern life forms, which suggests that some organisms have undergone little evolutionary change.

Comparative Anatomy.

Another line of evidence for evolution comes from observations of basic structural, or anatomical, similarities between organisms. **Homologous structures** are anatomical parts found in different organisms that are similar in origin and structure, although they may function differently. For example, the flippers of whales, the wings of bats, the forelimbs of cats, and the arms of humans are homologous structures; they serve different functions, but their basic bone structures are similar (Figure 6-1). The presence of such homologous structures suggests that these organisms have evolved from a common ancestor.

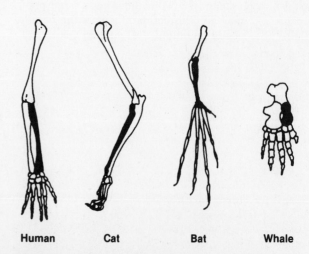

Human   Cat   Bat   Whale

Figure 6-1. Homologous structures in whales, cats, bats, and humans.

Fish   Tortoise   Chicken   Human

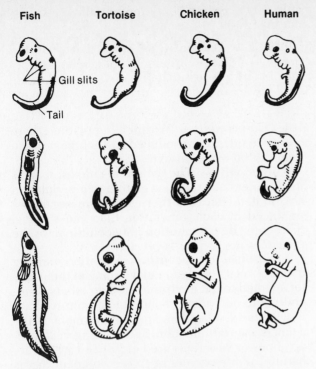

Gill slits

Tail

Figure 6-2. Some stages of embryonic development in fish, reptiles, birds, and humans.

Comparative Embryology.

Although certain adult organisms may be very different from each other, a comparison of the early stages of their embryonic development may show similarities that suggest a common ancestry. For example, the early embryos of fish, reptiles, birds, and humans closely resemble one another (Figure 6-2). As development continues, the characteristic traits of each species become apparent.

Comparative Cytology.

All living things are made up of cells. Cell organelles, including the cell membrane, ribosomes, and mitochondria, are structurally and functionally similar in most organisms.

Comparative Biochemistry.

All living things contain similar biochemical compounds. For example, the structure and function of DNA, RNA, and proteins (including enzymes) are similar in all organisms. The closer the relationship between organisms, the greater their biochemical similarity.

QUESTIONS

1. The forelegs of a frog and a horse are examples of structures that are (1) heterotrophic (2) homozygous (3) hermaphroditic (4) homologous

2. The similarity among the blood proteins of all the mammals may be taken as evidence for evolutionary relationships based upon (1) comparative anatomy (2) geographic distribution (3) comparative embryology (4) comparative biochemistry

3. The diagram below represents a cross section of undisturbed rock layers.

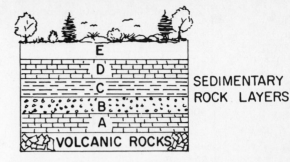

SEDIMENTARY ROCK LAYERS

A scientist discovers bones of a complex vertebrate species in layers *B* and *C*. In which layer would an earlier, less complex form of this vertebrate most likely first appear? (1) *A* (2) *E* (3) *C* (4) *D*

4. Which conclusion may be made when comparing fossils found in previously undisturbed strata of sedimentary rock? (1) The fossils in the upper strata are younger than those in the lower strata. (2) The fossils in the upper strata are older than those in the lower strata. (3) The fossils in the upper strata are generally less complex than those in the lower strata. (4) There are no fossils in the upper strata that resemble those in the lower strata.

5. Many related organisms are found to have the same enzymes and hormones. This suggests that (1) enzymes work only on specific substrates (2) enzymes act as catalysts in biochemical reactions (3) organisms living in the same environment require identical enzymes (4) these organisms may share a common ancestry

6. Which assumption is the basis for the use of the fossil record as evidence for evolution? (1) Fossils have been found to show a complete record of the evolution of all mammals. (2) In undisturbed layers of the earth's crust, the oldest fossils are found in the lowest layers. (3) All fossils can be found embedded in rocks. (4) All fossils were formed at the same time.

7. Which is an example of evidence of evolution based on comparative biochemistry? (1) Sheep insulin can be substituted for human insulin. (2) The structure of a whale's flipper is similar to that of a human hand. (3) Human embryos have a tail-like structure at one stage in their development. (4) Both birds and bats have wings.

8. If a rabbit is sensitized to human blood, the blood of the rabbit will react to chimpanzee blood very much the way it does to human blood. This is an example of which type of evidence supporting the theory of evolution? (1) comparative habitat (2) comparative anatomy (3) comparative embryology (4) comparative biochemistry

9. The presence of gill-like slits in a human embryo is considered to be evidence for the (1) theory that fish and mammals have a common ancestry (2) theory that the first organisms on Earth were heterotrophs (3) close relationship between fish and mammalian reproductive patterns (4) close relationship between humans and annelids

10. The diagram below represents a section of undisturbed rock and the general location of fossils of several closely related species. According to current theory, which is the most probable correct assumption to be made concerning species *A, B, C,* and *D?*

species C & D
species C
species A & B & C
species A & B
species A

(1) *A* is the ancestor of *B, C,* and *D.*   (2) *B* was extinct when *C* evolved.   (3) *C* evolved more recently than *A, B,* and *D.*   (4) *D* is the ancestor of *A, B,* and *C.*

11. Discuss some information scientists learn about organisms when studying the fossil record.

12. List and describe five evidences for evolution.

THEORIES OF EVOLUTION

Theories of evolution attempt to explain the similarities and differences among species. These theories must also account for the wide variety of adaptations in living things.

Lamarck.   The evolutionary theory of Jean-Baptiste Lamarck was based on his principle of use and disuse and the inheritance of acquired characteristics.

According to Lamarck's **principle of use and disuse,** new structures appeared in the course of evolution because they were needed. Structures that were present and were used became better developed and increased in size; structures that were not needed or not much used decreased in size, and eventually disappeared.

Based on the **inheritance of acquired characteristics,** evolutionary changes occurred when traits acquired during the lifetime of an individual were passed on to its offspring. It is assumed that traits that became well developed during the life of an individual were beneficial. As these traits were strengthened and passed on to each new generation, the species became better adapted to its environment.

Weismann.   The theory that traits acquired during the lifetime of an individual could be passed on to the next generation was disproved by August Weismann. In a series of experiments, Weismann removed the tails of mice. Offspring produced by the mating of the tailless mice had tails of normal length. Weismann removed the tails of these mice, and allowed them to mate. Again their offspring had tails of normal length. Weismann continued the experiment for many generations, but the newborn mice all had normal tails. The acquired condition of taillessness was not inherited.

Darwin.   Darwin's theory was based on the presence of variations among members of a species and the process that he called "natural selection." Darwin's theory includes the following ideas:

1. *Overpopulation.* Within a population, there are more offspring produced in each generation than can possibly survive.

2. *Competition.* The natural resources, such as food, water, and space, available to a population are limited. Because there are more organisms produced in each generation than can survive, there must be competition between them for the resources needed for survival.

3. *Survival of the fittest.* Variations among members of a population make some of them better adapted to the environment than others. Generally, the best-adapted individuals survive.

4. *Natural selection.* The environment is the agent of **natural selection,** determining which adaptations or variations are helpful and which are harmful. For example, in an environment that is undergoing an unusual cold period, animals born with fur that is thicker than normal will survive more easily than animals with thinner fur. In this case, the variation—thicker fur—is helpful in terms of the environmental pressure.

5. *Reproduction.* Individuals with helpful variations tend to survive and reproduce, transmitting these variations to their offspring.

6. *Speciation.* The development of new species, or **speciation,** occurs as variations or adaptations accumulate in a population over many generations.

In Darwin's theory, environmental pressures act as a force for the natural selection of the best-adapted individuals—those with helpful adaptations that enable them to survive and reproduce successfully. Darwin's theory did not explain how variations arise in members of a species.

QUESTIONS

1. The wings of experimental fruit flies were clipped short each generation for fifty generations. The fifty-first generation emerged with normal-length wings. This observation would tend to disprove the theory of evolution based on   (1) inheritance of mutations   (2) inheritance of acquired characteristics   (3) natural selection   (4) survival of the fittest

2. Darwin's theory of evolution did *not* contain the concept that   (1) genetic variations are produced by mutations and sexual recombination   (2) organisms that survive are best adapted to their environment   (3) population sizes remain constant due to a struggle for survival   (4) favorable traits are passed from one generation to another

3. An athlete explains that his muscles have become well-developed through daily activities of weight lifting. He believes that his offspring will inherit this trait of well-developed muscles. This belief would be most in agreement with the theory set forth by (1) Darwin (2) Lamarck (3) Weismann (4) Mendel

4. Natural selection can best be defined as (1) survival of the strongest organisms (2) elimination of the smallest organisms by the largest organisms (3) survival of those organisms genetically best adapted to the environment (4) survival and reproduction of those organisms that occupy the largest area in an environment

5. A supporter of the evolutionary theory set forth by Lamarck would probably theorize that the giraffe evolved a long neck due to (1) need and inheritance of acquired traits (2) mutations and genetic recombination (3) variations and survival of the fittest (4) overproduction and struggle for survival

6. Although similar in many respects, two species of organisms exhibit differences that make each well adapted to the environment in which it lives. The process of change that helps account for these differences is (1) evolution (2) parthenogenesis (3) comparative embryology (4) inheritance of acquired traits

7. The pig has four toes on each foot. Two of the toes are very small and do not have a major function in walking. Lamarck would probably have explained the reduced size of the two small toes by his evolutionary theory of (1) natural selection (2) mutation (3) use and disuse (4) synapsis

8. Weismann's experiments with mice produced results that helped to (1) support Darwin's assumption of a struggle for survival (2) disprove Lamarck's theory of the inheritance of acquired characteristics (3) disprove DeVries' concept of evolution (4) support Lamarck's theory of use and disuse

9. In a short paragraph, summarize Darwin's theory of evolution. Compare Darwin's theory to Lamarck's theory.

MODERN EVOLUTIONARY THEORY

The modern theory of evolution includes both Darwin's ideas of variation and natural selection and the genetic basis of variations in populations.

Sources of Variations.
Variations within a population result from two kinds of genetic events. First, recombination of alleles during sexual reproduction is a source of variations. Second, random and spontaneous gene and chromosome mutations produce genetic variations.

Natural Selection.
Natural selection involves the struggle of organisms to survive and reproduce in a given environment. As a result of natural selection, traits that are helpful to the survival of the organisms tend to be retained and passed on to new generations. Such favorable traits tend to increase in frequency within a population because the organisms that have them survive and reproduce more successfully than those that lack them. Unfavorable traits tend to decrease in frequency from generation to generation.

If environmental conditions change, traits that formerly had low survival value may have greater survival value. The survival value of traits that formerly were neither helpful nor harmful may also change. In both of these cases, traits that prove to be favorable under the new environmental conditions will increase in frequency in the population.

It has been found that the genetic makeup of some insects makes them resistant to the effects of insecticides. Before the widespread use of insecticides, this trait was of no particular survival value. With the increased use of insecticides, however, this trait developed a very high survival value. Since insects with resistance to insecticides survived and reproduced, the frequency of insecticide resistance has increased greatly in insect populations. Resistance to penicillin in populations of bacteria has followed the same pattern. The frequency of resistant organisms in populations has increased with increasing use of penicillin.

Resistance to insecticides and antibiotics did not arise as a result of exposure to these substances. The traits were already present in some members of the populations, and the insecticides and antibiotics acted as selecting agents.

Geographic Isolation.
Changes in gene frequencies that lead to the development of a new species are more likely to occur in small populations than in large populations. Small groups may be segregated from the main population by a geographic barrier, such as a body of water or a mountain range. As a result of this **geographic isolation,** the small population cannot interbreed with the larger, main population. In time, the isolated population may evolve into a new species.

The following factors may be involved in the evolution of a new species:

1. The gene frequencies in the isolated population may have been different from the gene frequencies in the main population to begin with. This difference in gene frequencies is known as the *founder effect.*

2. Different mutations occur in the isolated population and the main population.

3. Different environmental factors exert different selection pressures on each population.

Darwin observed the effect of geographic isolation in his study of the finches of the Galapagos Islands. Darwin hypothesized that the fourteen different species he observed had evolved from a single species that had migrated to the islands from the mainland. Over time, the different environment of each of the islands had gradually resulted in the evolution of the separate species.

Reproductive Isolation.
Geographic isolation may eventually lead to **reproductive isolation**. The isolated population becomes so different from the main population that members of the two groups cannot interbreed, even if the geographic barriers are removed. When two populations can no longer interbreed and produce fertile offspring, they have become two distinct species.

Time Frame for Evolution.
Although scientists generally agree on the basic factors involved in evolutionary change, there is currently a disagreement about the time frame in which such change occurs.

According to one theory, evolutionary change occurs slowly, gradually, and continuously. This theory, called **gradualism**, assumes that new species develop as a result of the gradual accumulation of small variations that eventually, together, cause reproductive isolation and a new species.

The theory of **punctuated equilibrium** proposes that species have long periods of relative stability (several million years) interrupted by geologically brief periods during which major changes occur, possibly leading to the evolution of a new species.

In the fossil records of some evolutionary pathways, there are transitional forms that support the theory of gradualism. However, in many evolutionary pathways, there is an apparent lack of transitional forms, which supports the theory of punctuated equilibrium.

QUESTIONS

1. A population of mosquitos is sprayed with a new insecticide. Most of the mosquitos are killed, but a few survive. In the next generation, the spraying continues, but still more mosquitos hatch that are immune to the insecticide. How could these results be explained according to the present concept of evolution? (1) The insecticide caused a mutation in the mosquitos. (2) The mosquitos learned how to fight the insecticide. (3) A few mosquitos in the first population were resistant and transmitted this resistance to their offspring. (4) The insecticide caused the mosquitos to develop an immune response, which was inherited.

2. What would be the most probable effect of geographic isolation in a population? (1) It has no effect on variations in the species. (2) It favors the production of new species. (3) It prevents the occurrence of mutations. (4) It encourages the mixing of gene pools.

3. Two organisms can be considered to be of different species if they (1) cannot mate with each other and produce fertile offspring (2) live in two different geographical areas (3) mutate at different rates depending on their environment (4) have genes drawn from the same gene pool

4. Certain strains of bacteria that were susceptible to penicillin have now become resistant. The probable explanation for this is that (1) the mutation rate must have increased naturally (2) the strains have become resistant because they needed to do so for survival (3) a mutation was retained and passed on to succeeding generations because it had high survival value (4) the principal forces influencing the pattern of survival in a population are isolation and mating

5. The theory of continental drift hypothesizes that Africa and South America were once a single landmass, but have drifted apart over millions of years. The "Old World" monkeys of Africa, although similar, show several genetic differences from the "New World" monkeys of South America. Which factor is probably the most important for maintaining these differences? (1) fossil records (2) comparative anatomy (3) use and disuse (4) geographic isolation

6. A change in the frequency of any mutant allele in a population most likely depends on the (1) size of the organisms possessing the mutant allele (2) adaptive value of the trait associated with the mutant allele (3) degree of dominance of the mutant allele (4) degree of recessiveness of the mutant allele

7. Many modern evolutionists have accepted much of Darwin's theory of evolution, but have added genetic information that gives a scientific explanation of (1) overproduction (2) the struggle for existence (3) the survival of the fittest (4) variations

8. As a result of sexual reproduction, the rate of evolutionary change in plants and animals has been greatly speeded up because (1) the offspring show more diversity than in asexual reproduction (2) characteristics change less frequently than in asexual reproduction (3) environmental changes never affect organisms produced by asexual reproduction (4) two parents have fewer offspring than one parent

9. Populations of a species may develop traits different from each other if they are isolated geographically for sufficient lengths of time. The most likely explanation for these differences is that (1) acquired traits cannot be inherited by offspring (2) environmental conditions in the two areas are identical (3) genetic recombination tends to be different in both populations (4) mutations are likely to be the same in both populations

10. Explain how sources of variation and natural selection drive the evolutionary process.

11. How did Darwin explain how 14 finch species evolved from a single mainland ancestor? Use the terms geographic isolation and reproductive isolation in your answer.

THE HETEROTROPH HYPOTHESIS

The **heterotroph hypothesis** is one proposed explanation for how life arose and evolved on the primitive earth. According to this hypothesis, the first life forms were heterotrophic, and had to obtain organic nutrients from the environment.

The Primitive Earth.
It is assumed that during the period preceding the development of the first life forms the primitive earth was an exceptionally hot body consisting of inorganic substances in solid, liquid, and gaseous states.

The atmosphere of the primitive earth had no free oxygen; instead, it was thought to consist of hydrogen (H_2), ammonia (NH_3), methane (CH_4), and water vapor. As the earth cooled, much of the water vapor condensed and fell as rain, which carried dissolved atmospheric gases (ammonia, methane, and hydrogen) and some minerals into the seas that formed. The seas became rich in these dissolved substances and minerals and are often described by biologists as a "hot, thin soup."

The primitive earth provided an energy-rich environment. It was very hot, and in addition to heat, there was electrical energy in the form of lightning, X rays and ultraviolet rays from sunlight, and radioactivity from rocks.

Synthesis of Organic Compounds.
The large amount of available energy was the driving force for synthesis reactions on the primitive earth. In these reactions, the inorganic raw materials in the seas became chemically bonded to form organic molecules, including simple sugars and amino acids. These organic molecules were the building blocks for the first life forms.

The scientist Stanley Miller devised an apparatus in which he simulated the conditions thought to exist in the primitive environment. His experiments showed that in the presence of heat and electrical energy, dissolved gases could combine to form simple organic compounds.

Formation of Aggregates.
In time, the simple organic molecules accumulated in the seas. Eventually, they combined chemically in synthesis reactions to form more complex organic molecules. (Such interactions between organic molecules have been demonstrated in the laboratory by Sidney Fox.) Some of the large, complex molecules formed groupings or clusters called *aggregates*. The aggregates developed a surrounding "membrane," which made it possible for the internal composition of the aggregate to differ from that of the surrounding water. It is believed that aggregates absorbed simple organic molecules from the environment for "food." Thus they carried on a form of heterotrophic nutrition.

Reproduction.
The aggregates became more complex and highly organized. Eventually, they developed the ability to reproduce. At the point where the ability to reproduce had evolved, the aggregates were considered to be living cells.

Heterotroph to Autotroph.
It is thought that these early heterotrophic life forms carried on a form of anaerobic respiration, or fermentation. As a result of extended periods of fermentation, carbon dioxide was added to the atmosphere. Eventually, as a result of evolution, some heterotrophic forms developed the capacity to use carbon dioxide from the atmosphere in the synthesis of organic compounds. These organisms were the first autotrophs.

Anaerobes to Aerobes.
Autotrophic activity (photosynthesis) added free oxygen to the atmosphere. Over time, the capacity to use free oxygen in respiration (aerobic respiration) evolved in both autotrophs and heterotrophs.

On the modern earth, there are both autotrophs and heterotrophs. Some life forms still carry on anaerobic respiration, but in most, respiration is aerobic.

QUESTIONS

1. According to the heterotroph hypothesis, the first living things probably were anaerobic because their environment had no available (1) food (2) energy (3) water (4) oxygen

2. Which is one basic assumption of the heterotroph hypothesis? (1) More complex organisms appeared before less complex organisms. (2) Living organisms did not appear until there was oxygen in the atmosphere. (3) Large autotrophic organisms appeared before small photosynthesizing organisms. (4) Autotrophic activity added molecular oxygen to the environment.

3. The heterotroph hypothesis is an attempt to explain (1) how the earth was originally formed (2) why simple organisms usually evolve into complex organisms (3) why evolution occurs very slowly (4) how life originated on the earth

4. The heterotroph hypothesis states that heterotrophic forms appeared before autotrophic forms as the first living things. A major assumption for this hypothesis is that (1) sufficient heat was not available for a foodmaking process (2) heterotrophic organisms were able to use molecules from the sea as food (3) lightning and radiational energy were limited to terrestrial areas (4) moisture in liquid form was limited to aquatic areas

5. Explain the transition from heterotroph to autotroph. What is the source of carbon dioxide and oxygen in the atmosphere?

UNIT 7 Ecology

Ecology is the study of the relationships between organisms and between organisms and their physical environment. No organism in nature exists as an entity separate from its environment.

ECOLOGICAL ORGANIZATION

In ecology, the relationships between organisms and the environment may be considered at various levels. The smallest, least inclusive level in terms of ecological organization is the population; the largest and most inclusive level is the biosphere.

1. All members of a species living in a given location make up a population. For example, all the water lilies in a pond make up a population.

2. All the interacting populations in a given area make up a community. For example, all the plants, animals, and microorganisms in a pond make up a pond community.

3. An ecosystem includes all the members of a community plus the physical environment in which they live. The living and nonliving parts of an ecosystem function together as an interdependent and relatively stable system.

4. The biosphere is the portion of the earth in which living things exist. The biosphere, which is composed of numerous complex ecosystems, includes the water, soil, and air.

QUESTIONS

1. All the different species within an ecosystem are collectively referred to as the (1) niche (2) community (3) consumers (4) population

2. Which term includes the three terms that follow it? (1) population: community, ecosystem, organism (2) community: ecosystem, organism, population (3) ecosystem: organism, population, community (4) organism: ecosystem, community, population

3. Which sequence shows increasing complexity of levels of ecological organization? (1) biosphere, ecosystem, community (2) biosphere, community, ecosystem (3) community, ecosystem, biosphere (4) ecosystem, biosphere, community

4. The members of the species *Microtus pennsylvanicus* living in a certain location make up a (1) community (2) succession (3) population (4) phylum

5. Which term includes all of the terrestial and aquatic regions on Earth where life exists? (1) marine biome (2) climax community (3) biosphere (4) tundra

6. List and explain the four levels of ecological organizations. Give examples of each.

CHARACTERISTICS OF ECOSYSTEMS

Ecosystems are the structural and functional units studied in ecology.

Requirements of Ecosystems.
An ecosystem, which involves interactions between living and nonliving factors, is a self-sustaining unit when the following conditions are met:

1. There must be a constant flow of energy into the ecosystem, and there must be organisms in the ecosystem that can use the energy for the synthesis of organic compounds. The primary source of energy for ecosystems on earth is sunlight; the organisms that can use this energy for the synthesis of organic compounds are green plants, algae, and other photosynthetic autotrophs.

2. There must be a cycle of materials between living organisms and the environment in an ecosystem.

Abiotic Factors of Ecosystems.
The components of an ecosystem include nonliving, or abiotic, factors, and living, or biotic, factors. The abiotic factors of the environment are physical factors that sustain the lives and reproductive cycles of organisms. These factors are:

1. intensity of light
2. temperature range
3. amount of water
4. type of soil
5. availability of minerals and other inorganic substances
6. supply of gases, including oxygen, carbon dioxide, and nitrogen
7. pH (acidity or alkalinity)

Abiotic factors vary from one environmental area to another. The abiotic conditions in any particular environment determine the types of plants and animals that can exist there. Thus, abiotic factors are limiting factors. For example, the small amount of available water limits the kinds of plants and animals that can live in the desert.

Biotic Factors of Ecosystems.
The biotic factors of an ecosystem are all the living things that directly or indirectly affect the environment. The organisms of an ecosystem interact in many ways. These interactions include nutritional and symbiotic relationships.

Nutritional Relationships. Nutritional relationships involve the transfer of nutrients from one organism to another within the ecosystem.

Autotrophs are organisms that can use energy from the environment to synthesize their own food from inorganic compounds. Most autotrophs are photosynthetic, using energy from sunlight and carbon dioxide and water from the environment to synthesize organic compounds.

Heterotrophs cannot synthesize their own food, and must obtain nutrients from other organisms. Depending on their source of food, heterotrophs are classified as saprophytes, herbivores, carnivores, or omnivores.

Saprophytes are organisms, including heterotrophic plants, fungi, and bacteria, that obtain nutrients from the remains of other organisms. For example, mushrooms are saprophytes that obtain nourishment from dead plants.

Herbivores are animals, such as deer, that feed on plants.

Carnivores are animals that consume other animals. Carnivores include **predators**, which kill and consume their prey, and **scavengers**, which feed on the remains of animals they have not killed.

Omnivores are animals that consume both plants and animals.

✱ **Symbiotic Relationships.** Different kinds of organisms sometimes live together in a close association. Such **symbiotic relationships** may or may not be beneficial to the organisms involved.
✱ 1. A type of symbiotic relationship in which one organism benefits and the other is not adversely affected is called **commensalism**. Barnacles living on whales and orchids living on large, tropical trees both obtain favorable places to live without harm to the other organism.
✱ 2. A symbiotic relationship in which both organisms benefit is called **mutualism**. For example, certain protozoans live in the digestive tracts of termites. Wood eaten by the termite is digested by the protozoans. The nutrients released supply both organisms. Another example of mutualism is found in lichens, which are made up of both algal and fungal cells. The algal cells carry on photosynthesis, which provides food for the lichen, while the fungal cells provide moisture and minerals and anchor the lichen to a surface.
✱ Nitrogen-fixing bacteria live in the roots of legumes. The relationship between these organisms is mutualistic because the bacteria provide nitrogen compounds for the plant, while the plant provides the bacteria with nutrients and a good environment in which to live.
✱ 3. A symbiotic relationship in which one organism (the **parasite**) benefits and the other (the **host**) is harmed is called **parasitism**. Examples include the athlete's foot fungus, which lives on humans, and tapeworms and heartworms in dogs.

1. Different species of animals in a community would most likely be similar in (1) physical structure (2) size (3) abiotic requirements (4) number of offspring produced
2. Interactions between organisms which influence their development and survival are known as (1) biotic factors (2) inorganic substances (3) physical conditions (4) chemical factors
3. In a study made over a period of years in a certain part of the country, the research showed that there was a low amount of rainfall, a wide seasonal variation in temperature, and short periods of daylight. These environmental factors are (1) abiotic factors of little importance to biotic factors (2) abiotic factors that limit the type of organisms present in the area (3) abiotic factors important to saprophytes in the area (4) biotic factors that are affected by the abiotic factors
✱ 4. The presence of nitrogen-fixing bacteria in nodules on the roots of legumes such as the peanut plant illustrates an association known as (1) commensalism (2) mutualism (3) parasitism (4) saprophytism
5. At times hyenas will feed on the remains of animals they, themselves, have not killed. At other times they will kill other animals for food. Based on their feeding habits, hyenas are best described as (1) herbivores and parasites (2) herbivores and predators (3) scavengers and parasites (4) scavengers and predators
6. Which is an abiotic factor in the environment? (1) water (2) earthworm (3) fungus (4) human
7. The organisms that prevent the earth from becoming covered with the bodies of dead organisms are known as (1) herbivores (2) parasites (3) producers (4) saprophytes
8. A particular species of fish has a very narrow range of tolerance for changes in water temperature and dissolved oxygen content. For the fish, the temperature and oxygen content represent (1) autotrophic conditions (2) a community (3) limiting factors (4) symbiosis
9. Which occurs within self-sustaining ecosystems? (1) Consumers produce most of the oxygen. (2) Consumers eventually outnumber producers. (3) Energy is created and destroyed. (4) Organisms interact with their environment.
✱ 10. Which of the following is an example of parasitism? (1) tapeworms living in the digestive tract of dogs (2) algal and fungal cells living together in the form of a lichen (3) barnacles living on whales (4) wood-digesting protozoa living in the digestive tract of termites
✱ 11. Parasitism is a type of nutritional relationship in which (1) both organisms benefit (2) both organisms are harmed (3) neither organism benefits (4) one organism benefits and the other is harmed
12. For an ecosystem to be self-sustaining, it must (1) contain more animals than plants (2) receive a constant flow of energy (3) have a constant supply of water (4) contain only heterotrophs

Ecology

13. Heterotrophs include (1) autotrophs, saprophytes, and herbivores (2) omnivores, carnivores, and autotrophs (3) saprophytes, herbivores, and carnivores (4) herbivores, autotrophs, and omnivores

14. The primary source of energy for ecosystems is (1) radioactivity (2) sunlight (3) animal proteins (4) carbon dioxide

15. Describe the conditions which must exist for an ecosystem to be self-sustaining.

16. Explain why abiotic factors are limiting factors.

Energy Flow Relationships.
For an ecosystem to be self-sustaining, there must be a flow of energy between organisms. The pathways of chemical energy from food through the organisms of an ecosystem are represented by food chains and food webs.

Food Chains. The transfer of energy from green plants through a series of organisms with repeated stages of eating and being eaten is described as a **food chain** (Figure 7-1). Green plants obtain energy for their life processes from the radiant energy of sunlight, which they convert to usable chemical energy by photosynthesis. For all other organisms in the food chain, energy is obtained from the breakdown of food. The organisms in a food chain are described in terms of the following categories.

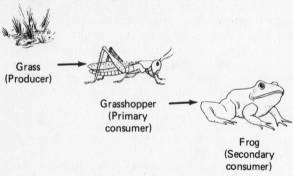

Figure 7-1. A food chain.

Green plants and other autotrophs are the **producers** in the food chain. All the energy for a community is derived from the organic compounds synthesized by the producers.

All the heterotrophic organisms in a community are **consumers**. They must obtain energy from food that they eat. Animals that feed on green plants are called **primary consumers**, or herbivores. Animals that feed on primary consumers are called **secondary consumers**, or carnivores (meat-eaters). Omnivores may be either primary or secondary consumers.

Saprophytes are **decomposers**, organisms that break down the remains of dead organisms and organic wastes. Decomposers return substances in the remains and wastes of plants and animals to the environment, where they can be used by other living organisms. Most decomposers are bacteria or fungi.

Food Webs. In a natural community, most organisms eat more than one species and may be eaten, in turn, by more than one species. Thus, the various food chains in a community are interconnected, forming a **food web** (Figure 7-2). Food webs have the same levels of organisms (producers, consumers, and decomposers) as food chains, but the flow of energy and materials is much more complex.

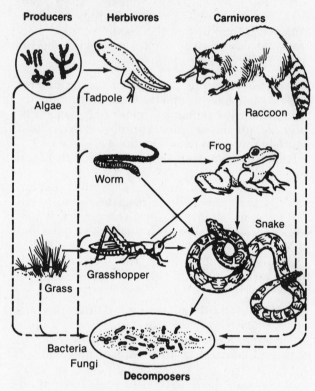

Figure 7-2. A food web.

Pyramid of Energy. The greatest amount of energy in a community is present in the organisms that make up the producer level. Only a small portion of this energy is passed on to primary consumers, and only a small portion of the energy in the primary consumers is passed on to secondary consumers. **A pyramid of energy** can be used to illustrate the loss of usable energy at each feeding level (Figure 7-3).

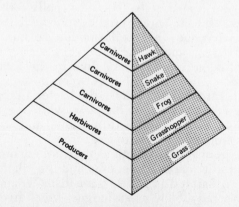

Figure 7-3. A pyramid of energy.

At each consumer level in an energy pyramid, only about 10 percent of the ingested nutrients are used to synthesize new tissues, which represent the food available for the next feeding level. The remaining energy is used by the consumers for their life functions and is eventually converted to heat, which is lost from the ecosystem. Thus, an ecosystem cannot sustain itself without the constant input of energy from the sun.

* Pyramid of Biomass. In general, the decrease in available energy at each higher feeding level means that less organic matter, or **biomass**, can be supported at each higher level. Thus, the total mass of producers in an ecosystem is greater than the total mass of primary consumers, and the total mass of primary consumers is greater than the total mass of secondary consumers. The decrease in biomass at each higher feeding level is illustrated by a **pyramid of biomass** (Figure 7-4).

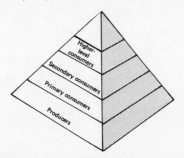

*Figure 7-4. A pyramid of biomass.

QUESTIONS

1. Which food chain relationship illustrates the nutritional pattern of a primary consumer? (1) seeds and fruits eaten by a mouse (2) an earthworm eaten by a mole (3) a mosquito eaten by a bat (4) a mold growing on a dead frog

2. Which term describes the bird and the cat in the following pattern of energy flow?

sun → grass → grasshopper → bird → cat

(1) herbivores (2) saprophytes (3) predators (4) omnivores

3. The elements stored in living cells of organisms in a community will eventually be returned to the soil for use by other living organisms. The organisms that carry out this process are (1) producers (2) herbivores (3) carnivores (4) decomposers

4. In the food chain below, what is the function of the rabbit?

lettuce plant → rabbit → coyote

(1) parasite (2) saprophyte (3) consumer (4) producer

5. Fly larvae consume the body of a dead rabbit. In this activity, they function as (1) producers (2) scavengers (3) herbivores (4) parasites

Base your answers to questions 6 through 9 on the diagram below and on your knowledge of biology. The diagram represents different species of organisms interacting with each other in and around a pond environment.

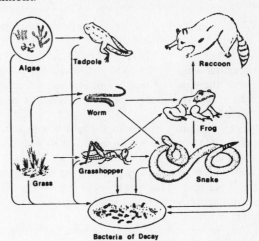

6. The adult frog represents a type of consumer known as a (1) producer (2) carnivore (3) saprophyte (4) parasite

7. Which organisms are classified as herbivores? (1) algae, tadpole, raccoon (2) worm, snake, bacteria (3) tadpole, worm, grasshopper (4) grasshopper, bacteria, frog

8. Which statement about the algae and grass is true? (1) They are classified as omnivores. (2) They parasitize the animals that consume them. (3) They contain the greatest amount of stored energy. (4) They decompose nutrients from dead organisms.

9. The interactions among organisms shown in this diagram illustrate (1) a food web (2) geographic isolation (3) abiotic factors (4) organic evolution

* 10. Which level of this food pyramid represents the largest biomass? (1) bass (2) minnows (3) copepods (4) algae

* 11. Which diagram best represents the usual relationships of biomass in a stable community? (1) 1 (2) 2 (3) 3 (4) 4

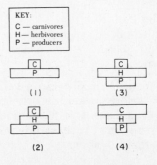

Base your answers to questions 12 through 14 on the food chain represented below and on your knowledge of biology.

rosebush → aphid → ladybird beetle → spider → toad → snake

12. Which organism in the food chain can transform light energy into chemical energy? (1) spider (2) ladybird beetle (3) rosebush (4) snake

13. At which stage in the food chain will the population with the smallest number of animals probably be found? (1) spider (2) aphid (3) ladybird beetle (4) snake

14. Which organism in this food chain is a primary consumer? (1) rosebush (2) aphid (3) ladybird beetle (4) toad

15. Which level in an energy pyramid has the greatest amount of energy? (1) highest level consumers (2) secondary consumers (3) primary consumers (4) producers

16. Draw, using specific organisms as examples, a pyramid of energy. Distinguish between a pyramid of energy and a pyramid of biomass. Explain the relationship between them.

17. Explain why an ecosystem could not sustain itself without the constant input of energy from the sun.

Base your answers to questions 18 through 21 on the diagram below, which represents four possible pathways for the transfer of energy stored by green plants.

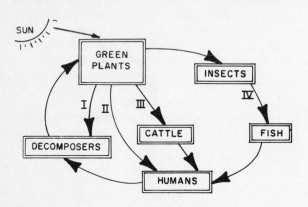

18. The pathway labeled IV represents (1) a food chain (2) a population (3) an ecosystem (4) an abiotic factor

19. Through which pathway would the sun's energy be most directly available to humans? (1) I (2) II (3) III (4) IV

20. In this diagram, humans are shown to be (1) herbivores, only (2) carnivores, only (3) omnivores (4) parasites

21. The cattle in the diagram represent (1) primary consumers (2) secondary consumers (3) producers (4) autotrophs

Cycles of Materials.

In a self-sustaining ecosystem, various materials are recycled between the organisms and the abiotic environment. The recycling process allows materials to be used over and over again.

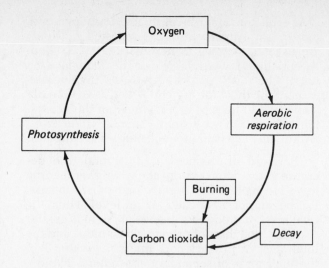

Figure 7-5. The carbon-hydrogen-oxygen cycle.

Carbon-Hydrogen-Oxygen Cycle. Carbon, hydrogen, and oxygen are recycled through the environment by the processes of respiration and photosynthesis (Figure 7-5). Carbon dioxide is released by the breakdown of glucose in aerobic cellular respiration, which uses oxygen from the air. In photosynthesis, carbon dioxide from the air is used in the synthesis of glucose, and oxygen is given off as a by-product.

Water Cycle. In the water cycle, water moves between the earth's surface and the atmosphere (Figure 7-6). The main processes involved in this cycle are **evaporation** and **condensation**. Liquid water on the earth's surface changes to a gas by the process of evaporation, and enters the atmosphere in the form of water vapor. As a result of condensation, water vapor is returned to the liquid state and falls to earth (precipitation). Some water vapor is added to the atmosphere by aerobic respiration in plants and animals and by transpiration in plants.

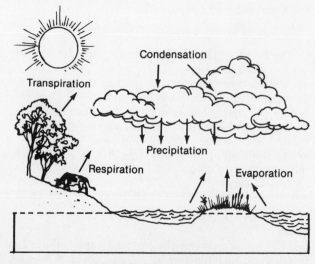

Figure 7-6. The water cycle.

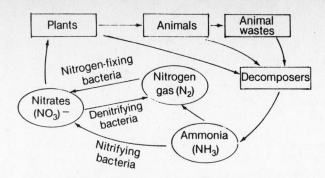

*Figure 7-7. The nitrogen cycle.

Nitrogen Cycle. Nitrogen is needed by all living things because it is part of the structure of amino acids and proteins. Plants absorb nitrogen-containing compounds from the soil; animals obtain nitrogen in the form of proteins in the foods they eat. The proteins are broken down by digestion to amino acids, which are then used in the synthesis of animal proteins.

* The nitrogen cycle involves decomposers and other soil bacteria. Figure 7-7 shows the various components of the nitrogen cycle, which are described below.

1. **Nitrogen-fixing bacteria**, which live in nodules in the roots of some plants (legumes), convert free nitrogen (N_2) from the air into **nitrates** (compounds containing $-NO_3$).

2. Nitrates are absorbed from the soil by plants and used in protein synthesis.

3. Animals that eat plants convert plant proteins into animal proteins.

4. The nitrogenous wastes of living animals and the nitrogen compounds in the remains of dead plants and animals are broken down by decomposers and converted to ammonia.

5. **Nitrifying bacteria** in the soil convert ammonia into nitrates, which can be used by plants.

6. **Denitrifying bacteria** break down some nitrogen-containing compounds into free nitrogen, which is released into the atmosphere.

QUESTIONS

* 1. In which form is nitrogen normally absorbed from the soil by grasses? (1) nitrates (2) uric acid (3) ammonia (4) molecular nitrogen

2. The processes involved in the recycling of carbon, hydrogen, and oxygen are (1) evaporation and condensation (2) photosynthesis and respiration (3) nitrification and denitrification (4) respiration and transpiration

* 3. Nitrogen is both removed from the atmosphere and returned to the atmosphere by the activities of (1) plants, only (2) animals, only (3) plants and animals (4) bacteria

4. Animals obtain nitrogen from (1) food (2) the soil (3) the atmosphere (4) bacteria in their intestines

5. Carbon dioxide is added to the atmosphere by (1) photosynthesis in plants (2) evaporation (3) respiration in animals, only (4) respiration in plants and animals

6. Oxygen is added to the atmosphere by (1) evaporation and photosynthesis (2) respiration in plants (3) photosynthesis, only (4) denitrifying bacteria

7. Which of the following processes is *not* involved in the water cycle? (1) condensation (2) nitrification (3) evaporation (4) transpiration

* 8. Nitrogen compounds in animal wastes and in the remains of dead organisms are broken down and converted into other compounds that can be used by living organisms by (1) bacteria (2) photosynthesis (3) aerobic respiration (4) absorption

Base your answers to questions 9 through 11 on the diagram below, which represents a cycle, and on your knowledge of biology.

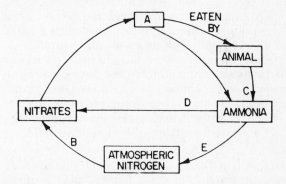

* 9. Nitrifying bacteria are represented by letter (1) A (2) E (3) C (4) D

* 10. The letter B most likely represents (1) bacteria of decay (2) denitrifying bacteria (3) a leguminous plant (4) nitrogen-fixing bacteria

* 11. The cycle represented by the diagram is the (1) nitrogen cycle (2) carbon cycle (3) water cycle (4) oxygen cycle

12. Describe two cycles which restore abiotic materials to the environment.

ECOSYSTEM FORMATION

Ecosystems tend to change over a long period of time until a stable ecosystem is formed. Both the communities (living things) and the nonliving part of the ecosystem change.

Succession.
The replacement of one kind of community by another in an ecosystem is called **ecological succession**. The kind of stable ecosystem that eventually develops in a particular geographical area depends on climate.

* **Pioneer Organisms.** Depending on climate and other abiotic environmental factors, succession on land can begin in an area with no living

things and end with a forest. Succession begins with **pioneer organisms,** which are the first plants to populate a given area. Lichens and algae may be pioneer organisms on bare rock.

✱ Starting with pioneer plants, each community modifies the environment, often making it less favorable for itself and more favorable for other kinds of communities. One sequence of plant succession in New York State might be: lichens, grasses, shrubs, conifers (pine trees), and deciduous (beech and maple) woodlands.

✱ Since plants are the basic source of food for a community, the types of plants present in a community determine the types of animals in the community. As the plant populations change, the animal populations also change.

✱ **Climax Communities.** Succession ends with the development of a **climax community** in which populations of plants and animals exist in balance with each other and with the environment. In New York State, for example, the oak-hickory and hemlock-beech-maple associations represent two climax communities. In the midwest, where there is less rain, grasslands are the climax community.

✱ The climax community remains until a catastrophic change, such as a volcanic eruption or forest fire, alters or destroys it. Thereafter, succession begins again, leading to the development of a new climax community. This new community may be of the same type as the previous one, or if the catastrophe has changed the environment in some basic way, it may be of another kind.

Competition.
Different species living in the same environment, or **habitat,** may require the same resources. When the resources, including food, space, water, light, oxygen, or minerals, are limited, competition occurs among the species. **Competition** is the struggle between different species for the same, limited resources. The more similar the needs of the species, the more intense the competition.

✱ Each species occupies a niche in the community. A **niche** is the role the species plays, and includes the type of food it eats or nutrients it requires, where it lives, where it reproduces, and its relationships with other species. When two species compete for the same niche, the weaker species is usually eliminated, establishing one species per niche in a community.

QUESTIONS

✱ **1.** In an ecological succession in New York State, lichens growing on bare rock are considered to be (1) climax organisms (2) pioneer organisms (3) primary consumers (4) decomposers

2. When two different species live in the same environment and use the same limited resources, which will usually occur? (1) competition (2) succession (3) commensalism (4) mutualism

3. The natural replacement of one community with another until a climax stage is reached is known as (1) ecological balance (2) organic evolution (3) dynamic equilibrium (4) ecological succession

✱ **4.** In an ecological succession leading to the establishment of a pond community, which of the following organisms would be among the first to establish themselves? (1) grasses (2) algae (3) minnows (4) deciduous trees

5. In New York State, bluebirds and sparrows inhabit nearly the same ecological niche. In many areas, bluebirds are being replaced by the sparrows as a result of (1) symbiosis (2) competition (3) mutualism (4) equilibrium

✱ **6.** Ecological succession ends with the development of a stable (1) climax community (2) pioneer community (3) niche (4) abiotic community

✱ **7.** The role a species plays in a community is its (1) habitat (2) biotic factor (3) succession (4) niche

✱ **8.** In a freshwater pond community, a carp eats decaying material from around the bases of underwater plants, while a snail scrapes algae from the leaves and stems of the same plant. They can survive at the same time because they occupy (1) the same niche, but different habitats (2) the same habitat, but different niches (3) the same habitat and the same niche (4) different habitats and niches

✱ **9.** Which two groups of organisms are most likely to be pioneer organisms? (1) songbirds and squirrels (2) lichens and algae (3) deer and black bears (4) oak and hickory trees

✱ **10.** Following a major forest fire, an area that was once wooded is converted to barren soil. Which of the following schemes describes the most likely sequence of changes in vegetation in the area following the fire? (1) shrubs → maples → pines → grasses (2) maples → pines → grasses → shrubs (3) pines → shrubs → maples → grasses (4) grasses → shrubs → pines → maples

✱ **11.** Describe the various stages which precede a beech-maple forest in New York State.

BIOMES

The earth can be divided into broad geographic regions by climate. The kind of climax ecosystem that develops in these large climatic areas is called a **biome.** Biomes may be terrestrial (land biomes) or aquatic (water biomes). A tropical rain forest found near the equator is a land biome. The ocean is an aquatic biome.

✱ **Terrestrial Biomes.** The major plant and animal associations (biomes) on land are determined by the large climate zones of the earth. These climate zones are, in turn, determined by geographic factors, including **latitude** (distance north or south of the equator) and **altitude** (distance above or below sea level). Other major geo-

Biome	Characteristics	Plants	Animals
Tundra	Permanently frozen subsoil	lichens, mosses, grasses	caribou, snowy owl
Taiga	Long, severe winters; summers with thawing subsoil	conifers	moose, black bear
Temperate-deciduous forest	Moderate precipitation; cold winters, warm summers	deciduous trees (maple, oak, beech)	gray squirrel, fox, deer
Tropical forest	Heavy rainfall; constant warmth	many species of broad-leaved plants	snake, monkey, leopard
Grassland	Considerable variability in rainfall and temperature; strong prevailing winds	grasses	pronghorn antelope, prairie dog, bison
Desert	Sparse rainfall; extreme daily temperature fluctuations	drought-resistant shrubs and succulent plants	kangaroo rat, lizard

graphic features, including large bodies of water, mountains, and deserts, modify the climate of nearby regions.

✱ Climate includes the temperature range and the amounts of precipitation and solar radiation received by a region. The presence or absence of water is a major limiting factor for terrestrial biomes and determines the kinds of plant and animal associations that can be established.

✱ **Kinds of Terrestrial Biomes.** Land biomes are described in terms of, and sometimes named for, the dominant kind of climax vegetation found there. Table 7-1 lists the major land biomes, their characteristics and dominant vegetation, and some representative animals.

✱ **Effects of Latitude and Altitude.** At the equator, the temperature and amount of rainfall remain relatively constant throughout the year. With increasing distance from the equator, temperature and rainfall show more variation during the year.

✱ Increasing altitude may have the same effect on climate as increasing latitude. Thus, the temperature and kind of climax vegetation found at the top of a high mountain near the equator may be very much like a region far north of the equator. This relationship is shown in Figure 7-8.

✱ Aquatic Biomes. Aquatic biomes make up the largest ecosystem on earth. More than 70 percent of the earth's surface is covered by water; the majority of living things on earth are water-dwellers.

✱ Aquatic biomes are more stable than terrestrial biomes; they show less variation in temperature because water has a great capacity to absorb

and hold heat. The kinds and numbers of organisms present in an aquatic biome are affected by various factors, including the amounts of dissolved oxygen and carbon dioxide, water temperature, intensity of light, and the kinds and amounts of dissolved minerals and suspended particles in the water.

✱ Aquatic organisms are well adapted for the removal of dissolved oxygen from water. They also have adaptations for maintenance of proper water balance in their cells. Water balance is affected by the concentration of salts in the water.

✱ In aquatic biomes, most photosynthesis takes place near the surface since the light intensity is greater there. At greater depths, where light does not penetrate, there is no photosynthesis.

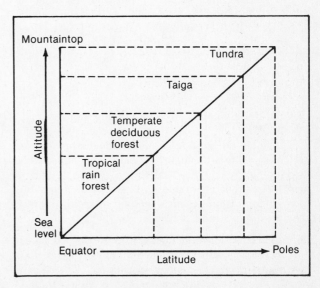

✱Figure 7-8. Relationship between latitude and altitude.

✱ Marine Biome. The marine, or saltwater, biome includes all the oceans of the earth, which make up a continuous body of water. Following are the most important characteristics of the marine biome.

1. It is the most stable environment on earth.

2. It absorbs and holds large quantities of solar heat, thereby stabilizing the earth's temperature.

3. It contains a relatively constant supply of nutrients and dissolved salts.

4. It serves as a habitat for a large number and wide variety of organisms.

5. Much of the photosynthesis on earth occurs in the oceans along the edges of the land masses (coastal waters).

✱ Freshwater Biomes. The freshwater biome includes ponds, lakes, and rivers. Because these are separate bodies of water, they vary widely in size, temperature, oxygen and carbon dioxide concentrations, amounts of suspended particles, current velocity, and rate of succession.

✱ Ponds and lakes tend to fill in over time. Dead plant material accumulates on the bottom and around the banks, gradually making the body of water shallower and smaller. Thus, in all but the largest lakes, there is a succession from a freshwater to a terrestrial climax community.

QUESTIONS

✱ 1. In which of the following biomes does most of the photosynthesis on earth occur? (1) deciduous forests (2) oceans (3) deserts (4) coniferous forests

✱ 2. Drastic changes in air temperature would be *least* likely to affect which biome? (1) tundra (2) temperate deciduous forest (3) marine (4) taiga

✱ 3. Land biomes are characterized and named according to the (1) secondary consumers in the food webs (2) primary consumers in the food webs (3) climax vegetation in a region (4) pioneer vegetation in a region

✱ 4. The largest and most stable ecosystems are the (1) aquatic biomes (2) terrestrial biomes (3) high-altitude biomes (4) high-latitude biomes

✱ 5. Which is the most common sequence of major land biomes encountered from the equator to the polar region? (1) tundra, taiga, temperate deciduous forest, tropical forest (2) tropical forest, temperate deciduous forest, taiga, tundra (3) temperate deciduous forest, tropical forest, taiga, tundra (4) tropical forest, temperate deciduous forest, tundra, taiga

For each description in questions 6 through 10, select the biome, chosen from the list below, that is most closely associated with that description.

    (1) Desert   (4) Temperate deciduous forest
    (2) Grassland   (5) Tundra
    (3) Taiga

✱ 6. This area has a short growing season and low precipitation, mostly in the form of snow. The soil is frozen permanently and vegetation includes lichens and mosses. (1) 1 (2) 3 (3) 2 (4) 5

✱ 7. This area has 10 to 30 inches of rainfall annually. The growing season does not produce trees, but the soil is rich and well-suited for growing domesticated plants such as wheat and corn. Grazing animals are found here. (1) 1 (2) 3 (3) 2 (4) 5

✱ 8. There are many lakes in this area and vegetation is coniferous forest composed mainly of spruce and fir. There are many large animals like bear and deer. (1) 1 (2) 2 (3) 3 (4) 4

✱ 9. This area had broad-leaved trees which shed their leaves in the fall. Winters are fairly cold, and the summers are warm with well-distributed rainfall. (1) 2 (2) 3 (3) 4 (4) 5

✱ 10. This area has a low annual rainfall and a rapid rate of evaporation. In order for plants to survive, they must be adapted to conserve moisture. Animals here are active mainly at night. (1) 5 (2) 1 (3) 4 (4) 3

✱ 11. Which biome is characterized by its ability to absorb and hold large quantities of solar heat, which helps to regulate the earth's temperature? (1) desert (2) marine (3) grassland (4) taiga

✱ 12. Generally, an increase in altitude has the same effect on the habitat of organisms as (1) an increase in latitude (2) an increase in moisture (3) a decrease in available light (4) a decrease in longitude

✱ 13. Discuss the relationship between latitude, altitude, and the types of organisms that inhabit a biome.

HUMANS AND THE BIOSPHERE

Humans, more than any other organisms, have the capacity to change the environment. Some human activities have negative effects on the environment, while others have positive effects.

Negative Aspects. Some human activities have upset the natural balance of ecosystems. These activities have brought about undesirable and lasting changes in one or more of the biotic or abiotic factors in some ecosystems, harming humans and other living things.

Human Population Growth. The human population of the earth is increasing at a rapid rate (Figure 7-9). A major factor in this increase involves medical advances that have increased the average life span. In most parts of the world, population growth is no longer limited by disease to the extent that it was in the past. However, in many ecosystems, the human population has grown faster than the food-producing capacity, resulting in hunger and starvation.

Human Activities. Some human activities have led to the endangerment or extinction of numerous species of plants and animals, and also produced less favorable living conditions for many species, including humans. Such activities in-

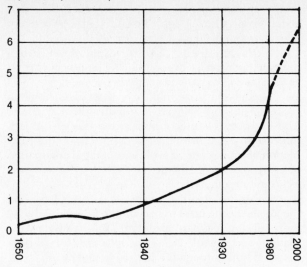

Population (in billions)

Figure 7-9. Human population growth.

clude overhunting, importation of organisms, exploitation of wildlife, poor land use management, and technological oversights.

1. Uncontrolled hunting, fishing, and trapping, which still occur in many parts of the world, have resulted in the extinction of some species and endangered others. The dodo bird and passenger pigeon were hunted to extinction; the blue whale is an endangered species because of overhunting.

2. Humans have accidentally or intentionally imported species into areas where they have no natural enemies. These imported organisms have increased in numbers, leading to the disruption of existing ecosystems. Imported organisms that have caused serious damage include the Japanese beetle, the gypsy moth, and the organism that causes Dutch elm disease.

3. Humans have exploited animal and plant wildlife for their own use. For example, trees in tropical rain forests have been cut wastefully for plywood; the African elephant and Pacific walrus have been overhunted for their ivory tusks; Colombian parrots have been captured and sold as pets.

4. The building of cities (urbanization) and suburbs (suburbanization) has reduced the amount of farmland and disrupted natural habitats, threatening the existence of various wildlife species. Overgrazing, overcropping, and failure to use cover crops have resulted in the loss of valuable soil nutrients and topsoil in many areas.

5. Some technological developments have contributed to the pollution of water, air, and land.

In many areas, water has been polluted by chemical wastes from homes and factories. Major chemical wastes include phosphates, heavy metals, and PCBs. Radioactive materials have been dumped or have leaked into the water supply from factories and waste-storage areas. The temperature of river water has been raised when water taken from the river has been used for cooling in factories and plants and then returned to the waterway. Untreated sewage has been dumped into rivers and oceans. Water pollutants have killed fish and other animals, as well as plant life.

Exhaust gases from factories, automobiles, and other sources have polluted the air. The major air pollutants include carbon dioxide, carbon monoxide, hydrocarbons, and particulate matter. Nitrogen oxides and sulfur dioxides are gaseous pollutants that combine with water vapor in the atmosphere, forming acids. Precipitation of the acids, or **acid rain,** kills vegetation. It also changes the pH of lakes and ponds, which kills many organisms.

Some biocides (generally pesticides or herbicides) used to kill insects and prevent the growth of weeds have had negative effects on the environment. Biocides have contaminated the soil, air, and water supplies. They have also entered food chains and caused the deaths of some organisms, thereby disrupting whole food webs. The pesticide DDT, for example, has killed many bald eagles and falcons.

Technological developments have resulted in the increased production of solid, chemical, and nuclear wastes. Disposal of these wastes, many of them highly toxic, is a major problem.

Positive Aspects.
Humans are becoming increasingly aware of possible negative effects of their activities on the environment. As a result, they are making many efforts to correct past damage and avoid future negative effects.

Population Control. Methods of controlling the human reproduction rate have been, and continue to be, developed.

Conservation of Resources. Measures have been taken to conserve water, fossil fuels (oil, coal, and natural gas), and other natural resources. Soil erosion is being controlled by reforestation projects and use of cover crops. People are now realizing the economic significance of recycling various materials.

Pollution Control. Laws are being enacted to control the pollution of air and water. New techniques of sanitation and disposal of hazardous wastes are being developed.

Species Preservation. Endangered species are being protected, and efforts are being made to increase the size of existing populations of endangered species. This is being accomplished by protection of habitats, including the setting up of wildlife refuges and national parks. Management of various forms of wildlife includes laws limiting hunting and the development of fisheries.

Animals that were once endangered but are now reproducing successfully and increasing in number are bisons and egrets. Endangered animals that are currently responding to conservation efforts and are beginning to make a comeback are the whooping crane, bald eagle, and peregrine falcon. However, the future of some species is still in doubt.

Biological Control. Biological control of insect pests reduces the use of chemical pesticides. One method of biological control involves the use of sex hormones to attract and trap insect pests. Another method of biological control involves the use of natural parasites that kill harmful insects. Biological control methods are less likely than chemical methods to affect species that are beneficial to humans, disrupt food webs, and contaminate the land.

The Future.
A greater awareness of ecological principles and careful use of energy and other natural resources will help to assure a suitable environment for succeeding generations.

QUESTIONS

1. Which accomplishment by humans has made the most positive ecological impact on the environment? (1) the importation of organisms such as the starling and Japanese beetle into the United States (2) reforestation and soil-cover planting measures to prevent soil erosion (3) the extinction or near extinction of many predators to prevent the death of prey animals (4) the use of pesticides and other similar crop-improvement chemicals to regulate the insect population

2. When a garden became infested with a large population of aphids, ladybird beetles were introduced into the community as predators on the aphids. The resultant decrease in the aphid population was due to (1) biological control (2) parthenogenesis (3) vegetative propagation (4) chemosynthesis

3. Recent studies have found traces of the insecticide DDT accumulated in fat tissue. A correct explanation for this accumulation is that (1) fat tissue absorbs DDT directly from the air (2) fat tissue cells secrete DDT (3) DDT is needed for proper metabolic functioning (4) DDT is passed along food chains

4. An increased use of coal could cause additional tons of sulfur dioxide to be emitted into the atmosphere, which could create severe environmental problems with (1) acid rain (2) PCBs (3) DDT (4) dioxin

5. The number of African elephants has been drastically reduced by poachers who kill the animals for the ivory in their tusks. This negative aspect of human involvement in the ecosystem could best be described as (1) poor land use management (2) importation of organisms (3) poor agricultural practices (4) exploitation of wildlife

6. Gypsy moth infestations of rural areas of New York State may pose a potentially serious threat to many forested areas. Which would probably be the most ecologically sound method of gypsy moth control? (1) widespread application of DDT (2) introduction of a biological control (3) removal of its forest habitat (4) contamination of its food sources

7. Recent evidence indicates that lakes in large areas of New York State are being affected by acid rain. The major effect of acid rain in the lakes is (1) an increase in game fish population levels (2) the stimulation of a rapid rate of evolution (3) the elimination of many species of aquatic life (4) an increase in agricultural productivity

8. Compared to other organisms, humans have had the greatest ecological impact on the biosphere due to their (1) internal bony skeleton (2) homeostatic regulation of metabolism (3) adaptations for respiration (4) ability to modify the environment

9. The rapid rise of the human population level over the past few hundred years has been due mainly to (1) increasing levels of air and water pollution (2) loss of topsoil from farmable lands (3) removal of natural checks on population growth (4) increasing resistance level of insect species

10. Which illustrates the human population's increased understanding and concern for ecological interrelationships? (1) importing organisms in order to disrupt existing ecosystems (2) allowing the air to be polluted only by those industries that promote technology (3) removing natural resources from the earth at a rate equal to or greater than the needs of an increasing population (4) developing animal game laws in order to limit the number of organisms that may be killed each year

11. When species of plants and animals are introduced into a new habitat, they often become pests in the new habitat, even though they were not pests in their native habitats. The most probable reason for this is that in the new habitat they (1) have fewer natural enemies (2) have a much lower mutation rate (3) develop better resistance to the new climate (4) learn to use different foods

Base your answers to questions 12 through 16 on the information below and on your knowledge of biology.

Polychlorinated biphenyls (PCB's) are microcontaminants which are found in some water. Microcontaminants do not change the appearance, smell, or taste of water, yet they affect parts of the surrounding ecosystem. After PCB's get into water, they are absorbed by some algae, which concentrate them. Then fish, which feed on the algae, concentrate the PCB's many more times. PCB's are usually thousands of times more concentrated in fish than they are in the water in which the fish live. At this level of contamination, the survival of some species in the food web is endangered. The health of other species, including humans who may consume some predator fish such as salmon, is also endangered.

Identifying microcontaminants in huge bodies of water is a painstaking and time-consuming procedure.

The procedure involves a long chain of activities which include filtering, extracting with solvents, and analyzing by chromatographic techniques. Although detecting microcontaminants is a difficult process, it is essential that humans continuously monitor the environment for their presence to help preserve our food webs.

12. In which of the following are PCB's usually most concentrated? (1) dissolved oxygen (2) water molecules (3) algae (4) fish

13. Which is a harmful effect of microcontaminants on an aquatic ecosystem? (1) They decrease the density of the water. (2) They cause water used for human consumption to have an unpleasant taste. (3) They accumulate in certain organisms, making them toxic to other organisms. (4) They cause water to appear cloudy.

14. The producer organisms in the aquatic food web described in the passage are (1) bacteria (2) fish (3) humans (4) algae

15. The presence of microcontaminants such as PCB's in a water supply is an example of a negative way in which humans have modified their environment by (1) technological oversight (2) pollution controls (3) importation (4) overcropping

16. Based on the passage above, which is a laboratory procedure used to identify microcontaminants such as PCB's? (1) tissue staining (2) chromatographic separation (3) use of a compound light microscope (4) preparation of wet mounts

Base your answers to questions 17 through 21 on the information following and on your knowledge of biology.

Acid rain is a serious environmental problem in large areas of Canada and the northeastern United States, including New York State. It is partly created as rain "washes out" sulfur and nitrogen pollutants from the air. Acid rain alters the fundamental chemistry of sensitive freshwater environments and results in the death of many freshwater species. The principal sources of this pollution have been identified as smokestack gases released by coal-burning facilities located mainly in the midwestern United States.

"Unpolluted" rain normally has a pH of 5.6. Acid rain, however, has been measured at pH values as low as 1.5, which is more than 10,000 times more acidic than normal. Commonly, acid rain has a pH range of 3 to 5, which changes the acidity level of the freshwater environment into which it falls. The effect of the acid rain depends upon the environment's ability to neutralize it. Evidence is accumulating, however, that many environments are adversely affected by the acid rain. As a result, the living things within lakes and streams that cannot tolerate the increasing acidity gradually die off.

There are many environmental problems that result from acid rain. Most of these problems center around the food web upon which all living things, including humans, depend. If freshwater plants, animals, and protists are destroyed by the acid conditions, then terrestrial predators and scavengers dependent on these organisms for food are forced to migrate or starve. These changes in a food web can eventually affect the human level of food consumption.

17. The accompanying scale shows the pH of four common household substances. Acid rain has a pH closest to that of which of these substances? (1) ammonia (2) tap water (3) baking soda (4) vinegar

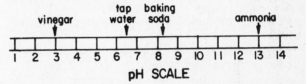

pH SCALE

18. What is most likely the source of acid rain in New York State? (1) far western United States (2) midwestern United States (3) far eastern Canada (4) far western Europe

19. Which food chain includes organisms that would most immediately be affected by acid rain?
(1) grass → rabbit → fox → decay bacteria
(2) algae → aquatic insect → trout → otter
(3) shrub → mouse → snake → hawk
(4) tree → caterpillar → bird → lynx

20. Acid rain is generally considered a negative aspect of human involvement with the ecosystem. As such, it would most correctly be classified as a type of (1) biological control (2) conservation of resources (3) technological oversight (4) land use management

21. A strain of fish that could survive under conditions of increased acidity could best be obtained by (1) binary fission (2) vegetative propagation (3) selective breeding (4) budding

22. List and describe some positive and negative impacts that humans have on the environment.

23. In your opinion, what are some of the most important precautions we must take to protect our environment for succeeding generations?

Laboratory Skills

As part of the Regents biology course, students are expected to master a number of specific skills. Some of these skills involve application of the scientific method, while others are actual laboratory procedures.

Skills using the scientific method:

1. Formulate a question or define a problem for investigation and develop a hypothesis to be tested in an investigation.

2. Distinguish between controls and variables in an experiment.

3. Collect, organize, and graph data.

4. Make predictions based on experimental data.

5. Formulate generalizations or conclusions based on the investigation.

Skills involving laboratory procedures:

6. Given a laboratory problem, select suitable lab materials, safety equipment, and appropriate observation methods.

7. Demonstrate safety skills in heating materials in test tubes or beakers, use of chemicals, and handling dissection equipment.

8. Identify the parts of a light microscope and their functions. Use the microscope correctly under low and high power.

9. Determine the size of microscopic specimens in micrometers.

10. Prepare wet mounts of plant and animal cells and apply stains, including iodine and methylene blue.

11. With the use of a compound microscope, identify cell parts, including the nucleus, cytoplasm, chloroplasts, and cell walls.

12. Use indicators, including pH paper, Benedict's solution (or Fehling's solution), iodine solution (or Lugol's solution), and bromthymol blue. Interpret changes shown by the indicators.

13. Use measurement instruments, such as metric rulers, Celsius thermometers, and graduated cylinders.

14. Dissect plant and animal specimens, exposing major structures for examination.

The Scientific Method

1. Defining a problem and developing a hypothesis. Scientists do research to answer a question or solve a problem. Thus, the first step in planning a research project is to define specifically the problem to be solved.

After the research problem has been defined, the next step is to develop an idea of the possible solution to the problem. This educated guess, or *hypothesis*, provides the researcher with the factor (or factors) to be tested in the experiment.

For example, a scientist interested in studying the enzyme amylase might want to measure the rate of enzyme action at various temperatures. The basic hypothesis for such an experiment would be that the rate at which amylase hydrolyzes, or breaks down, starch is affected by temperature. The scientist might also hypothesize that the maximum rate of enzyme action would occur at normal body temperature (37°C).

2. Designing and conducting an experiment. Biologists often use controlled experiments when doing research. In one kind of controlled experiment, there are actually two setups: an experimental setup and a control setup. The experimental and control setups are identical except for a single factor, or variable, which is being tested.

In another type of controlled experiment, all conditions are kept constant except for one, which is varied. Any changes observed during the experiment can then be explained in terms of the variable factor.

In an experiment to determine the effect of temperature on the rate of action of the enzyme amylase, temperature is the variable.

The scientist could set up two types of controls in this experiment. A basic controlled experiment would use two setups—one containing a starch solution only, the second containing exactly the same amount of the same starch solution plus the enzyme amylase. Both setups would then be tested at various temperatures to determine how much starch had undergone hydrolysis. The setup with no enzyme is the control; the setup with the enzyme is the experimental one. The control can show that no hydrolysis occurs without the enzyme.

In the experimental setup, all conditions are kept constant except temperature. Thus, the scientist knows that the changes in the rate of hydrolysis are caused by the effects of temperature on the enzyme amylase.

3. Collecting, organizing, and graphing data. During an experiment, the scientist collects data. These data are the results of the experiment. The data may be recorded in a log in the form of a chart, or data table. Sometimes the results are plotted on a graph. Scientists also use computers to record and organize experimental results.

In an experiment to determine the rate of action of amylase at various temperatures, the data collected might be written in a table, as shown in Figure 1.

Figure 1. Data Table

Temperature (°C)	Grams of Starch Hydrolyzed Per Minute
0	0.0
10	0.2
20	0.4
30	0.8
40	1.0
50	0.3
60	0.2

The relationship between two varying factors can often be shown clearly on a line graph. The graph in Figure 2 shows the same information as the data table above.

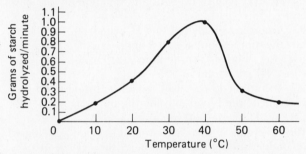

Figure 2. A line graph.

4. Making predictions based on experimental data. Scientists may make predictions based on experimental data. The validity of these predictions can then be tested by further experimentation.

For example, on the basis of the data shown in Figure 1, a scientist might predict that the number of grams of starch hydrolyzed at normal body temperature (37°C) would be between 0.8 and 1.0 grams/minute. Further measurements might show that the prediction was correct, or they might show that at 37°C the rate was higher than 1.0 grams/minute. Scientists must be extremely careful not to make any assumptions that are not supported by the data.

5. Making generalizations and drawing conclusions. The results of an experiment are collected and analyzed. For a conclusion to be meaningful, the experiment must be repeated many times, and all the results obtained must be included in the analysis. The scope of the conclusion must be limited by the experimental data.

In the experiment on the effect of temperature on the rate of action of amylase, the data in the table show that the enzyme functions most efficiently at 40°C. However, if measurements were made only at 10° intervals, you cannot say definitely that 40°C is the optimum temperature for amylase without measurements at other, inter-

mediate, temperatures. It is probably safe to conclude that the optimum temperature is close to 40°C.

QUESTIONS

1. The diagram below represents a setup at the beginning of a laboratory investigation.

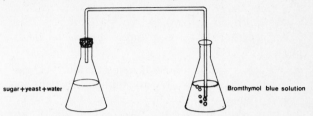

Which hypothesis could most likely be supported by observing and collecting data from this investigation? (1) The fermentation of a yeast-sugar solution results in the production of carbon dioxide. (2) Yeast cells contain simple sugars. (3) Oxygen is released when a yeast-sugar solution is illuminated with green light. (4) Yeast cells contain starches.

Base your answers to questions 2 and 3 on the information and chart below.

A green plant was placed in a test tube, and a light was placed at varying distances from the plant. The bubbles of O_2 given off by the plant were counted. The chart below shows the data collected during this experiment.

Distance of Light from Plant (cm)	Number of Bubbles Per Minute
10	60
20	25
30	10
40	5

2. A variable in this investigation is the (1) color of the light used (2) distance between the light and the plant (3) size of the test tube (4) type of plant used
3. Which conclusion can be drawn from this investigation? (1) As the distance from the light increases, the number of bubbles produced decreases. (2) As the distance from the light increases, the number of bubbles produced increases. (3) As the distance from the light decreases, the number of bubbles decreases. (4) There is no relationship between the number of bubbles produced and the distance of the plant from the light.

Base your answers to questions 4 through 6 on the following information, diagram, and data table, and on your knowledge of biology.

A student is studying the effect of temperature on the hydrolytic action of the enzyme gastric protease, which is contained in gastric fluid. An investigation is set up using 5 identical test tubes, each containing 40 milliliters of gastric fluid and 20 millimeters of glass tubing filled with cooked egg white, as shown in the diagram below. After 48 hours, the amount of egg white hydrolyzed in each tube was measured. The data collected are shown in the data table below.

	Tube	Temperature (°C)	Amount of Enzymatic Hydrolysis in 48 hours
40ml Gastric Fluid / Glass Tube Containing Egg White	1	4	0.0 mm
	2	8	2.5 mm
	3	21	4.0 mm
	4	37	7.5 mm
	5	100	0.0 mm

4. Which is a variable in this investigation? (1) gastric fluid (2) length of glass tubing (3) temperature (4) time

5. If an additional test tube were set up identical to the other test tubes and placed at a temperature of 15°C for 48 hours, what amount of hydrolysis might be expected? (1) less than 2.5 mm (2) between 2.5 mm and 4.0 mm (3) between 4.0 mm and 7.5 mm (4) more than 7.5 mm

6. The best graph of the results of this investigation would be made by plotting the data on which set of axes? (1) 1 (2) 2 (3) 3 (4) 4

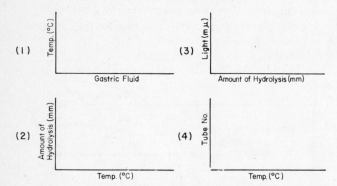

Base your answers to questions 7 through 11 on the two charts below and your knowledge of biology. Chart I shows the percentages of certain materials in the blood entering the kidney and the percentages of the same materials in the urine leaving the body. Chart II shows the number of molecules in the beginning and end of the kidney tubule for every 100 molecules of each substance entering the glomerulus.

Chart I

Substance	% of blood	% of urine
Protein	7.0	0.0
Water	91.5	96.0
Glucose	0.1	0.0
Sodium	0.33	0.29
Potassium	0.02	0.24
Urea	0.03	2.7

Chart II

Substance	Number of Molecules		
	in blood entering glomerulus	Beginning of Tubule	End of Tubule
Protein	100	0	0
Water	100	30	1
Glucose	100	20	0
Sodium	100	30	1
Potassium	100	23	12
Urea	100	50	90

7. According to chart I, which substance is more highly concentrated in the urine than in the blood? (1) water (2) sodium (3) protein (4) glucose

8. According to charts I and II, which substance enters the tubules, but does *not* appear in the urine leaving the body? (1) protein (2) water (3) glucose (4) potassium

9. According to the data, which substance did *not* pass out of the blood into the tubule? (1) water (2) urea (3) glucose (4) protein

10. The data in the charts would best aid a biologist in understanding the function of the (1) heart of a frog (2) nephron of a human (3) nerve net of a hydra (4) contractile vacuole of a paramecium

11. Which substances enter the tubule and then are reabsorbed back into the blood as they pass through the tubule? (1) urea and potassium (2) water and sodium (3) urea and protein (4) protein and glucose

Base your answers to questions 12 through 14 on the information provided by the graph below. The graph shows the average growth rate for 38 pairs of newborn rats. One member of each pair was injected with anterior pituitary extract. The other member of each pair served as a control.

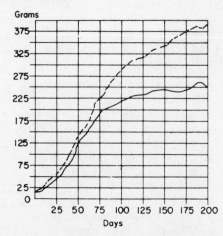

—— Average growth of 38 untreated littermates (control)

--- Average growth of 38 rats injected with anterior pituitary extract (experimental)

12. At 75 days, what was the average weight of the rats injected with pituitary extract? (1) 65 grams (2) 125 grams (3) 200 grams (4) 225 grams

13. Based on the graph, it can be correctly concluded that the pituitary extract (1) is essential for life (2) determines when a rat will be born (3) affects the growth of rats (4) affects the growth of all animals

14. The graph shows the relationship between the weight of treated and untreated rats and the (1) age of the rats (2) sex of the rats (3) size of the rats' pituitary glands (4) type of food fed to the rats

Base your answers to questions 15 and 16 on your knowledge of laboratory procedures used in biology and on the information below. Diagrams *A* through *E* show the general appearance of five tree fruits that were used by a science class in an experiment to determine the length of time necessary for each type of fruit to fall from a second-floor balcony to the lobby floor of their school. One hundred fruits of each type were selected by the students and the average time of fall for each type of fruit is shown in the chart below.

FRUITS (NOT DRAWN TO SCALE)

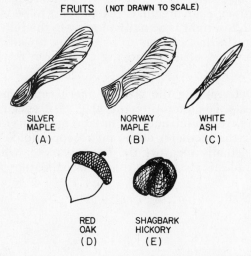

Tree Type	*Average Fall Time of 100 Fruits*
Silver Maple	3.2 sec
Norway Maple	4.9 sec
White Ash	1.5 sec
Red Oak	0.8 sec
Shagbark Hickory	0.8 sec

15. Based on this experimental evidence, what inference seems most likely to be true concerning the distribution of these fruits during windstorms in nature? (1) Silver maple fruits would land closer to the base of their parent tree than would shagbark hickory fruits. (2) White ash fruits would land farther from the base of their parent tree than would silver maple fruits. (3) White ash fruits would land closer to the base of their parent tree than would shagbark hickory fruits. (4) Norway maple fruits would land farther from the base of their parent tree than would silver maple fruits.

16. Which graph best shows the average fall time for each fruit type tested during this experiment?

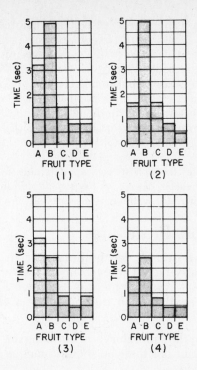

17. The graph below was developed as a result of an investigation of bacterial counts of three identical cultures grown at different temperatures. Which conclusion might be correctly drawn from this graph?

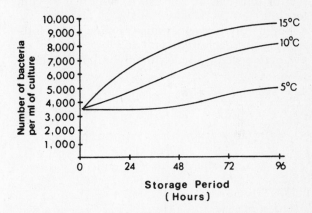

(1) The culture contains no bacteria. (2) Refrigeration retards bacterial reproduction. (3) Temperature is unrelated to the bacteria reproduction rate. (4) Bacteria cannot grow at a temperature of 5°C.

Base your answers to questions 18 through 20 on the graphs below showing data on some environmental factors acting in a large New York lake.

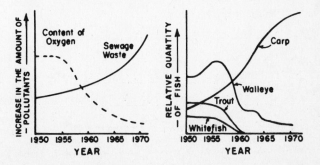

18. Which relationship can be correctly inferred from the data presented? (1) As sewage waste increases, oxygen content decreases. (2) As sewage waste increases, oxygen content increases. (3) As oxygen content decreases, carp population decreases. (4) As oxygen content decreases, trout population increases.

19. The greatest change in the lake's whitefish population occurred in the years between (1) 1950 and 1955 (2) 1955 and 1960 (3) 1960 and 1965 (4) 1965 and 1970

20. Which of the fish species appears able to withstand the greatest degree of oxygen depletion? (1) trout (2) carp (3) walleye (4) whitefish

Laboratory Procedures

6. Selecting suitable lab equipment. In planning and carrying out an experiment, knowledge of the correct lab equipment is essential. Figure 3 shows the basic lab equipment you should know.

7. Safety in the laboratory. Following are some safety precautions that you should practice in the laboratory.

- Do not handle chemicals or equipment unless you are told by your teacher to do so.
- If any of your lab equipment appears to be broken or unusual, do not use it. Report it to your teacher.
- Report any personal injury or damage to clothing to your teacher immediately.
- Never taste or inhale directly unknown chemicals.

- Never pour reagents back into stock bottles or exchange stoppers.
- When heating a liquid in a test tube, make sure that the opening of the test tube is pointed away from you and away from anyone nearby.

8. Using a compound microscope. Review the parts of the compound microscope and their functions by studying Figure 1-2 (page 5) and Table 1-2 (page 6).

In using the compound microscope, the observer should begin by viewing the specimen with the low-power objective, focusing first with the coarse adjustment, then with the fine adjustment. The objectives can then be switched from low power to high power. All focusing under high power should be done with the fine adjustment. The field appears dimmer under high power than under low power. Opening the diaphragm allows more light to reach the specimen.

The image of an object seen under the microscope is enlarged, reversed (backward), and inverted (upside-down). When viewed through the microscope, an organism that appears to be moving to the right is actually moving to the left. An organism that appears to be moving toward the observer is actually moving away from the observer.

9. Determining the size of microscopic specimens. To determine the size of a specimen being examined under a microscope, you must know the diameter of the microscope field. You can actually measure the field diameter with a clear plastic centimeter ruler. Place the ruler over

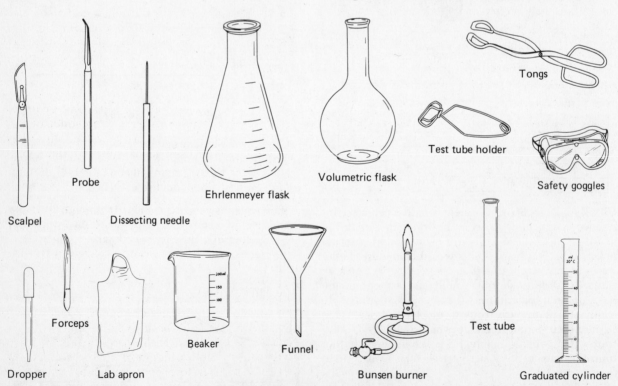

Scalpel Probe Dissecting needle Ehrlenmeyer flask Volumetric flask Tongs Test tube holder Safety goggles

Dropper Forceps Lab apron Beaker Funnel Bunsen burner Test tube Graduated cylinder

Figure 3. Laboratory equipment.

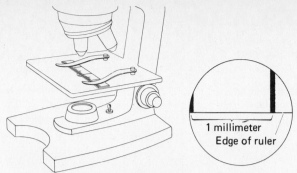

Figure 4. Measuring with a microscope.

the opening in the stage of the microscope, as shown in Figure 4. Focus on the ruler markings and adjust the position of the ruler so that a millimeter marking is at the left. Once you have estimated the field diameter under low power, you can estimate the size of specimens observed under low power by how much of the field they cover. For example, if the diameter of the field is 1.5 mm and a specimen is about one-third the diameter of the field, the specimen is about 0.5 mm in length.

The unit most commonly used in measuring microscopic specimens is the micrometer, symbol μm, which is one-thousandth of a millimeter.

$$1 \text{ mm} = 1,000 \ \mu m \qquad 1 \ \mu m = 0.001 \text{ mm}$$

In the example above, the field diameter is 1.5 mm, which is equal to 1,500 μm. The specimen is 0.5 mm long, which equals 500 μm.

When you switch from low power to high power, the field diameter decreases. For example, if the magnification under low power is $100\times$ and under high power is $400\times$, the field diameter under high power will be one-fourth that under low power. If the low-power magnification is $100\times$ and high-power magnification is $500\times$, then the diameter of the high-power field will be one-fifth that of the low-power field.

10. Preparing a wet mount and applying stains. A wet mount is a temporary slide preparation used for viewing specimens with a compound microscope. Any specimen to be examined must be thin enough for light to pass through it.

The preparation of a wet mount involves the following steps:

1. Use a medicine dropper to put a drop of water in the center of the slide.
2. Place the tissue or organism to be examined in the drop of water on the slide.
3. Cover the specimen with a cover slip, as shown in Figure 5.
4. To stain the section, add a drop of iodine solution or methylene blue at one edge of the cover slip. Touch a small piece of paper towel to the opposite side of the cover slip to draw the stain across the slide and through the specimen.

11. Identifying cell parts with a compound microscope. Review the structure of plant and an-

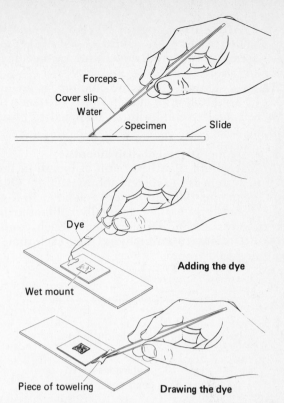

Figure 5. Making a wet mount and staining a specimen.

imal cells and the functions of cell organelles (pages 4 and 5).

Unstained cells viewed with a compound microscope show relatively little detail. The use of stains, such as iodine or methylene blue, enhances contrast. With such stains, the nucleus becomes clearly visible, and in plant and algal cells the cell wall becomes visible. Chloroplasts are visible as small oval green structures. Most other cell organelles, including mitochondria and the endoplasmic reticulum, are not visible with the compound light microscope.

12. Using indicators and interpreting changes. Indicators are used to test for the presence of specific substances or chemical characteristics.

Litmus paper is an indicator used to determine whether a solution is an acid or a base. In an acid, blue litmus paper turns red. In a base, red litmus paper turns blue.

pH paper is an indicator that is used to determine the actual pH of a solution. When a piece of pH paper is dipped into a test solution, it changes color. The color of the pH paper is then matched against a color chart, which shows the pH.

Bromthymol blue is an indicator used to detect the presence of carbon dioxide. In the presence of carbon dioxide, bromthymol blue turns to bromthymol yellow. If the carbon dioxide is removed from the bromthymol yellow, the indicator changes back to bromthymol blue.

Benedict's solution is an indicator used to test for the presence of simple sugars (monosaccharides). When heated in the presence of simple sugars, Benedict's solution turns from blue to yellow, green, or brick red, depending on the sugar concentration.

Lugol's solution, or iodine solution, is an indicator used to test for starch. In the presence of starch, Lugol's solution turns from red to blue-black.

13. Using measurement instruments.

• **Metric rulers.** The basic unit of length in the metric system is the meter, abbreviated *m*. One meter contains 100 centimeters. As shown in Figure 6, metric rulers are generally calibrated in centimeters and millimeters (mm). Each centimeter contains 10 millimeters, thus each meter contains 1,000 mm.

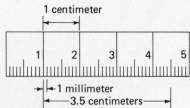

Figure 6. A centimeter ruler.

• **Celsius thermometers.** In the metric system, temperature is commonly measured in degrees Celsius. On the Celsius scale, 0° is the freezing point of water and 100° is the boiling point of water. Figure 7 shows a thermometer calibrated in degrees Celsius. Each degree is marked by a short line, and every tenth degree is labeled.

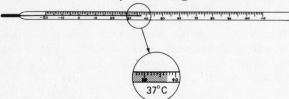

Figure 7. A Celsius thermometer.

• **Graduated cylinders.** The basic unit for measuring the volume of a liquid in the metric system is the liter, symbol *L*. A liter contains 1,000 milliliters (*mL*). Most laboratory measurements involve milliliters, rather than liters.

The volume of a liquid is frequently measured in graduated cylinders, which come in many sizes. When you need an accurately measured amount of liquid, use a graduated cylinder of appropriate size—that is, to measure 5 mL of liquid, use a 10-mL graduated cylinder, not a 1,000-mL graduated cylinder.

The surface of water and similar liquids curves upward along the sides of the cylinder (Figure 8). This curved surface, or **meniscus**, is caused by the strong attraction of liquid molecules to the glass surface. For an accurate measurement, the reading should be done at eye level, and the measurement should be taken from the bottom of the meniscus, as shown. With other types of liquids, the meniscus curves the other way. A meniscus of this type should be read across the top.

100

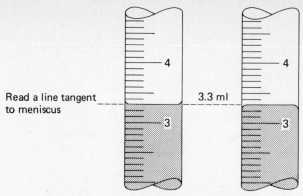

Figure 8. Using a graduated cylinder.

14. Dissecting plant and animal specimens. Dissections are done to expose major structures for examination. The specimen is generally placed in a dissection pan and fastened down with pins. In doing a dissection, you should be very careful with the dissection instruments, which are sharp. You should also be careful in cutting into and handling the specimen so that you do not damage important structures. Follow all instructions and record your observations by making labeled diagrams as you proceed with the dissection.

QUESTIONS

Base your answers to questions 1 through 3 on the four sets of laboratory materials listed below and on your knowledge of biology.

Set A	Set C
Light source	Scalpel
Colored filters	Forceps
Beaker	Scissors
Test tubes	Pan with wax bottom
Test tube stand	Pins
Set B	Stereomicroscope
Droppers	Goggles
Benedict's solution	**Set D**
Iodine	Compound micro-
Test tubes	scope
Test tube rack	Glass slides
Heat source	Water
Goggles	Forceps

1. Which set should a student select to test for the presence of a carbohydrate in food? (1) Set *A* (2) Set *B* (3) Set *C* (4) Set *D*

2. Which set should a student select to determine the location of the aortic arches in the earthworm? (1) Set *A* (2) Set *B* (3) Set *C* (4) Set *D*

3. Which set should a student use to observe chloroplasts in elodea (a green water plant)? (1) Set *A* (2) Set *B* (3) Set *C* (4) Set *D*

4. To view cells under the high power of a compound microscope, a student places a slide of the cells on the stage and moves the stage clips over to secure the slide. She then moves the high-power objective into place and focuses on the slide with the coarse adjustment. Two steps in this procedure are incorrect. For this procedure to be correct, she should have focused under (1) low power using coarse and fine adjustments and then under high power using only the fine adjustment (2) high power first, then low power using only the fine adjustment (3) low power using the coarse and fine adjustments and then under high power using coarse and fine adjustments (4) low power using the fine adjustment and then under high power using only the fine adjustment

Base your answers to questions 5 and 6 on the diagram below.

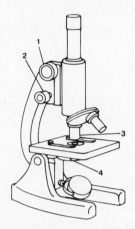

5. The part labeled 1 is used (1) to increase the amount of light reaching the specimen (2) for focusing with the high-power objective (3) to hold the lenses (4) for focusing with the low-power objective
6. To adjust the amount of light reaching the specimen, you would use the part labeled (1) 1 (2) 2 (3) 3 (4) 4

Base your answers to questions 7 through 9 on the information below and on your knowledge of biology.

A student prepares a wet mount of onion epidermis and observes it under three powers of magnification of a compound light microscope ($40\times$, $100\times$, and $400\times$).

7. An adjustment should be made to allow more light to pass through the specimen when the student changes magnification from (1) $100\times$ to $400\times$ (2) $400\times$ to $100\times$ (3) $400\times$ to $40\times$ (4) $100\times$ to $40\times$
8. Iodine stain is added to the slide. Under $400\times$ magnification, the student should be able to observe a (1) mitochondrion (2) nucleus (3) ribosome (4) centriole
9. A specimen that is suitable for observation under this microscope should be (1) stained with Benedict's solution (2) moving and respiring (3) alive and reproducing (4) thin and transparent
10. A microscope is supplied with $10\times$ and $15\times$ eyepieces, and with $10\times$ and $44\times$ objectives. What is the maximum magnification that can be obtained from this microscope? (1) $59\times$ (2) $150\times$ (3) $440\times$ (4) $660\times$
11. Under low power ($100\times$) a row of eight cells can fit across the field of a certain microscope. How many of these cells could be viewed in the high power ($400\times$) visual field of this microscope? (1) 1 (2) 2 (3) 8 (4) 32

12. A compound light microscope has a $10\times$ ocular, $10\times$ low-power objective, and a $40\times$ high-power objective. A student noted that under high power, four cells end to end extended across the diameter of the field. If the microscope were switched to low power, approximately how many cells would fit across the field? (1) 1 (2) 8 (3) 16 (4) 4
13. The diagram below shows a section of a metric ruler scale as seen through a compound light microscope. If each division represents one millimeter, what is the approximate width of the microscope's field of view in micrometers? (1) 3,700 μm (2) 4,200 μm (3) 4,500 μm (4) 5,000 μm

Base your answers to questions 14 through 17 on your knowledge of biology and on the diagrams below, which represent fields of vision under the low power of the same compound microscope ($100\times$). Diagram A shows the millimeter divisions of a plastic ruler and diagram B shows a sample of stained onion epidermal cells.

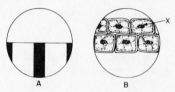

14. Structure X in diagram B was most likely stained by adding (1) water (2) iodine solution (3) Benedict's solution (4) bromthymol blue
15. Structure X in diagram B indicates (1) a nucleus (2) a mitochondrion (3) the cell wall (4) the cytoplasm
16. The diameter of the field of vision in diagram A is approximately (1) 500 μm (2) 1,000 μm (3) 1,500 μm (4) 2,000 μm
17. What is the approximate length of each onion epidermal cell in field B? (1) 200 μm (2) 660 μm (3) 1,000 μm (4) 2,500 μm
18. Iodine solution is used in the test for (1) proteins (2) simple sugars (3) oxygen (4) starch
19. In the presence of carbon dioxide, bromthymol blue (1) shows no color change (2) turns yellow (3) turns blue-black (4) turns red-orange
20. Benedict's solution is used to test for (1) disaccharides (2) oxygen (3) starch (4) simple sugars
21. Which piece of equipment should be used to transfer a hydra onto a microscope slide? (1) scissors (2) dissecting needles (3) medicine dropper (4) forceps
22. While a student is heating a liquid in a test tube, the mouth of the tube should always be (1) corked with a rubber stopper (2) pointed toward the student (3) allowed to cool (4) aimed away from everybody

A Clone of Your Own

Imagine selecting a popular student in your school and then placing an order for 25 copies of that student from a science laboratory. Sounds like science fiction? Well, you may be surprised to learn that, in the future, scientists might develop the technique to make copies of, or *replicate*, individual people. In fact, as long ago as the 1950s, researchers first succeeded in producing living copies of some amphibians, such as frogs and salamanders, by cloning them. *Cloning* is the process by which a group of organisms is produced, each of which is identical to the one original, or parent, organism.

In 1961, University of Oxford embryologist J. B. Gurdon successfully cloned several identical offspring of a South African clawed frog. How did he actually accomplish this? First, Gurdon exposed an unfertilized frog's egg to radiation in order to destroy its nucleus. Next, he removed a functioning nucleus from an intestinal cell of a tadpole of the same species. Unlike the egg cell nucleus, the nucleus of the intestinal cell—which was still in an early stage of development—contained a full set of chromosomes. (In fact, all body cells contain a full set of chromosomes, making them *totipotent*, that is, capable of developing into a complete organism.) Gurdon injected this nucleus into the irradiated egg cell. The egg cell then began to divide, giving rise to new cells just as if it had been normally fertilized. Continued cell division and embryonic development resulted in a young frog identical to the parent frog, the one that had donated the intestinal cell nucleus.

Gurdon's experiment was repeated several times by scientists using nuclei from tadpole intestinal cells that were at later stages of development. Results showed that the more developed nuclei could not produce clones. Evidently, as the nuclei matured, they became too specialized as digestive cells. With such increased specialization, these cells lost their ability to divide like a fertilized egg to produce a complete new organism. However, the results of the original experiment still could be duplicated in young clawed frogs if young intestinal cell nuclei were used.

Having successfully cloned frogs, researchers turned their attention to trying to clone mammals. This procedure proved to be much more difficult because mammalian eggs are tinier than those of amphibians and damage easily. In 1981, one laboratory claimed success in the cloning of mice. In 1997, researchers in Scotland announced that they had cloned a sheep from the udder cells of an adult sheep. The offspring was named Dolly.

Some scientists think that the cloning of sheep and other mammals could be useful for the development of preferred breeds of livestock. For example, researchers may be able to help farmers produce varieties of livestock that are more resistant to disease and to harsh environments.

Eventually, scientists might be able to attempt the cloning of humans. Some people think that cloning experiments on humans should be prohibited. They feel that it would be too risky to let anyone have the power to decide *who* should be replicated, and that such a risk outweighs any potential benefits. What do you think about the possible consequences of trying to clone people and other mammals? Is it worth the risk?

Questions

1. In the 1960s, a scientist worked with frog cell nuclei to produce
   a. sterile frogs.
   b. identical frogs.
   c. super frogs.
   d. salamanders.

2. Cloning is the process by which organisms are produced that are
   a. different from each other and the parent organism.
   b. the same as all other members of their species.
   c. the same as each other and the parent organism.
   d. the same as members of another similar species.

3. How might the ability to clone mammals, if developed, be of benefit to a dairy farmer? In saving endangered species?

4. Do library research on other forms of reproduction in which only one parent is involved. Describe some advantages and disadvantages of cloning and other types of asexual reproduction.

Barking Up the Right Tree for Taxol

Throughout the ages, chemicals from various plants have been used to treat various ailments and diseases in people. Scientists continue to search for chemical compounds in plants that may be of medical use. In 1983, doctors began conducting clinical studies of a promising new anticancer drug called *taxol*. This special drug is extracted from the bark of the Pacific yew, a slow-growing tree found in the ancient forests of the northwestern United States. Taxol's usefulness comes from its ability to target dividing cancer cells and prevent them from reproducing. Taxol prevents a dividing cell from assembling spindle fibers and so the cell cannot undergo mitosis. By 1988, the researchers found that taxol was effective in combating ovarian cancer. In 1993, the Food and Drug Administration approved the use of taxol for ovarian cancer. The drug has also been found to be useful in fighting breast and lung cancer as well as melanoma.

Until recently, the only way to obtain taxol was to take it directly from the bark of large old Pacific yew trees. The Pacific yew tree is on the endangered species list. To make matters worse, taxol is present in the bark in very small concentrations. For example, the bark from a large 100-year-old tree would yield only a single dose of taxol! Just think of the number of trees that would have to be sacrificed to treat the estimated 26,700 women who will be diagnosed with ovarian cancer this year. Only the oldest, largest trees could be used.

The first effort to produce taxol without causing the extinction of the Pacific yew was a procedure used since the early 1980s called *plant tissue culture*. This technique involves taking small pieces of plant tissue from tree bark, culturing them to produce more plant tissue cells in the laboratory, and then extracting the drug from cultured cells.

Two United States laboratories did produce taxol by this method. How do the technicians actually produce more taxol from plant tissue culture? First, small pieces of yew bark are placed in lab dishes on a medium full of nutrients. The bark cells then multiply, producing a mass of unspecialized tissue called a *callus*. Pieces of callus are used to make more tissue culture, which in turn, develops more callus. Special chemicals are added to the callus to stimulate it to produce more taxol than would normally be found in yew bark. After several weeks, the callus is carefully dried and the taxol extracted from it.

There are several advantages to this procedure. Considering that it takes 13,600 kilograms of bark to produce just one kilogram of pure taxol, this technique could save the lives of thousands of trees, especially since one old tree supplies only about 9 kilograms of bark. In 1991 alone, more than 360,000 kilograms of dried yew bark were collected to produce taxol for research and treatment purposes. Another advantage of tissue culture techniques is that cell cultures could produce more taxol than is produced in bark. And this process can continue year-round, regardless of changes in season and climate, plant diseases, forest fires, and other natural disasters.

In 1994, a team of researchers in California reported success in synthesizing the complete taxol molecule. The process is very complex and costly. It was not a practical way to produce taxol. However, in early 1995, the Food and Drug Administration approved a semi-synthetic form of taxol for treating cancers of the ovaries and breast. A chemical extracted from the English yew is synthesized into taxol. The English yew is a hardy tree which is in good supply and grows throughout northern temperate zones. Although it is slow growing, it can be propagated easily by seeds or by cuttings. Today, taxol is mass-produced at a relatively low cost by these semi-synthetic methods.

In recent years, a new chemical has been synthesized that could prove better than taxol

in the fight against cancer. Researchers have succeeded in producing cell-killing chemicals called *epothilones*. Naturally produced by bacteria, epothilones work in exactly the same way as taxol. Some scientists think that the epothilones will work even better, because they seem to kill those cancer cells that have become resistant to taxol.

Questions

1. A special drug obtained from yew bark is used to fight
   - a. arthritis.
   - b. obesity.
   - c. cancer.
   - d. calluses.

2. A mass of unspecialized plant tissue is referred to as
   - a. bark.
   - b. callus.
   - c. taxol.
   - d. nutrient.

3. The most important reason why epothilones may replace taxol as a weapon against cancer is that epothilones are
   - a. cheaper to make.
   - b. mass-produced by bacteria.
   - c. natural chemicals.
   - d. able to kill cancer cells resistant to taxol.

4. Write a short paragraph stating why it is better to obtain taxol from the English yew rather than from the Pacific yew.

5. Do library research and write a brief report about the efforts being made to protect and preserve rare plant species while trying to obtain food and drug products from them.

Transplants, T-Cells, and the Thymus

Imagine someone who has a liver from a pig and a heart from a sheep. Does this sound inhuman, or maybe even inhumane, to you? Well, someday scientists may perfect the techniques necessary to perform successful transplants of other mammals' organs into ailing humans. While most of us take our good health for granted, thousands of people are desperately in need of specific organs or body parts that are in better shape than their own.

Transplants of tissues and organs between humans do take place every day. Body parts such as bone, bone marrow, cartilage, tendons, ligaments, kidneys, livers, corneas, pancreases, hearts, and lungs can all be transplanted. It is even possible for us to donate bone marrow, or one of our kidneys, to someone else while we are still alive. In fact, kidneys taken for transplants from live donors survive better in the recipient than those taken from cadavers. But most healthy organs and tissues used for transplants still come from the bodies of people who legally agreed to donate their usable body parts after their death. (In most cases, permission from the family is also obtained by a doctor before any use of the body for transplants actually takes place.)

Although increasingly common, organ and tissue transplants are still risky procedures. Not all patients survive even the first year after the operation. According to a 1988 survey conducted by the United Network for Organ Sharing (UNOS), the first-year survival rate for over 12,700 recipients of major organs in America was as follows: heart, 83%; liver, 76%; pancreas, 89%; kidneys (from live donors), 97%; lung, 48%; and heart-lung, 57%. And the organs themselves do not always function that well after one year.

Risks are high because of the delicate nature of transplant operations. Often, during such a procedure, veins and arteries must be blocked to prevent blood loss. Parts of the body are then starved of oxygen and nutrients and, as a result, may be damaged.

In addition, the body usually recognizes the transplanted organ or tissue as foreign and undergoes an *immune response*. The immune system's job is to destroy foreign materials in the body. So it will attack the transplanted body part, and the patient may die.

Special drugs, called *immunosuppressants*, are given to transplant patients to try to prevent their immune systems from rejecting the foreign tissue or organ. Since the early 1980s, drugs such as cyclosporine and prednisone have aided the recovery and survival of transplant patients. Another drug, called FK-506, is currently being tested on such patients by doctors in Pennsylvania. However, some of these drugs further increase the risks for transplant recipients because they weaken the body's ability to fight disease, leaving the patients vulnerable to all sorts of infections. Despite these risks, transplant operations are able to save, or at least extend and improve, the lives of many people each year. Estimates for 1989 indicate that transplants were successful for more than 13,000 Americans in that year alone.

Unfortunately, organs and tissues for transplants are in short supply. As of 1992, there were over 22,000 Americans on the UNOS waiting list for organ donations. Understandably, many people find it difficult to think of their own death, and so avoid making the decision whether or not to donate their organs. Another difficulty can be locating a suitable organ or tissue in time, although the UNOS serves the purpose of networking with doctors in over 250 hospitals and clinics to help match donors with recipients. So, scientists are looking for new ways to make sure that the precious few organs that *are* donated are not rejected by those lucky enough to receive them.

One new technique devised to prevent transplant rejection involves the *thymus gland*. Researchers in the United States and Italy have successfully transplanted tissues and organs (such as pancreatic cells and kidneys) in rats which were accepted by the recipients'

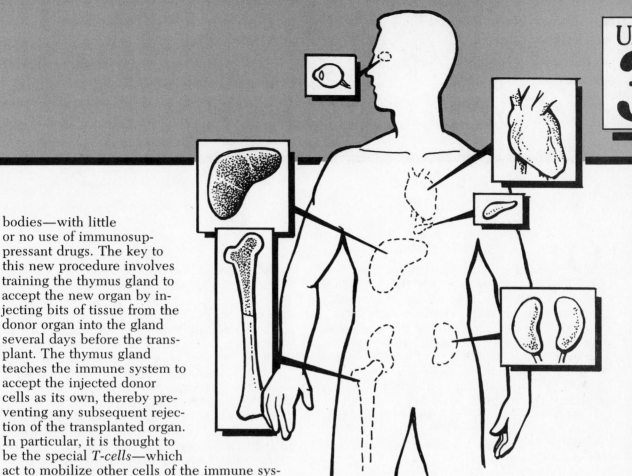

bodies—with little
or no use of immunosup-
pressant drugs. The key to
this new procedure involves
training the thymus gland to
accept the new organ by injecting bits of tissue from the
donor organ into the gland
several days before the transplant. The thymus gland
teaches the immune system to
accept the injected donor
cells as its own, thereby preventing any subsequent rejection of the transplanted organ.
In particular, it is thought to
be the special *T-cells*—which
act to mobilize other cells of the immune system to reject foreign tissues—that are trained
by the thymus to accept the new organ.

Knowing that all immune system cells first
form in the body's bone marrow, American sur-
geon Dr. Suzanne Ilstad was able to develop a
different technique to prevent transplant rejec-
tions. She transplanted bone marrow from
donor rats into the bodies of mice. When the
immature T-cells in the donor marrow passed
through each mouse's thymus, they were
trained by the gland to recognize all donor tissue as "self." As a result, transplants from the
donor rat were then accepted by the recipient
mouse's immune system.

Since there is such a shortage of human donors, and since scientists have been successful
in transplanting tissue between two rodent species, some doctors hope to eventually transplant organs from various mammals into
humans. This might help save the lives of
many patients who would otherwise die while
waiting for compatible human organs. What do
you think about the possible use of animal organs for humans? Do you think it is ethical? Or
should more people be encouraged to donate
their own organs?

Questions

1. *Most* tissues and organs used in transplants
   are obtained from
   a. animals.   c. cadavers.
   b. robots.   d. living people.

2. Transplanted organs are often attacked and
   rejected by this body system:
   a. immune   c. circulatory
   b. respiratory   d. digestive

3. Briefly describe the main benefit and main
   risk associated with the use of *immunosup-
   pressant* drugs in a transplant patient's
   body.

4. Do library research to find out about the use
   of animals in the early development of transplant procedures. Briefly discuss the pros
   and cons of applying animal models to
   human medicine and explore the idea of
   using animal parts for humans.

Surrogate Children and Grandchildren

On August 5, 1991, an article in a New York City newspaper described the situation of a 42-year-old woman who was pregnant with her own grandchildren. The woman, whom we'll call Granny, was carrying twins produced from eggs that were surgically removed from the ovary of her daughter and then fertilized *in vitro* by sperm from her son-in-law. In the process of *in vitro* fertilization, a mature egg from a woman is mixed in a laboratory dish with sperm from a man; there, fertilization can take place. The fertilized egg is then implanted into the womb of a woman, where it develops as a normal embryo.

Why was Granny willing to function as a *surrogate* mother, that is, as a woman who carries and bears a child for another woman? Because her daughter was born without a uterus, so she could produce mature eggs, but was unable to conceive and bear her own children.

More and more stories of surrogate motherhood are making the headlines these days, but they usually describe less than ideal situations. The practice of surrogacy raises many moral and legal questions. While Granny was not paid by her daughter to carry and bear her twins, surrogate mothers usually charge a substantial fee for providing this service. Opponents of this procedure feel that it is unethical to receive money for having babies.

Another troublesome issue centers around the right, if any, of the surrogate mother to keep the child she bears. One recent court case in California involved a woman who was paid to be a surrogate mother. But after giving birth, she refused to turn the baby over to its biological parents (the couple who contributed the sex cells). Although the woman who bears a child is usually considered by law to be its natural mother, in this case the court awarded custody to the biological parents.

Even more difficult to resolve are the custody conflicts that can arise when a surrogate mother not only "sells" use of her womb for a fetus, but contributes the egg as well. In such cases, the surrogate *is* the biological mother of the offspring, too. This type of arrangement may occur when a woman is unable to use her own eggs, and so her husband's sperm is used to fertilize the egg of another woman, who agrees to give up the baby at birth. It is much harder for a judge to decide who the rightful mother is in such an instance than when the surrogate is not related to the fetus. In at least one case, such a conflict led to joint custody arrangements between the surrogate and biological parents.

As for Granny, some people have praised her for assuming the role of surrogate mother for her own grandchildren. These advocates argue that there are no moral conflicts in this case because no fees were involved and it is very unlikely that the grandmother will want to keep the twins. Above all, they point out that the surrogacy was performed out of a mother's love for her daughter. However, others feel that this type of surrogacy could create emotional problems for the children. They may one day wonder, "Is Granny really our mother or our grandmother?" What do you think? Do you think surrogate mothers should or should not be related to the biological parents? To the offspring? And who should decide such matters?

Questions

1. *In vitro* fertilization is a helpful procedure
   for women who
   a. cannot conceive normally.
   b. have too many babies.
   c. have surrogate grandmothers.
   d. have infertile husbands.

2. A surrogate mother is the woman who helps
   another woman have a baby by
   a. adopting one for her.
   b. going to the hospital with her.
   c. "selling" use of her womb.
   d. finding her a husband.

3. Write a brief paragraph explaining why a
   surrogate mother may or may not feel enti-
   tled to keep the baby after its birth. Discuss
   the rights of the biological parents *vs.* the
   surrogate's.

4. Do library research to find out about any
   recent court case involving *in vitro* fertilization and surrogacy. Describe the basic ar-
   guments involved and state your own views
   about the outcome of the case.

Transgenic Animals: Are They Mice or Men?

Imagine a species of fish that develops at an unusually fast rate and grows to be twice as large as normal. Imagine sheep that produce milk containing disease-fighting substances normally found in human blood. And imagine a type of chicken that has a superior ability to combat viruses. You need not imagine any further because, in this age of *transgenic* animals, these breeds already exist.

A transgenic animal's genetic makeup includes a foreign gene intentionally inserted by scientists. This foreign gene, which usually comes from another animal species, gives the organism different characteristics. For example, insertion of a foreign gene for growth may increase the quality or quantity of an animal's meat. A different gene might cause an organism to produce chemicals needed by a sick person to survive. And other inserted genes may help strengthen an animal's resistance to disease.

Genetic researchers have developed successful gene-insertion techniques. To create a transgenic animal, a technician attaches a gene from one type of animal to the DNA of a different one. This can be done by injecting the foreign DNA into a fertilized egg of the animal. Once the fertilized egg has the new genetic information, it is allowed to develop into an embryo. The embryo is placed inside the womb of a mature female of the same species, who has been treated with drugs to prepare her for pregnancy.

Inserting foreign genes into embryos and implanting those embryos into wombs are relatively easy tasks. Few embryos, however, will actually incorporate the foreign gene into their genetic code. To ensure the success of the gene transplant, technicians must carry out the procedure with large numbers of embryos, in the hope that at least one will accept the new genetic information. Those embryos that do accept the foreign gene eventually develop into mature organisms that can be mated to produce more transgenic organisms.

Thus far, scientists have created over 1000 types of transgenic mice, each carrying a different foreign gene. There are also more than a dozen varieties of transgenic pigs, in addition to many transgenic breeds of rabbits, birds, rats, and fish. The more than twelve varieties of transgenic fish include genes from humans, rats, cows, chickens, and other species of fish.

One of the most useful transgenic animals developed so far is a mouse that carries the human gene to produce *tissue plasminogen activator* (TPA) in its milk. TPA, a substance normally found in human blood, functions to dissolve blood clots. Now TPA can be purified from the mouse milk and used to treat heart attack patients.

Although transgenic animals can prove very useful to society, some people object to the practice of gene transplants. They feel that transgenic animals can accidentally upset the balance of nature. For example, scientists have altered the genetic makeup of several breeds of fish by adding growth hormone genes from other species to their DNA. These laboratory fish now grow larger at a much faster rate than normal. If these transgenic fish were to escape to a natural environment, they might eat more than their usual amount of food, in addition to preying on smaller fish species. Such results could seriously decrease the populations of other naturally occurring breeds of fish.

However, as gene transplants become easier to perform, the variety and importance of transgenics will grow. Eventually, members of the government, the scientific community, and society at large will have to decide if the benefits of transgenics outweigh the possible burdens. Are the risks worth taking? What do you think?

Questions

1. A *transgenic* animal's genetic composition always
   a. has fewer than normal genes.
   b. contains a foreign gene.
   c. has super-growth genes.
   d. contains a mouse gene.

2. Scientists can develop transgenic animals by inserting genes into
   a. a sperm cell.
   b. an unfertilized egg cell.
   c. a fertilized egg cell.
   d. a developed embryo.

3. As mentioned above, scientists have developed breeds of transgenic sheep and mice that produce medically valuable substances in their milk. Briefly describe how you think this method of obtaining a human substance from an animal may or may not be harmful to the organism being used.

4. Do library research to investigate the development of one specific breed of transgenic animal. Discuss the importance of the product for which the animal is bred, and explain why that species is used.

Climate Change and Human Evolution

Sealed within the shells of tiny marine organisms may be the key to understanding important steps in human evolution. Oceanic evidence seems to show that two periods of worldwide cooling coincide with major turning points in hominid evolution. But how was this connection made?

Scientists have discovered that during periods of global cooling, higher concentrations of oxygen-18 (an oxygen isotope) exist in ocean water. This isotope is preserved in the shells of tiny animals called *foraminifera*, which are found buried in layers in the ocean floor. When researchers analyzed deep-sea sediment cores, they discovered evidence of two episodes of major global cooling: one happened about five million years ago, around the time when the line of hominids first separated from that of the apes; and a second, more severe cooling occurred about 2.5 million years ago, when the genus *Homo*, to which we belong, first appeared. Hominid fossil evidence can give us an idea of when and where different forms arose in the human evolutionary tree. However, it is the foraminiferan fossil evidence that may help tell us why and how.

Some researchers have suggested that each period of worldwide cooling also caused a drying of the African climate. The drier climate in turn led to a dwindling of tropical forests, giving way to more open savannas. Fossil evidence indicates that as the environment changed, some existing species either died out or moved away, and new species took their place on the savanna. For example, fossils of certain antelopes show that species more adapted to a grassland habitat emerged during the two ancient periods of cooling.

Apparently, antelopes were not the only African mammals to undergo a change. Anthropologists who study human origins hypothesize that one or more species of tree-dwelling ape might have successfully adapted to the disappearance of much of its forest habitat by coming down from the trees five million years ago. Once on the ground, these apes would have found themselves wandering longer distances in search of food—and walking upright on two legs is the most practical means of doing so. It turns out that the earliest hominid fossils that show bipedal ability (the *australopithecines*) date back 4.5 to 5 million years.

When yet another episode of cooling and drying occurred about 2.5 million years ago, there was more than one species of bipedal hominid on the African continent. One type, the *robust* australopithecine, faced the challenge of a drier environment by specializing in eating more seeds and tubers within its limited habitat. Another species of australopithecine learned to search for a greater variety of foods over a bigger range, and in the process became more skillful and intelligent in its use of the habitat. And this species was to lead to the first hominid in our own genus—the bigger-brained, tool-using *Homo habilis*—about two million years ago.

All the fossil experts may not be convinced that the effects of global cooling directly caused the evolution of hominids from apes, but some researchers feel that the evidence certainly shows a strong connection. And while fossil hominid bones can tell us only the basic facts about their owners' origins and lifestyles, the shells of some long-dead protozoans have helped to flesh out the bigger picture.

Questions

1. Scientists have learned
   about changes in the
   global climate by studying oxygen-18 content
   in the shells of ancient
   a. clams.
   b. snails.
   c. foraminiferans.
   d. corals.

2. The mammal closest to
   modern humans in our
   evolutionary history
   would be
   a. savanna-adapted antelopes.
   b. tree-dwelling apes.
   c. robust australopithecines.
   d. *Homo habilis*.

3. As mentioned above, some anthropologists
   believe that periods of global cooling may
   have had an effect on hominid evolution.
   Describe how climatic cooling may have affected the course of human evolution. In
   particular, explain how you think a change
   in climate affected competition for food
   resources between the early hominid
   species.

4. Do library research on other periods of
   global cooling that affected the course of
   human evolution and history. In particular,
   research the ice age episode that affected
   Neanderthal populations (which may or may
   not be ancestral to modern humans) in Europe. There is currently much controversy
   about possible changes in climate, like
   global warming, that may be brought on by
   various human activities. Based on your
   readings, describe how you think such
   changes could affect human evolution—
   physical or cultural—in the future.

Trashing Our Cities

Have you ever stopped to wonder what happens to all the trash you throw away each day? Statistics for 1988 show that the average American throws away nearly 4 lbs. of garbage, or solid waste, every day. That's more than 1000 lbs. per year! All Americans together produce over 160 million tons of solid waste per year from residential and commercial sources—more than any other country generates. Where does it all go?

In pre-industrial times, most garbage in cities was simply thrown out into the streets. This led to filthy and disease-ridden environments. Nowadays, most garbage is carted away by the truckload to be disposed of in soil-covered dumps called *landfills*. In fact, about 75% of all solid wastes are dumped in landfills across the nation. Some landfills that have been filled to their capacity are seeded over with grass and converted into public parks. Others become building sites, with whole communities built on top of them.

There are some serious drawbacks to the use of landfills. For one thing, toxic chemicals in certain discarded items can seep out of improperly sealed landfills and contaminate the soil and groundwater of nearby communities. More importantly, as the amount of garbage created continues to increase each year, the remaining space in landfills becomes smaller and scarcer. The U.S. Environmental Protection Agency (EPA) has estimated that one-third of all existing landfills will be filled up by 1993. Furthermore, nearly half the states in the country are expected to run out of landfill space by the year 2000. And no one wants a new dump site in his or her own community. It seems, therefore, that our nation must find other ways of dealing with its tons of trash.

One obvious alternative to dumping more and more garbage into our landfills is to generate less trash in the first place. Industry can certainly try to use less packaging material in its products. And individuals can try to reuse containers and other items when possible. In addition, many large items, such as furniture and appliances, that end up in the city dump can be repaired or salvaged for parts.

Another method of dealing with trash is to burn it. About 14% of our solid wastes are burned in large municipal incinerators, many of which convert waste to energy. Unfortunately, the burning process also converts some garbage to toxic ash and air pollution, particularly when plastics are burned. So incineration is not the best choice either.

A new way of handling garbage that is becoming more popular is to recycle it. *Recycling* is the process by which used items are treated so that their materials can be used again. About 13% of all solid wastes are recycled. Experts estimate that American communities could eventually recycle as much as 50% of their solid wastes. By 1990, there were more than 140 state recycling laws passed. More than 30 states have passed laws that encourage people to sort recyclables from other trash, and that require a statewide recycling plan.

A large cost associated with recycling has been the only factor preventing the government from mandating nationwide recycling laws. The cost of recycling a ton of garbage may be about $270 as opposed to $150 for dumping it. However, as overflowing landfills and waste-to-energy incinerators get more expensive to use, recycling becomes more economically feasible. And recycling helps save our natural resources and energy, too.

Glass and metal products can be melted down and reused time and again. Some plastics and paper can be recycled into new products, but they have a more limited life span since their fibers weaken each time they are recycled. One of the most profitable materials to recycle is metal, which comprises about 8.5% of all garbage by weight. In 1990, Americans recycled about 56 billion aluminum cans, totaling over 60% of all cans made. It is less polluting and more energy efficient to recycle aluminum, steel, and tin products than to produce them from raw ores. In total, almost 15% of all metals are recycled each year.

Nearly 8% of all solid wastes, by weight, is glass. By the late 1980s, Americans were sorting and recycling about five billion glass containers, equaling about 12% of the total amount that was discarded. Plastics also make up about 8% of all garbage by weight, but they take up 20–30% of the waste volume. By the end of the 1980s, only about 1% of all plastics was being recycled. Although sorting and processing may be more difficult because of their variety, used plastic items can be made into many new products.

By far the largest component of all solid wastes is paper, making up nearly 40% of all garbage produced in our homes and offices. That's a total of 50 million tons per year! About one-fourth of all paper waste was recycled in 1988, and that amount probably will increase as people become more aware of deforestation and the need to save trees. Many useful products, such as newspapers and cardboard boxes, can be made from recycled paper. The only problem is that, in the process of cleaning dyes and ink off used paper during recycling, some chemical pollutants are produced.

Given the current situation of vanishing resources, loss of natural habitats, and environmental pollution, maybe it's time for the federal government to pass a law insisting on the recycling of more solid wastes at home and at work. And maybe the government should help pay for the recycling process, too. What do you think?

Questions

1. Altogether, Americans produce about how much solid waste per year?
   a. 160 tons
   b. 160,000 pounds
   c. 160,000 tons
   d. 160 million tons

2. The item that makes up most of our garbage, by weight, is
   a. glass. b. paper. c. plastic. d. metal.

3. Metal is one of the most profitable materials to recycle. Based on your reading of this feature, briefly explain why it makes good sense—economically and environmentally—to recycle as much aluminum, steel, and other metals as possible.

4. Do library research on the pros and cons of recycling paper. Explore why the burning of waste paper, to produce energy, may or may not be environmentally sound (consider pollution and global warming); and compare the environmental impacts of recycling used paper *vs.* milling new paper (consider trees, water, and energy).

Glossary

Acid rain: The precipitation of acids formed by reactions of pollutants with water vapor in the atmosphere.

Active immunity: Immunity that develops when the body produces its own antibodies against a disease-causing organism.

Active site: The specific region on the enzyme surface that attaches to the substrate.

Active transport: A process by which substances are transported through the cell membrane; requires an expenditure of energy by the cell.

Adaptation: A physical feature or behavior pattern that enables an organism to function efficiently in its environment.

Addition: A chromosomal alteration in which a segment breaks off one chromosome and becomes reattached to the homologous chromosome.

ADP (adenosine diphosphate): An energy transfer compound that is converted to ATP during cellular respiration.

Adrenal gland: An endocrine gland that secretes adrenaline and various steroid hormones.

Adrenaline: A hormone produced by the adrenal medulla; released at times of stress and causes an increase in the rate of the heartbeat and breathing.

Aerobic respiration: Cellular respiration requiring free oxygen.

Allantois: In egg-laying vertebrates, an embryonic membrane that serves as a storage site for nitrogenous wastes; also functions in the exchange of respiratory gases.

Alleles: The two genes on homologous chromosomes that control the same trait.

Allergy: An immune response to a common material that does not act as an antigen in most people.

Alveolus: In the lungs, a small, hollow air sac surrounded by capillaries; site of exchange of respiratory gases between the lungs and blood.

Ameboid motion: Locomotion in which the cytoplasm flows into cell extensions called pseudopods.

Amino acid: The building block of proteins; an organic compound containing a carboxyl group, an amino group, and a variable side chain.

Amniocentesis: A technique for obtaining fetal cells.

Amnion: The membrane that surrounds the developing embryo.

Amniotic fluid: The fluid within the amnion; provides a watery environment for the embryo and cushions it from shocks.

Amylase: An enzyme that breaks down starch.

Anaerobic respiration: Cellular respiration in which a substance other than oxygen is the final hydrogen acceptor; also called *fermentation*.

Anemia: A condition in which the blood cannot carry an adequate amount of oxygen; may be caused by too few red blood cells or too little hemoglobin.

Angina pectoris: A condition characterized by pain in the chest and left arm; caused by blockage of a coronary artery.

Anther: Oval-shaped part of the stamen in which pollen grains are produced.

Antibody: Protein molecule that reacts with foreign substances in the body and destroys them; produced by lymphocytes.

Anticodon: A three-nucleotide sequence on a transfer RNA molecule that is complementary to a codon on a messenger RNA molecule.

Antigen: Any substance that stimulates the production of antibodies by lymphocytes.

Aorta: In humans, the largest artery in the body; in insects, the vessel that carries blood from the "heart" to the sinuses.

Appendix: A small pouch located at the beginning of the large intestine; serves no function in humans.

Artery: A thick-walled vessel that carries blood away from the heart.

Artificial selection: The selection by a breeder of individuals with certain desirable traits for mating.

Asexual reproduction: Reproduction in which there is only one parent, and the offspring are genetically identical to the parent.

Asthma: An allergic condition characterized by a narrowing of the bronchial tubes and difficulty in breathing.

Atom: The smallest particle of an element that has the properties of that element.

ATP (adenosine triphosphate): An energy transfer compound produced by cellular respiration; used as source of energy for cell metabolism.

Atrium: One of the upper chambers of the heart.

Autonomic nervous system: Part of the nervous system that includes the nerves that control smooth muscle, cardiac muscle, and glands; not under voluntary control.

Autosomes: All the chromosomes of a cell other than the sex chromosomes.

Autotrophic nutrition: A form of nutrition in which the organism can synthesize needed organic compounds from simple inorganic compounds; photosynthesis is the most common form of autotrophic nutrition.

Auxin: A plant hormone that influences division, elongation, and differentiation of plant cells.

Bile: A substance produced by the liver; it passes through ducts to the gallbladder and then into the small intestine, where it emulsifies fats.

Binary fission: A form of asexual reproduction in which two new individuals of equal size are formed as a result of mitotic cell division.

Binomial nomenclature: A system of using the genus and species names to identify each kind of organism.

Biomass: Mass of living matter.

Biome: A large geographic region with a particular type of climax community determined by the climate.

Biosphere: The portion of the earth in which living things are found.

Bladder: See **urinary bladder**.

Blastula: A stage of development in which the embryo is in the form of a hollow ball made up of a single layer of cells.

Blood pressure: The pressure exerted by the blood on the walls of the arteries during the heartbeat cycle.

Bowman's capsule: Part of a nephron of a kidney; a cup-shaped structure that surrounds the glomerulus.

Bronchiole: One of the small tubes formed by the repeated branching of the bronchi.

Bronchus: One of the two tubes that are formed where the lower end of the trachea divides: each bronchus extends into a lung.

Bryophyte: A simple, multicellular plant that lacks specialized conducting tissues; mosses and liverworts.

Budding: A form of asexual reproduction in which the cytoplasm divides unequally so that one of the daughter cells is much larger than the other.

Bulb: An underground stem surrounded by fleshy leaves.

Cambium: A meristematic tissue between the xylem and phloem; increases the diameter of stems and roots.

Capillary: A small, thin-walled blood vessel that connects an artery and a vein.

Carbohydrate: An organic compound made up of carbon, hydrogen, and oxygen, with a 2:1 ratio of hydrogen to oxygen.

Carbon-fixation reactions: See **dark reactions.**

Cardiac muscle: The type of muscle tissue that makes up the walls of the heart.

Cardiovascular disease: A disease of the heart or blood vessels.

Carnivore: An animal that feeds on other animals.

Cartilage: A type of flexible, fibrous connective tissue found at the ends of bones and in the nose, ears, and trachea.

Cast: A type of fossil formed when minerals fill a fossil mold and harden.

Catalyst: A substance that affects the rate of a chemical reaction, but is itself unchanged by the reaction.

Cell: The basic unit of structure and function in all living things.

Cell body: The part of a neuron that contains most of the organelles; generally receives impulses from the dendrites and transmits them to the axon.

Cell membrane: The selectively permeable membrane that surrounds the cell and controls the passage of materials into and out of the cell; also known as the *plasma membrane.*

Cell plate: In plant cells, a structure that forms at the end of mitosis and divides the cytoplasm in two; develops into new cell wall.

Cellular respiration: The process by which the chemical energy in nutrients is released.

Cellulose: A polysaccharide that makes up the cell walls of plants and algae.

Cell wall: A rigid, nonliving structure found outside the cell membrane in plants, fungi, and some microorganisms.

Central nervous system: The brain and spinal cord.

Centrioles: A pair of cylindrical organelles found near the nucleus in animal cells; function in cell division.

Centromere: The region on a double-stranded chromosome where the two chromatids are attached.

Cerebellum: The part of the brain that coordinates movements of the body and maintains balance; located below and behind the cerebrum.

Cerebral palsy: A group of diseases caused by brain damage during embryonic development; affects voluntary movement.

Cerebrum: The part of the brain that is the center for thought, memory, learning, and all voluntary activities; in humans, the largest part of the brain.

Cervix: The lower end of the uterus.

Chitin: A polysaccharide that makes up the exoskeleton of arthropods and the cell walls of fungi.

Chlorophyll: The green pigment found in plants, algae, and some protists that absorbs light energy, which is then converted to chemical energy in photosynthesis.

Chloroplast: A chlorophyll-containing organelle found in green plants, algae, and some protists; the site of photosynthesis.

Chorion: In shelled eggs, the membrane that lines the inside of the shell; also functions with the allantois in gas exchange.

Chromatid: One of the strands of a double-stranded chromosome.

Chromatin: The material of the chromosomes in dispersed form between cell divisions.

Chromatography: A technique used to separate and identify the components of a mixture.

Chromosome: A structure in the nucleus, made up of DNA and protein, on which the genes are arrayed.

Cilia: Short, hairlike organelles that cover the outside of some cells; capable of waving motion.

Cleavage: A series of rapid mitotic cell divisions at the beginning of embryonic development.

Climax community: A stable community that remains in balance until it is destroyed by a catastrophic event; the final stage of ecological succession.

Cloning: A process in which a group of genetically identical offspring are produced from the cells of an organism.

Closed circulatory system: A circulatory system in which the blood is confined within vessels.

Codominance: A type of intermediate inheritance in which both alleles are expressed in the heterozygous individual.

Codon: A sequence of three nucleotides in messenger RNA that specifies the insertion of a particular amino acid in polypeptide formation.

Coenzyme: A nonprotein component necessary for the functioning of a particular enzyme; often, a vitamin.

Color blindness: A sex-linked, inherited disorder in which the ability to see certain colors is affected.

Commensalism: A type of symbiotic relationship in which one organism benefits and the other is not affected.

Community: All the interacting populations in a particular area.

Competition: The struggle between members of different species for the same, limited natural resources.

Compound: A substance made up of two or more elements chemically bonded together.

Consumer: An organism that must obtain nutrients from the environment; a heterotroph.

Contractile vacuole: In protists, a vacuole in which excess water is stored until it is expelled from the cell.

Coronary circulation: The system of blood vessels that supplies blood to the heart.

Coronary thrombosis: A blockage in an artery that supplies blood to the heart.

Corpus luteum: The progesterone-secreting structure that forms from the ruptured follicle after ovulation.

Cotyledon: The part of the embryo plant that contains stored food; also known as the *seed leaf*.

Covalent bond: A chemical bond in which two atoms share electrons.

Crop: In some animals, an organ of the digestive system in which food is stored temporarily.

Crossing-over: An exchange of segments between homologous chromosomes during synapsis.

Cross-pollination: The transfer of pollen from an anther of one plant to a stigma of another plant.

Cuticle: In plants, the waxy layer that covers the epidermis of leaves.

Cyclosis: The natural streaming of the cytoplasm that occurs in all cells.

Cytoplasm: The watery material that fills the cell between the cell membrane and the nucleus; contains the cell organelles and is the site of many metabolic reactions.

Dark reactions: The series of photosynthetic reactions that do not require light, and end with the synthesis of glucose; also known as the *carbon-fixation reactions*.

Deamination: The removal of the amino group from an amino acid.

Decomposer: An organism that breaks down the remains of dead organisms; a saprophyte.

Dehydration synthesis: A reaction in which two molecules bond together where a hydrogen (H) is removed from one and a hydroxyl group (OH) is removed from the other; the H and OH form water.

Deletion: A chromosomal alteration in which a segment breaks off a chromosome and is lost.

Denaturation: The inactivation of an enzyme caused by excess heat or some other physical factor that changes the shape of the active site.

Dendrites: The branched extensions of the cell body of a neuron that receive impulses from the axon of an adjacent neuron.

Denitrifying bacteria: Bacteria that can break down some nitrogen-containing compounds, and release nitrogen gas into the atmosphere.

Deoxyribonucleic acid: See **DNA**.

Deoxyribose: A 5-carbon sugar found in DNA nucleotides.

Desert: A biome characterized by low annual rainfall and a wide variation in temperature between night and day.

Diabetes: A disorder in which the blood sugar level is abnormally elevated because of inadequate amounts of insulin in the blood.

Diaphragm: A large muscle at the bottom of the chest cavity that functions in breathing; in microscopes, a structure that controls the amount of light reaching the specimen.

Diastole: The relaxation phase of the heartbeat cycle.

Diffusion: The process in which molecules and ions move from regions of high concentration to regions of low concentration until an equilibrium is reached.

Digestion: The process by which large molecules in food are broken down into smaller molecules that can be used by the cells.

Dihybrid: Heterozygous for two traits.

Dihybrid cross: A cross between two organisms that are heterozygous for two traits.

Dipeptide: A compound formed when two amino acids are joined by dehydration synthesis.

Diploid chromosome number (2n): The full, normal number of chromosomes in the body cells.

Disaccharide: A sugar formed when two monosaccharides are bonded together by dehydration synthesis.

Disjunction: The separation of the two members of each pair of homologous chromosomes during the first meiotic division.

Dissecting microscope: A microscope that has an ocular and an objective lens for each eye; also known as a *binocular microscope*.

DNA (deoxyribonucleic acid): A double-stranded nucleic acid found in the chromosomes; contains the hereditary information that is passed from generation to generation.

Dominant gene: A gene whose phenotype is always expressed when present.

Dorsal: The upper, or back, side of an animal.

Down syndrome: In humans, a hereditary disorder caused by the presence of an extra chromosome number 21.

Ecological succession: The process in which one type of community is gradually replaced by another until a stable, climax community develops.

Ecology: The study of the relationships between organisms and between organisms and the environment.

Ecosystem: All the members of a community plus the physical environment in which they live.

Ectoderm: The outer germ layer.

Effector: A muscle or a gland.

Egestion: The process by which undigested and indigestible food is eliminated from the body.

Egg cell: The female gamete; the *ovum*.

Electron: A negatively charged particle found in the space around the nucleus of an atom.

Element: A substance that cannot be broken down into simpler substances by ordinary chemical reactions.

Emphysema: A disease in which the walls of the alveoli break down, which decreases the surface area for gas exchange.

Emulsification: The process by which fats are physically broken down into small droplets.

Endocrine glands: Glands that release their secretions directly into the bloodstream; also known as *ductless glands*.

Endoderm: The innermost germ layer.

Endoplasmic reticulum: A network of membrane-lined channels in the cytoplasm.

Endoskeleton: An internal bony skeleton that functions with attached muscles in locomotion.

Enzyme: A protein that acts as a catalyst; each reaction of cellular metabolism is catalyzed by an enzyme.

Epicotyl: In flowering plants, the upper portion of the plant embryo, which develops into the leaves and upper part of the stem.

Epidermis: In plants, the outermost cell layer of the leaf; in animals, the outer layer of the skin.

Epiglottis: A flap of tissue that covers the opening of the trachea in the throat during swallowing.

Esophagus: The part of the digestive tract that connects the mouth and stomach.

Essential amino acid: An amino acid that cannot be synthesized by the body, and must be present in the diet.

Estrogen: A female sex hormone produced by the ovaries; stimulates development of female secondary sex characteristics and production of egg cells.

Evolution: The process of change through time.

Excretion: The process by which the wastes of cell metabolism are removed from the body.

Exocrine gland: A gland whose secretion passes into a duct, not into the blood.

Exoskeleton: An external skeleton that functions with attached muscles in locomotion.

External development: The development of an embryo outside the body of the female.

External fertilization: Fertilization that occurs outside the body of the female.

Extracellular digestion: Digestion that occurs outside the body cells.

Fallopian tube: See **oviduct**.

Fat: A lipid that is solid at room temperature.

Feces: The digestive wastes that are egested from the body.

Fermentation: See **anaerobic respiration**.

Fertilization: In sexual reproduction, the fusion of the nuclei of two monoploid gametes to form the diploid zygote, the first cell of the new individual.

Filament: In a stamen, the stalk that supports an anther.

Filtration: The process by which water, salts, urea, and other substances diffuse out of the blood in the glomerulus and into Bowman's capsule.

Flagellum: A long, hairlike organelle that can move back and forth; functions in locomotion in some organisms.

Follicle: In an ovary, a small sac that contains an egg cell.

Follicle-stimulating hormone (FSH): A pituitary hormone that stimulates the development of follicles in the ovaries of females.

Food chain: The transfer of energy from green plants through a series of organisms with repeated stages of eating and being eaten.

Food web: The interconnected food chains of a community.

Fossil: The remains or traces of an organism that no longer exists.

Fraternal twins: Twins that develop from two different eggs.

Fruit: In flowering plants, the structure that contains the seeds; forms from the ripened ovary.

Fungi: The kingdom that includes heterotrophic, mostly multicellular organisms with cell walls and a filamentous, multinucleate structure.

Gallbladder: A pouch that temporarily stores bile produced by the liver.

Gamete: A specialized sex cell that contains the monoploid number of chromosomes; a sperm or an egg.

Gametogenesis: The production of gametes; involves meiosis and differentiation.

Ganglion: A mass of nerve cells.

Gastric caeca: In insects, pouches that secrete enzymes into the intestine.

Gastric gland: A gland in the stomach lining that secretes hydrochloric acid and gastric protease.

Gastric protease: An enzyme secreted by the gastric glands that begins digestion of proteins in the stomach; also known as *pepsin*.

Gastrointestinal tract: The digestive tract of an animal.

Gastrula: A stage of embryonic development that begins with the formation of the endoderm.

Gastrulation: In embryonic development, an inward movement of cells resulting in the formation of a two-layered gastrula.

Gene: A section of a DNA molecule that controls the synthesis of a polypeptide.

Gene frequency: The percentage of organisms in a population that carry an allele.

Gene mutation: A change in the chemical makeup of the DNA.

Gene pool: All the inheritable genes in a population.

Gene splicing: See **genetic engineering**.

Genetic engineering: The transfer of genetic material from one organism into the genetic material of another organism; also called *gene splicing*.

Genetics: The branch of biology that deals with heredity.

Genotype: The genetic makeup of an organism.

Geographic isolation: The segregation of a small population from the main breeding population by a geographic barrier between them.

Geotropism: In plants, a growth response to the force of gravity.

Germ layers: In embryonic development, the three basic cell layers from which all the tissues and organs of the body develop; the endoderm, mesoderm, and ectoderm.

Gestation period: The time between fertilization and birth.

Gizzard: In some animals, an organ of the digestive tract that grinds food.

Glomerulus: A ball of capillaries in a nephron of the kidneys.

Glucagon: A hormone produced by the islets of Langerhans in the pancreas; raises blood glucose level.

Glycogen: A polysaccharide that is a food storage compound in animals.

Goiter: A disorder in which the thyroid gland becomes enlarged; may be caused by a deficiency of iodine in the diet.

Golgi complex: A cell organelle involved in the synthesis, packaging, and secretion of cell products; has the form of a stack of flattened membranes and vesicles.

Gonads: The sex organs—ovaries in females, testes in males.

Gout: A condition caused by the deposition of uric acid in the joints.

Gradualism: The theory that new species evolve as a result of the gradual accumulation of small variations that eventually cause reproductive isolation.

Grafting: A technique in which a cut twig from one plant is firmly attached to the stem of another, rooted plant, on which it grows.

Grassland: A biome in which the dominant plants are grasses; also known as *prairie*.

Growth-stimulating hormone: A pituitary hormone that stimulates the growth of the long bones of the body.

Guanine: A nitrogenous base found in DNA and RNA.

Guard cell: One of a pair of cells that controls the opening and closing of a stomate by changing shape.

Habitat: The part of the environment in which an organism lives.

Hardy-Weinberg principle: A statement of the conditions under which the gene frequencies in a sexually reproducing population remain constant.

Hemoglobin: A red, iron-containing pigment that carries oxygen in the blood of many animals.

Hemophilia: A sex-linked, inherited disorder in which the blood does not clot properly.

Herbivore: An animal that feeds on plants.

Hermaphrodite: An animal that has both male and female gonads.

Heterotroph: An organism that must ingest preformed organic nutrients.

Heterotroph hypothesis: A hypothesis that the first living things on earth were anaerobic heterotrophs.

Heterotrophic nutrition: A form of nutrition in which the organism must ingest preformed organic nutrients.

Heterozygous: Having two different, or contrasting, alleles for a trait; *hybrid.*

High blood pressure: See **hypertension**.

Histamine: A substance released by the body cells that causes the symptoms of an allergic reaction.

Homeostasis: The maintenance of a constant internal environment in spite of changes in the external environment.

Homologous chromosomes: A pair of chromosomes that contain genes that control the same traits.

Homologous structures: Anatomical parts of different organisms that are similar in origin and structure.

Homozygous: Having two identical alleles for a trait.

Hormone: In animals, a secretion of an endocrine gland that is released into the blood and affects the activity of a distant tissue; in plants, a cellular product that affects the growth of various tissues.

Host: The organism that is harmed in a parasitic relationship.

Hybrid: See **heterozygous**.

Hybridization: The crossing of two varieties to produce offspring with the best traits of both.

Hydrolysis: A type of chemical reaction in which a large molecule is broken down into smaller molecules by the addition of water.

Hypertension: Abnormally high blood pressure in the arteries during the heartbeat cycle.

Hypocotyl: In flowering plants, the lower portion of the plant embryo, which develops into the roots and lower part of the stem.

Hypothalamus: A part of the brain that produces hormones that influence the activities of the pituitary gland.

Identical twins: Twins that develop from one fertilized egg that has separated into two equal halves early in cleavage.

Immune response: An antigen-antibody reaction.

Immunity: The capacity of the body to resist a particular disease.

Imprint: A type of fossil found in sedimentary rock; formed when a living thing leaves a mark or depression in mud that later turns to rock.

Impulse: A region of electrical and chemical change that travels over the membrane of a nerve cell.

Inbreeding: The crossing of closely related individuals to increase the chance of producing offspring with a desirable trait present in the parents.

Incomplete dominance: A type of intermediate inheritance in which the phenotype of the heterozygous individual is intermediate between the contrasting homozygous traits.

Independent assortment: A principle of Mendelian genetics stating that different traits are inherited independently of one another.

Ingestion: The process in which materials from the environment are taken into the body of an organism.

Inhalation: The taking of air into the lungs.

Inorganic compound: A compound that does not contain both carbon and hydrogen.

Insulin: A hormone produced by the islets of Langerhans in the pancreas; lowers blood glucose level.

Intercellular fluid (ICF): Fluid that bathes the cells of the body; formed from plasma that is forced out of the capillaries.

Intermediate inheritance: A type of inheritance in which the heterozygous individual is different from both the homozygous dominant and homozygous recessive individual.

Internal development: Development of an embryo within the body of the female.

Internal fertilization: Fertilization that occurs within the reproductive tract of the female.

Interneuron: A neuron within the spinal cord or brain that transmits impulses from a sensory neuron to a motor neuron.

Intestinal glands: Glands in the lining of the small intestine that secrete protein-, lipid-, and carbohydrate-digesting enzymes.

Intestine: The part of the digestive tract in which most digestion and absorption of nutrients occur.

Intracellular digestion: Digestion of food inside a cell, generally within a food vacuole.

In vitro **fertilization:** Fertilization of an egg outside the body of a female mammal.

Ion: An atom or group of atoms that has lost or gained electrons and has an electrical charge.

Ionic bond: A chemical bond formed by the transfer of electrons from one atom to another.

Islets of Langerhans: Endocrine cells in the pancreas that secrete the hormones insulin and glucagon.

Joint: A place in the skeleton where bones are connected.

Karyotyping: A technique for preparing an enlarged photograph of the chromosomes of a cell so that they can be examined for abnormalities in number and structure.

Kidney: One of a pair of excretory organs that filter urea from the blood and regulate the chemical makeup of body fluids.

Lacteal: A small lymphatic vessel found in a villus.

Large intestine: Part of the digestive tract in which water is reabsorbed from the digestive wastes.

Larynx: The voice box.

Lenticel: A small opening in the stem of a woody plant.

Leukemia: A form of cancer that affects the production of white blood cells.

Ligament: Connective tissue that attaches bones together at a movable joint.

Light reactions: The initial reactions of photosynthesis in which ATP is produced and water is split in the presence of light; also called the *photochemical reactions*.

Lipid: An organic compound made up of carbon, hydrogen, and oxygen, with hydrogen and oxygen not in a 2:1 ratio; a fat, oil, or wax.

Liver: A large organ that functions in deamination of amino acids and conversion of the amino groups to urea; it also breaks down red blood cells and produces bile.

Locomotion: The ability to move from place to place.

Lymph: The fluid found in lymph vessels; formed from excess intercellular fluid.

Lymph node: An enlarged region in a lymph vessel where microorganisms and dead cells are filtered from the lymph.

Lymphocyte: A white blood cell that produces antibodies.

Lymph vessel: A vessel that arises in the body tissues and carries excess intercellular fluid (lymph) to the blood.

Lysosome: A small, saclike, membrane-bounded organelle that contains digestive enzymes.

Magnifying power: The amount of enlargement of an image produced by a microscope; magnification.

Malpighian tubules: The excretory organs of grasshoppers and other insects.

Marsupial: A type of mammal in which no placenta develops, and most development occurs after birth; a pouched mammal.

Medulla: The part of the brain that controls many involuntary activities; located at the base of the brain and continuous with the spinal cord.

Meiosis: The type of cell division that produces monoploid cells (gametes); also called *reduction division*.

Meningitis: An inflammation of the membranes that surround the brain and spinal cord.

Menopause: The cessation of the menstrual cycle.

Menstrual cycle: A monthly series of changes that prepares the uterus for pregnancy.

Menstruation: The periodic shedding of the lining of the uterus.

Meristem: In flowering plants, the tissues that have the capacity to undergo cell division.

Mesoderm: The middle germ layer.

Messenger RNA (mRNA): RNA that carries the hereditary information for protein synthesis from the nucleus to the cytoplasm.

Metabolism: All of the chemical reactions of the life processes of an organism.

Microdissection instruments: Very small instruments that are used only with the aid of a microscope.

Micrometer (μm): A unit of measurement equal to 0.001 millimeter or 0.000001 meter.

Mitochondrion: A slipper-shaped cell organelle in which most of the reactions of aerobic cellular respiration take place.

Mitosis: The process in which the chromosomes replicate and then separate, forming two identical nuclei.

Mitotic cell division: The process in which a cell nucleus divides by mitosis, and the cytoplasm divides into equal halves, forming two identical cells.

Mixed nerve: A nerve that contains both sensory and motor neurons.

Mold: A type of fossil formed when sediments harden around the remains of an organism, which then decompose, leaving the mold; a type of fungus.

Monera: The kingdom that includes bacteria and blue-green algae, the only organisms that lack a nuclear membrane.

Monoploid chromosome number (*n*): Half the diploid chromosome number; includes only one chromosome of each homologous pair.

Monosaccharide: A simple sugar.

Motile: Capable of locomotion.

Motor nerve: A nerve containing only motor neurons.

Motor neuron: A neuron that transmits impulses from the spinal cord to an effector—a muscle or a gland.

Multiple alleles: Inheritance in which there are more than two different forms of a gene for a trait.

Mutagenic agent: Anything that increases the frequency of mutation.

Mutation: A change in the genetic material.

Mutualism: A type of symbiotic relationship in which both organisms benefit.

Natural selection: In Darwin's theory of evolution, the concept that better-adapted organisms survive and reproduce more successfully than organisms that are less well adapted.

Negative feedback: The mechanism by which blood hormone levels are regulated.

Nephridia: The excretory organs of earthworms and other annelids.

Nephron: The functional unit of the kidney; consists of a glomerulus, Bowman's capsule, and a long, coiled tubule.

Nerve: A bundle of neurons or parts of neurons.

Nerve cord: A cord of nerve tissue that connects the peripheral nerves and the brain.

Nerve net: In coelenterates, interconnected, modified neurons that conduct impulses in all directions.

Neuron: A nerve cell.

Neutron: An electrically neutral particle found in the nucleus of an atom.

Niche: The role an organism plays in its community.

Nitrate: A nitrogen-containing compound that can be used by plants for protein synthesis.

Nitrifying bacteria: Bacteria that can convert ammonia to nitrates.

Nitrogen-fixing bacteria: Bacteria that can convert nitrogen gas to nitrates.

Nitrogenous base: One of the nitrogen-containing compounds that is a component of DNA and RNA nucleotides; adenine, cytosine, guanine, thymine, and uracil.

Nondisjunction: A type of chromosomal alteration in which one or more pairs of homologous chromosomes fail to separate during meiosis.

Nucleolus: A dense, granular structure found in the cell nucleus; site of some RNA synthesis.

Nucleotide: The basic structural unit of DNA and RNA; composed of a sugar, a phosphate group, and a nitrogenous base.

Nucleus: In an atom, the dense, positively charged central part that contains protons and neutrons; in a cell, the control center of the cell that contains the chromosomes and is surrounded by a double membrane.

Nutrition: The life process in which materials from the environment are taken in by an organism and converted to a form that can be used in cell metabolism.

Oil: A lipid that is liquid at room temperature.

Omnivore: An animal that feeds on both plant and animal matter.

One gene–one polypeptide hypothesis: The hypothesis that a gene is a sequence of nucleotides that contains the information for the synthesis of a single polypeptide.

Oogenesis: The development of egg cells.

Open circulatory system: A system in which the blood leaves the vessels and bathes the body cells directly.

Optimum temperature: The temperature at which an enzyme functions most efficiently.

Organelle: A substructure of a cell; each kind of organelle carries out a specific function.

Organic compound: A compound that contains both carbon and hydrogen.

Osmosis: The diffusion of water through a semipermeable membrane.

Ovary: A female gonad.

Oviduct: A tube through which an egg cell passes from an ovary to the uterus; also called *Fallopian tube.*

Ovulation: The release of a mature egg cell from the surface of an ovary.

Ovule: In a plant ovary, the structure in which egg cells are produced and fertilization occurs.

Palisade layer: In leaves, the cell layer in which most photosynthesis occurs.

Pancreas: The organ that produces pancreatic juice, which contains digestive enzymes, and the hormones insulin and glucagon.

Parasite: The organism that benefits in a parasitic relationship; lives on or in another organism from which it obtains nutrients.

Parasitism: A type of symbiotic relationship in which one organism (the parasite) benefits and the other (the host) is harmed.

Parathormone: The parathyroid hormone that controls calcium metabolism.

Parathyroid gland: An endocrine gland that secretes the hormone parathormone.

Passive immunity: A temporary immunity to a particular disease brought about by the injection of antibodies from the blood of another person or from an animal.

Passive transport: The transport of materials across cell membranes without the expenditure of cellular energy; diffusion or osmosis.

Penis: In mammals, the male organ through which urine and sperm pass out of the body.

Peptide bond: The type of chemical bond that forms when amino acids are joined together by dehydration synthesis.

Peripheral nervous system: All the nerves outside the brain and spinal cord.

Peristalsis: The rhythmic muscular contractions of the digestive organs that move food through the digestive tract.

Petal: In flowers, one of the leaflike structures inside the ring of sepals; may be white or brightly colored.

Petrifaction: The process by which the tissues of a dead organism are gradually replaced by minerals.

PGAL: A three-carbon compound produced in the dark reactions of photosynthesis and from which glucose is synthesized.

pH: A measure of the acidity or alkalinity of a solution based on the concentration of hydrogen ions.

Phagocyte: A white blood cell that engulfs and destroys microorganisms and other foreign matter in the blood and body tissues.

Phagocytosis: A process by which particles are surrounded by extensions of a cell (pseudopods) and taken into the cell.

Pharynx: The area where the oral and nasal cavities meet in the back of the mouth.

Phenotype: The physical appearance of a trait or an organism resulting from its genetic makeup.

Phenylketonuria: A genetic disorder in which the body lacks the enzyme necessary to metabolize the amino acid phenylalanine.

Phloem: The transport, or vascular, tissue of plants that carries dissolved foods from the leaves throughout the plant.

Photochemical reactions: See **light reactions**.

Photolysis: In the light reactions of photosynthesis, the use of energy from sunlight to split water into hydrogen and oxygen.

Photosynthesis: A type of autotrophic nutrition in which light energy is absorbed by chlorophyll and used to synthesize organic compounds.

Phototropism: A growth response of a plant to light coming from one direction.

Pinocytosis: A type of active transport in which large, dissolved molecules are taken into a cell by an inpocketing of the cell membrane.

Pioneer organism: One of the first living things in an otherwise lifeless area.

Pistil: The female reproductive organ of a flowering plant.

Pituitary gland: An endocrine gland that secretes several hormones; some of these hormones regulate the activities of other endocrine glands.

Placenta: In placental mammals, a temporary organ that forms from both maternal and fetal tissues; the site of exchange of materials between maternal and fetal blood.

Placental mammal: A mammal in which development is completed internally and the embryo obtains nutrients and gets rid of wastes through the placenta.

Plasma: The fluid portion of the blood.

Plasma membrane: See **cell membrane**.

Platelets: Small blood cell fragments that function in clotting reactions.

Polar body: A small cell produced during oogenesis by an unequal division of the cytoplasm.

Pollen grain: A tiny, sporelike capsule that contains sperm nuclei of a flowering plant.

Pollen tube: In flowering plants, the tube that grows down from a germinating pollen grain; the sperm nuclei pass down the pollen tube to the ovule, where fertilization occurs.

Pollination: The transfer of pollen grains from an anther to a stigma.

Polypeptide: A chain of three or more amino acids joined together by peptide bonds.

Polyploidy: The presence of one or more complete extra sets of chromosomes in a cell.

Polysaccharide: A carbohydrate that consists of three or more monosaccharides bonded together.

Population: All members of a species that live in a particular area.

Population genetics: A study of the factors that affect gene frequencies in populations of sexually reproducing organisms.

Predator: An animal that kills and consumes its prey.

Primary consumer: An animal that feeds on plants; a herbivore.

Producers: The autotrophs of a food chain.

Progesterone: A female sex hormone produced by the ovaries; stimulates thickening of the uterine lining in preparation for pregnancy.

Protein: A nitrogen-containing organic compound made up of amino acids.

Protista: The kingdom that includes one-celled organisms with a nucleus surrounded by a nuclear membrane and either photosynthetic or heterotrophic nutrition.

Proton: A positively charged particle found in the nucleus of an atom.

Pseudopod: An extension of the cell into which the cell contents flow.

Puberty: The stage at which an individual becomes capable of sexual reproduction.

Pulmonary circulation: The path of the blood between the heart and the lungs.

Pulse: The rhythmic expansion and contraction of the arteries caused by the heartbeat.

Punctuated equilibrium: The theory that species remain relatively unchanged for long periods of time and then show major changes that lead to the development of new species over a relatively short geologic time span.

Pyramid of biomass: The relative amounts of living matter, or biomass, at each feeding level in a community.

Pyramid of energy: The relative amounts of energy available at each feeding level in a community.

Receptor: A specialized structure in the nervous system that can detect a particular kind of stimulus; a sense organ.

Recessive gene: A gene whose phenotype is not expressed in the presence of a dominant gene.

Recombinant DNA: DNA formed by the insertion of genes from another organism by gene splicing.

Rectum: Portion of the large intestine where digestive wastes are stored temporarily before being egested from the body.

Red blood cells: Blood cells that contain the red pigment hemoglobin and that carry oxygen between the lungs and the body cells.

Reflex: An automatic, inborn response to a particular stimulus.

Reflex arc: An inborn nerve pathway for carrying out a reflex response.

Regeneration: The process by which an animal regrows a lost body part.

Regulation: The control and coordination of the life processes.

Rejection: An immune response that occurs when the

body of a recipient recognizes a transplanted organ as foreign and produces antibodies against it.

Replication: The process by which DNA makes an exact copy of itself.

Reproductive isolation: The inability of two populations to interbreed and produce fertile offspring.

Resolution: The capacity of a microscope to show separate images of two points that are very close together.

Respiration: The process by which organisms obtain energy from the breakdown of nutrients.

Response: The reaction of an organism to a stimulus.

Ribonucleic acid: See **RNA**.

Ribose: A 5-carbon sugar found in RNA.

Ribosomal RNA (rRNA): The type of RNA found in the ribosomes.

Ribosome: An organelle that is the site of protein synthesis; found suspended in the cytoplasm and attached to membranes of the endoplasmic reticulum.

RNA (ribonucleic acid): A single-stranded nucleic acid that functions in protein synthesis.

Root hair: In root tips, a hairlike extension of an epidermal cell that increases the surface area for absorption.

Roughage: Indigestible material in food, mainly cellulose.

Runner: A horizontal stem that grows close to the ground; where buds on the runner touch the ground, roots develop, and a new plant grows.

Saliva: The watery secretion of the salivary glands; contains the enzyme amylase, which begins starch digestion in the mouth.

Salivary glands: Exocrine glands that secrete saliva.

Saprophyte: An organism that obtains nutrients from the remains of other organisms; a decomposer.

Saturated fat: A fat that contains no double bonds and cannot add hydrogens.

Scavenger: An animal that feeds on the remains of animals that it has not killed.

Scion: In grafting, the cut twig that is attached to the rooted stock.

Screening: Simple chemical tests that are used to detect certain genetic disorders.

Scrotum: A sac that is an outpocketing of the body wall and contains the testes.

Secondary consumer: An animal that feeds on primary consumers; a carnivore.

Sedimentary rock: A type of rock that forms from thick layers of sediment that gradually harden from the pressure of overlying layers.

Seed: The structure that contains the embryo plant.

Seed coat: The outer covering of a seed.

Self-pollination: The transfer of pollen from an anther to a stigma on the same plant.

Semen: A mixture of sperm and various fluids.

Sensory nerve: A nerve that contains only sensory neurons.

Sensory neuron: A neuron that transmits impulses from a sense receptor to the spinal cord.

Sepal: One of the leaflike structures that form a circle at the base of a flower and enclose and protect the flower bud.

Sessile: Living permanently attached to a fixed object or surface.

Setae: Bristles found in pairs on the underside of earthworms and other annelids.

Sex chromosomes: The X and Y chromosomes, which determine sex.

Sex-linked genes: Genes found on the sex chromosomes.

Sexual reproduction: Reproduction in which the new individual develops from a single cell that has been formed by the fusion of two specialized sex cells, one from each parent.

Sickle-cell anemia: A genetic disorder characterized by abnormal hemoglobin and red blood cells.

Skeletal muscle: Voluntary muscle attached to the bones of the skeleton; also called *striated muscle*.

Small intestine: The part of the digestive tract in which digestion is completed and nutrients are absorbed into the blood.

Smooth muscle: Involuntary muscle found in the walls of internal organs.

Somatic nervous system: Part of the nervous system that includes all nerves that control voluntary muscles and all sensory nerves from sense receptors to the central nervous system.

Speciation: The process by which a new species evolves.

Species: All organisms of the same kind; all organisms capable of breeding with one another and producing fertile offspring.

Spermatogenesis: The development of sperm cells.

Sperm cell: The male gamete.

Spinal cord: A cord of nervous tissue that extends from the brain down the back of vertebrates; carries impulses to and from the brain, and is the center for many reflexes.

Spindle apparatus: A network of fibers that forms during mitosis; involved in the movement of chromosomes.

Spiracles: Small holes in the exoskeleton of insects through which respiratory gases enter and leave the body.

Spongy layer: In leaves, the layer of cells between the palisade layer and the lower epidermis; contains interconnecting air spaces continuous with the stomates.

Spore: A specialized, small reproductive cell produced by mitotic cell division.

Stamen: The male reproductive organ of a flower.

Starch: A polysaccharide that is a food storage compound in plants.

Stigma: The sticky, knoblike part of a pistil that is specialized for receiving pollen grains.

Stimulus: Any change or physical factor in the environment that initiates impulses in a sense receptor.

Stock: In grafting, the rooted plant to which the scion is attached.

Stomate: An opening in the surface of a leaf through which gases enter and leave the internal leaf tissues.

Striated muscle: See **skeletal muscle**.

Stroke: A disorder caused by an interruption in the blood flow to the brain.

Style: The part of a pistil that supports the stigma.

Substrate: A substance acted upon by an enzyme.

Sweat gland: A structure in the skin that filters water, salts, and a small amount of urea from the blood.

Symbiotic relationship: A type of close association in which two organisms of different kinds live together and one or both of them benefit.

Synapse: The junction between adjacent neurons.

Synapsis: The pairing of homologous chromosomes during the first meiotic division.

Synthesis: A chemical reaction in which small molecules combine to form larger ones.

Systemic circulation: The circulatory pathway between the heart and all parts of the body except the lungs.

Systole: The contraction phase of the heartbeat cycle.

Taiga: A biome with cold winters and a short growing season.

Temperate deciduous forest: A biome with cold winters and hot summers; the climax vegetation is deciduous trees (oaks, maples, beeches).

Tendon: A connective tissue cord that attaches muscle to bone.

Test cross: A cross done to determine whether an individual showing a dominant phenotype is homozygous dominant or heterozygous.

Testes: The male gonads.

Testosterone: A male sex hormone produced by the testes.

Thyroid gland: An endocrine gland that secretes the hormone thyroxin.

Thyroid-stimulating hormone (TSH): A pituitary hormone that stimulates the secretion of thyroxin by the thyroid gland.

Thyroxin: The thyroid hormone that regulates the rate of cell metabolism.

Trachea: The tube that carries air from the pharynx to the lungs.

Tracheophyte: A plant with vascular tissues and true roots, stems, and leaves.

Transfer RNA (tRNA): A type of RNA that carries an amino acid to the messenger RNA in protein synthesis.

Translocation: A chromosomal alteration in which a segment of a chromosome breaks off and becomes reattached to a nonhomologous chromosome.

Transpiration: In plants, the loss of water by evaporation through the stomates of the leaves.

Transpirational pull: The combination of transpiration and other upward-acting forces that allows water to rise in the xylem of a plant in a continuous column.

Transport: The processes by which materials are absorbed into and circulate through an organism.

Tropical rain forest: A biome found near the equator and characterized by a constant warm temperature and constant, plentiful rainfall.

Tropism: In plants, an unequal growth response to a stimulus that comes from one direction.

Tube nucleus: The nucleus that controls the growth of the pollen tube.

Tuber: An enlarged underground stem that contains stored food.

Tundra: A biome in which the winters are long and cold and the subsoil remains frozen, even during the short summer.

Ultracentrifuge: An instrument used to separate small particles or materials according to differences in density.

Umbilical cord: In placental mammals, the structure that connects the embryo to the placenta.

Unsaturated fats: Fats that contain one or more double bonds.

Urea: The nitrogenous waste product of mammals.

Ureter: One of a pair of tubes that carries urine from the kidneys to the urinary bladder.

Urethra: A tube that carries urine from the urinary bladder to the outside of the body; in the male, it also carries sperm.

Uric acid: A semisolid, crystalline nitrogenous waste product of various animals.

Urinary bladder: A sac that stores urine temporarily before it is excreted from the body.

Uterus: The organ of the female reproductive system in which embryonic development occurs.

Vacuole: A fluid-filled cell organelle surrounded by a membrane.

Vagina: The muscular tube that leads from the uterus to the outside of the body; also called the *birth canal*.

Vegetative propagation: A type of asexual reproduction in plants in which new plants develop from the roots, stems, or leaves of the parent plant.

Vein: In animals, a thin-walled vessel that carries blood from the body tissues toward the heart; in leaves, a bundle containing xylem and phloem.

Ventral: The lower, or belly, side of an animal.

Ventricle: One of the lower, muscular chambers of the heart.

Villus: A fingerlike projection of the inner lining of the small intestine.

White blood cells: Blood cells that protect the body from microorganisms and other foreign materials.

Xylem: In plants, the conducting, or vascular, tissue that carries water and dissolved materials upward from the roots to the rest of the plant.

Yolk: A stored nutrient in animal eggs.

Yolk sac: The embryonic membrane that surrounds the yolk of an egg.

Zygote: In sexual reproduction, the diploid cell formed by fertilization; the first cell of a new individual.

Index

Abiotic factors, of ecosystems, 87
ABO blood group, 36
  inheritance of, 66
Absorption, 1
  of nutrients, 33
Acetylcholine, 28
Acid rain, 91
Acquired characteristics,
    inheritance of, 78
Active immunity, 36
Active site, of enzymes, 10–11
Active transport, 19, 42
Addition, 68
Adenine, 71
Adenosine triphosphate, see ATP
Adhesion, 21
Adrenal glands, 45
Aerobic respiration, 24
Aggregates, 81
Aging, 58
Air pollution, 91
Albumen, 55
Alcoholic fermentation, 23–24
Algae, 2, 88
Allantois, 55
Alleles, 62
Allergy, 36
Altitude, and climate, 88–89
Alveoli, 39–40
Amber, 76
Ameboid motion, 31
Amino acids, 8–9
  absorption of, 33
  in diet, 34
  essential, 34
Amino group, 8–9
Ammonia, excretion of, 26–27
Amniocentesis, 70
Amnion, 55
Amniotic fluid, 55
Amylase, in pancreatic juice, 33
  in saliva, 32
Anaerobic respiration, 23–24
Anal pore, 18
Anemia, 38
  sickle-cell, 68, 70
Angina pectoris, 38
Angiosperms, reproduction in, 59
Animal kingdom, 2
Annelids, 2
Anther, 59
Antibody, 36
Anticodon, 72
Antigen, 36
Aorta, in grasshopper, 22
  in humans, 37
Appendicitis, 35
Aquatic biomes, 89–90
Artery, 37
Arthritis, 47
Arthropods, 2
Artificial selection, 70
Asbestos, 68
Asexual reproduction, 48

binary fission, 49
budding, 49–50
regeneration, 50
sporulation, 50
vegetative propagation, 50
Asthma, 40
Athlete's foot fungus, 83
Atom, 7
ATP, 1
  and aerobic respiration, 24
  and anaerobic respiration, 23–24
  in photosynthesis, 14
Atrium, of heart, 37
Autonomic nervous system, 43
Autosomes, 66
Autotrophic nutrition, 13–16, 83
Auxin, 30
Axon, 28

Bacteria, 2
  as decomposers, 84
  in nitrogen cycle, 86
Benedict's solution, 99
Benzene, 68
Bicarbonate ions, 40
Bile, 32
Binary fission, 49
Binocular microscope, 5
Binomial nomenclature, 2
Biological pest control, 92
Biomes, 88–90
Birth canal, 56
Biosphere, 82
Biotic factors, in ecosystems,
    82–83
Blastula, 54
Blood, cells of, 36
  circulation of, 36–38
  clotting of, 36
  composition of, 36
  and immunity, 36
  types, 36, 66
Blood pressure, 37
Blood type, 36
  inheritance of, 66
Blood vessels, 36–37
Blue-green algae, 2
Body temperature, 41
Bonds, chemical, 7
Bone, 46
Bone marrow, 36, 46
Bowman's capsule, 41–42
Brain, of earthworm, 29
  of grasshopper, 29
  of human, 43
Breathing, 40
Breeding, 70–71
Bromthymol blue, 99
Bronchiole, 39
Bronchitis, 40
Bronchus, 39
Brown, Robert, 3
Bryophytes, 2
  transport in, 20–21

Budding, 49–50
Bulb, 50

Calcium, metabolism of, 45
Cambium, 60
Cancer, 49
Capillaries, 37
Carbohydrates, 8
  in diet, 34
Carbon-14, 14
Carbon dioxide, 86
  in blood, 40
  in cellular respiration, 23–24
  in photosynthesis, 13–14
Carbon-fixation reactions, 14
Carbon-hydrogen-oxygen cycle, 86
Carboxyl group, 8–9
Cardiac muscle, 46–47
Cardiovascular disease, 38
Carnivore, 83
Carriers, 67
Cartilage, in respiratory system, 39
  in skeleton, 46
Cast, 76
Catalyst, 10
Cell, 3–5
Cell body, 28
Cell membrane, 4
  and active transport, 19
  and diffusion, 19
  and osmosis, 19
  and phagocytosis, 19
  and pinocytosis, 19–20
  structure of, 19
Cell plate, 48
Cell theory, 3
Cellular respiration, 23–24
  aerobic, 24
  anaerobic, 23
Cellulose, 8, 34
Cell wall, 4–5
Central nervous system, of
    earthworm, 29
  of grasshopper, 29
  of humans, 29, 43
Centrioles, 4
  in mitosis, 48
Centromeres, 48
Cerebellum, 43
Cerebral palsy, 44
Cerebrum, 43
Cervix, 56
Chemical bonds, 7
Chitin, 31
Chlorophyll, 13–14
Chloroplasts, 3–4, 16
  in dark reactions, 14
  in light reactions, 13–14
  structure of, 13
Chordates, 2
Chorion, 55
Chromatids, 48
Chromatin, 48

in aerobic respiration, 24
Mitosis, 48
Mixed nerves, 43
Molds, fossil, 76
Molecular formulas, 7–8
Monera, 2
Monoploid chromosome number, 51
Monosaccharides, 8
Morgan, Thomas H., 62
Mosses, 21
Motor nerves, 43
Motor neurons, 42–43
Multiple alleles, 66
Muscle, cardiac, 46
  skeletal, 46
  smooth, 46
Muscle fatigue, 39
Mutagenic agents, 68
Mutations, chromosomal, 67–68
  gene, 72
Mutualism, 83

Nasal cavity, 39
Natural resources, conservation of, 91
Natural selection, 78–79
Negative feedback, 45
Nephridia, 27
Nephron, 41–42
Nerve, 43
Nerve control, 28–29
  in earthworm, 29
  in grasshopper, 29
  in humans, 29, 42–43
  in hydra, 29
Nerve cord, of earthworm, 29
  of grasshopper, 29
Nervous system, of earthworm, 29
  of grasshopper, 29
  human, 42–43
Neurons, of humans, 42–43
  structure of, 28
Neurotransmitters, 28–29
Neutrons, 7
Niche, 88
Nitrates, 87
Nitrifying bacteria, 87
Nitrogen cycle, 87
Nitrogen-fixing bacteria, 83, 87
Nitrogenous base, 71
Nondisjunction, 67–68
Nostrils, 39
Nuclear membrane, 4
  in meiosis, 51
  in mitosis, 48
Nucleolus, 4
Nucleotides, 71
Nucleus, of atom, 7
  of cell, 4
Nutrition, 1, 13
  autotrophic, 13–16, 83
  in earthworm, 18
  in fungi, 17
  in grasshopper, 18
  heterotrophic, 13, 16–18, 83
  in humans, 18, 32–35
  in hydra, 18
  in protists, 17–18

Oils, 9
Omnivores, 83
One gene–one polypeptide hypothesis, 72
Oogenesis, 52–53
Open circulatory system, 22
Optimum temperature, 11
Oral cavity, 32
Oral groove, 18
Organic compounds, 8
Osmosis, 19
Ovary, of flower, 59
  of humans, 45, 57
Overhunting, 90
Ovulation, 57
Ovule, 59
Oxygen-18, 14

Palisade layer, 16
Pancreas, digestive functions of, 33
  endocrine functions of, 45
Pancreatic juice, 33
Parasite, 83
Parasitism, 83
Parathormone, 44–45
Parathyroid glands, 44–45
Passive immunity, 36
Passive transport, 19
Pedigree charts, 69
Pepsin, 11
Peptide bond, 9
Peripheral nerves, 29
Peripheral nervous system, human, 43
Petals, 59
Petrifaction, 76
PGAL, 14
pH, 11
  and enzyme action, 11–12
pH paper, 99
Phagocytes, 36
Phagocytosis, 19
  in ameba, 17
Pharynx, of earthworm, 18
  of grasshopper, 18
  of humans, 39
Phase-contrast microscope, 5
Phenotype, 62
Phenylketonuria, 70
Phloem, 21
Photochemical reactions, 13–14
Photolysis, 14
Photosynthesis, 13–16
  adaptations for, 15–16
Phototropism, 30
Pigments, photosynthetic, 13
Pinocytosis, 19–20
Pioneer organisms, 87–88
Pistils, 59
Pituitary gland, 44–45
PKU, 70
Placenta, 55
Placental mammals, 55
Plant kingdom, 2
Plants, 2
  excretion in, 27
  hormones of, 30
  nutrition in, 13–15

respiration in, 25
  sexual reproduction in, 59–60
  transport in, 21
  tropisms of, 30
  vegetative propagation of, 50
Plasma, 36
Plasma membrane, 4
Platelets, 36
Polar body, 52–53
Polar nuclei, 59–60
Polio, 44
Pollen grain, 59–60
Pollen tube, 59–60
Pollination, 59–60
Pollution, environmental, 91
Polypeptides, 9
Polyploidy, 68
Polysaccharides, 8
  digestion of, 33
Population, 75, 82
Population genetics, 75
Predators, 83
Producers, 84
Progesterone, 45, 56–57
Proteases, 33
Proteins, 8
  in diet, 34
  hydrolysis of, 33–34
  synthesis of, 9, 72
Protista, 2
Protists, binary fission in, 49
  locomotion in, 31
  nutrition in, 17–18
  respiration in, 25
  transport in, 22
Protons, 7
Protozoa, 2
Pseudopods, 17, 31
Puberty, 56, 58
Punctuated equilibrium, theory of, 80
Punnett squares, 63
Pyramid of biomass, 85
Pyramid of energy, 84–85
Pyruvic acid, 23–24

Radioactive dating, 76
Receptors, 29
Recessive alleles, 62
Recombination, 63
Rectum, 18, 33
Red blood cells, 36
  breakdown of, 41
Reflex, 43
Reflex arc, 43
Regeneration, 50
Regulation, 1, 28–30
  chemical control, 30
  nerve control, 28–29
Rejection, 36
Replication, of DNA, 71
Reproduction, 1
  asexual, 48–50
  sexual, 48, 51–53, 59–60
Reproductive isolation, 80
Resistance, 79
Resolution, 5
Resolving power, 5
Respiration, 1, 25–26, 39–40

Sample Examinations

BIOLOGY
JUNE 1998

Directions (1–59): For *each* statement or question, select the word or expression that, of those given, best completes the statement or answers the question. Record your answer on the separate answer paper in accordance with the directions on the front page of this booklet.

1 Which activity is illustrated in the diagram of an ameba shown below?

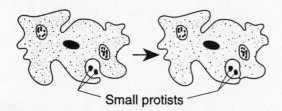

Small protists

1 egestion
2 synthesis
3 respiration
4 ingestion

2 During a race, the body temperature of a runner increases. The runner responds by perspiring, which lowers body temperature. This process is an example of

1 maintenance of homeostasis
2 an antigen-antibody reaction
3 an acquired characteristic
4 environmental factors affecting phenotype

3 The diagram below represents a freshwater protist.

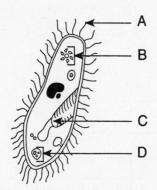

Which letter indicates a structure that prevents the accumulation of excess water in the protist?

(1) *A*   (3) *C*
(2) *B*   (4) *D*

4 In the cartoon below, *Canus nipponicus* refers to a proposed scientific name for an imaginary organism.

"What a find, Ms. Dinkins! ... It's Mailman, all right—but remarkably, this specimen is fully intact, with the *Canus nipponicus* still attached."

This proposed scientific name indicates the

1 kingdom and phylum
2 phylum and genus
3 genus and species
4 kingdom and species

5 Viruses are exceptions to the cell theory, but they have some characteristics of living things. What is one of these characteristics?

1 They are made up of many specialized cells.
2 They contain genetic material.
3 They reproduce by mitosis.
4 They contain chlorophyll.

6 Which formula represents an organic compound?

(1) $Mg(OH)_2$ (3) $C_{12}H_{22}O_{11}$
(2) $NaCl$ (4) NH_3

7 Hydrogen peroxide (H_2O_2) is a toxic by-product of cellular metabolism in aerobic organisms. The reaction below occurs within the cells to prevent the accumulation of hydrogen peroxide.

$$2H_2O_2 \xrightarrow{\text{catalase}} 2H_2O + O_2$$

In this reaction, catalase functions as an

1 enzyme in the breakdown of hydrogen peroxide
2 enzyme in the synthesis of hydrogen peroxide
3 emulsifier in the digestion of hydrogen peroxide
4 indicator in the detection of hydrogen peroxide

8 Which life process is classified as autotrophic in some organisms and heterotrophic in other organisms?

1 hormonal regulation   3 anaerobic respiration
2 nutrition   4 transport

9 What does the process of photosynthesis produce?

1 starch, which is metabolized into less complex molecules by dehydration synthesis
2 protein, which is metabolized into less complex molecules by dehydration synthesis
3 glycerol, which is metabolized into more complex carbohydrates by dehydration synthesis
4 glucose, which is metabolized into more complex carbohydrates by dehydration synthesis

10 The diagram below shows the same type of molecules in area A and area B. With the passage of time, some molecules move from area A to area B.

Molecules

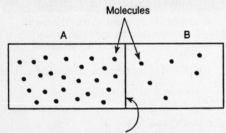

Selectively Permeable Membrane

This movement is the result of the process of

1 phagocytosis   3 diffusion
2 pinocytosis   4 cyclosis

11 Which statement correctly describes one characteristic of the tubelike digestive system of an earthworm?

1 Various parts of the system perform different digestive functions.
2 The shape of the system allows food to be processed by intracellular digestion.
3 The shape of the system eliminates the need for egestion.
4 Digestive enzymes are not used in the system.

12 The absorption and circulation of materials in a hydra are most similar to the absorption and circulation of materials in a

1 grasshopper   3 human
2 protozoan   4 frog

13 What are the primary components of the structure labeled X in the diagram below?

1 stomates and lenticels
2 xylem tissue and phloem tissue
3 epidermal cells and guard cells
4 cambium and root hairs

14 The fermentation of glucose by yeast normally yields

(1) lactic acid, CO_2, and 2 ATP
(2) alcohol, CO_2, and 36 ATP
(3) alcohol, CO_2, and 2 ATP
(4) CO_2, H_2O, and 36 ATP

15 Which waste product of a grasshopper may be retained and used in other metabolic activities?

1 water   3 carbon dioxide
2 uric acid   4 feces

16 Which diagram represents an organelle that contains the enzymes needed to synthesize ATP in the presence of oxygen?

(1)   (2)   (3)   (4)

17 Which title is an appropriate heading for column X?

Organism	X
A	Moist skin
B	Spiracles and tracheal tubes
C	Gills and capillaries

1 Structures Needed for Anaerobic Respiration
2 Structures Used in Gas Exchange
3 Excretory Systems
4 Sensory Receptors

18 Which organism is correctly paired with the excretory adaptation used for the removal of its nitrogenous wastes?

1 grasshopper — nephron
2 human — Malpighian tubules
3 hydra — kidney
4 earthworm — nephridia

19 Which substances are secreted at the endings of nerve cells?

1 antibodies   3 neurotransmitters
2 antigens   4 lipids

20 A drastic change in the metabolic rate of a human would most likely result from the

1 oversecretion of the salivary glands
2 overproduction of auxins
3 deterioration of the skeletal system
4 malfunction of the endocrine glands

21 Which set of terms would most likely be used in a description of the nervous system of chordates?

1 brain, dorsal nerve cord, highly developed receptors
2 brain, fused ganglia, ventral nerve cord
3 no brain, fused ganglia, tympana
4 no brain, nerve net, modified neurons

22 Three organisms possess some of the characteristics shown in the chart below. An **X** indicates that the characteristic is present.

Organism	Consumer	Structures for Locomotion		
		Cilia	Flagella	Pseudopods
A			X	
B	X			X
C	X	X		

Which statement best describes these organisms?

(1) A could be an alga, B could be an ameba, and C could be a paramecium.
(2) A could be a plant, and B and C could be coelenterates.
(3) A could be a yeast, and B and C could be bacteria.
(4) A could be a moss, B could be a hydra, and C could be an earthworm.

23 The diagram below shows a particle of food being moved along the human digestive tract by alternate waves of relaxation and contraction of the muscular walls of the esophagus.

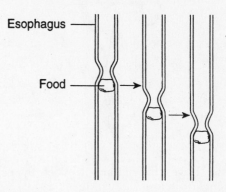

Which process causes the movement of the food down the esophagus?

1 circulation   3 peristalsis
2 active transport   4 osmosis

24 A malfunction of the lymph nodes would most likely interfere with the

1 release of carbon dioxide into the lymph
2 filtering of glucose from the lymph
3 release of oxygen into the lymph
4 filtering of bacteria from the lymph

25 A pulse can be detected most easily in

1 an artery   3 a capillary
2 a vein   4 a lacteal

26 The diagram below represents part of a capillary in a specific region of the human body.

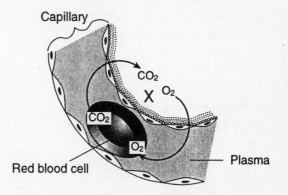

The region labeled X represents part of

1 a glomerulus   3 a villus
2 an alveolus   4 the liver

27 The diagram below represents a group of organs in the human body.

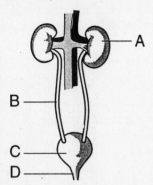

Urine leaves the urinary bladder by passing through structure

(1) A   (3) C
(2) B   (4) D

28 Which row in the chart below contains the words that best complete this statement?

The __I__ glands produce __II__, which are transported by the __III__ system.

Row	I	II	III
A	digestive	hormones	circulatory
B	endocrine	enzymes	lymphatic
C	endocrine	hormones	circulatory
D	digestive	enzymes	lymphatic

(1) A   (3) C
(2) B   (4) D

29 One function of the human endoskeleton is to

1 transmit impulses
2 produce blood cells
3 produce lactic acid
4 store nitrogenous wastes

30 What would most likely result if mitosis was *not* accompanied by cytoplasmic division?

1 two cells, each with one nucleus
2 two cells, each without a nucleus
3 one cell with two identical nuclei
4 one cell without a nucleus

31 Which structures are *not* involved in asexual reproduction?

1 centromeres   3 chromosomes
2 spindles   4 setae

32 Which statement best explains why invertebrates regenerate lost tissue more readily than most vertebrates do?

1 Invertebrates contain specialized cells that produce the hormones necessary for this process.
2 Invertebrate cells exhibit a higher degree of uncontrolled cell division than vertebrate cells do.
3 Invertebrate animals reproduce asexually, but vertebrate animals reproduce sexually.
4 Invertebrate animals have more undifferentiated cells than vertebrate animals have.

33 Which diagram represents binary fission?

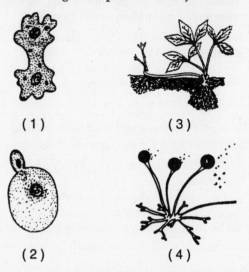

(1)   (3)

(2)   (4)

34 The process of meiotic cell division in a human male usually forms

1 one diploid cell, only
2 four diploid cells
3 one monoploid cell, only
4 four monoploid cells

35 Which reproductive adaptation is characteristic of most terrestrial vertebrates but *not* of most aquatic vertebrates?

1 external fertilization
2 internal fertilization
3 motile gametes
4 external development

36 Based on the fact that a watermelon contains many seeds, what can be inferred about a normal flower of a watermelon plant?

1 It contains many sepals and petals.
2 It contains very large anthers.
3 It contains a large number of ovules.
4 It contains a large number of stamens.

37 The spotted touch-me-not, a flowering plant, has seed pods that burst open when touched and forcefully eject their seeds. Such an adaptation is favorable because it

1 aids in the dispersal of the species
2 attracts insects that aid in pollination
3 prevents germination within the seed pod
4 can cause genetic changes to occur

38 Which chromosome pair below best illustrates the gene-chromosome theory?

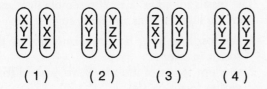

(1)   (2)   (3)   (4)

39 In squirrels, the gene for gray fur (G) is dominant over the gene for black fur (g). If 50% of a large litter of squirrels are gray, the parental cross that produced this litter was most likely

(1) $GG \times Gg$ (3) $Gg \times gg$
(2) $GG \times GG$ (4) $gg \times gg$

40 Which process is illustrated by the diagram below?

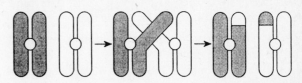

1 crossing-over
2 nondisjunction
3 sex determination
4 independent assortment

41 Which cross could produce a child with type O blood?

(1) $I^A i \times I^B I^B$ (3) $I^A I^B \times ii$
(2) $I^A I^A \times I^B i$ (4) $I^A i \times I^B i$

42 Breeders have developed a variety of chicken that has no feathers. Which methods were most likely used to produce this variety?

1 artificial selection and inbreeding
2 grafting and hybridization
3 regeneration and incubation
4 vegetative propagation and binary fission

43 A molecule of DNA is a polymer composed of

1 glucose   3 fatty acids
2 amino acids   4 nucleotides

44 The diagram below illustrates the change that occurred in the frequency of phenotypes in an insect population over 10 generations.

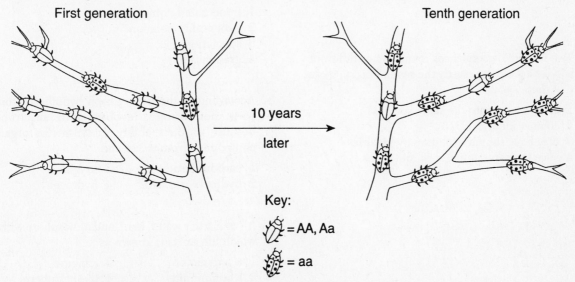

A probable explanation for this change would be that over time there was

1 a decrease in the adaptive value of gene a
2 an increase in the adaptive value of gene a
3 an increase in the population of this insect
4 a decrease in the mutation rate of gene A

45 In fruit flies with the curly wing mutation, the wings will be straight if the flies are kept at 16°C, but curly if they are kept at 25°C. The most probable explanation for this is that

1 fruit flies with curly wings cannot survive at high temperatures
2 the environment influences wing phenotype in these fruit flies
3 high temperatures increase the rate of mutations
4 wing length in these fruit flies is directly proportional to temperature

46 According to Darwin's theory of evolution, differences between species may be the result of

1 the disuse of body structures
2 the transmission of acquired characteristics
3 natural selection
4 mutagenic agents

47 The concept that new varieties of organisms are still evolving is best supported by the

1 increasing need for new antibiotics
2 increasing number of individuals in the human population
3 decreasing number of new fossils discovered in undisturbed rock layers
4 decreasing activity of photosynthetic organisms due to warming of the atmosphere

48 Two nucleotide sequences found in two different species are almost exactly the same. This suggests that these species

1 are evolving into the same species
2 contain identical DNA
3 may have similar evolutionary histories
4 have the same number of mutations

49 The diagram below shows undisturbed sedimentary strata at the bottom of an ocean.

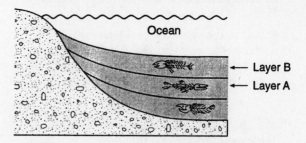

The fossils found in layer B resemble the fossils found in layer A. This similarity suggests that

1 the fossils in layer B were formed before the fossils in layer A
2 modern forms of life may have evolved from earlier forms of life
3 vertebrate fossils are only found in sediments
4 the fossils in layer A must be more complex than those in layer B

50 Variations within a species are most likely the result of

1 mutations and sexual reproduction
2 synapsis and disjunction
3 mitosis and asexual reproduction
4 overpopulation and recombination

51 The theory that evolutionary change is slow and continuous is known as

1 punctuated equilibrium
2 geographic isolation
3 speciation
4 gradualism

52 According to the heterotroph hypothesis, some early heterotrophs evolved into autotrophs because of their ability to synthesize organic compounds from water and

1 carbon dioxide   3 oxygen
2 hydrochloric acid   4 hydrogen

53 All of Earth's water, land, and atmosphere within which life exists is known as

1 a population   3 a biome
2 a community   4 the biosphere

54 An ecosystem is represented below.

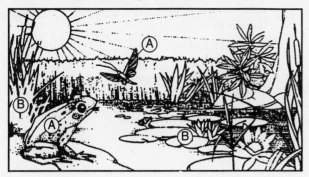

This ecosystem will be self-sustaining if

1. the organisms labeled *A* outnumber the organisms labeled *B*
2. the organisms labeled *A* are equal in number to the organisms labeled *B*
3. the type of organisms represented by *B* are eliminated
4. materials cycle between the organisms labeled *A* and the organisms labeled *B*

55 A certain plant requires moisture, oxygen, carbon dioxide, light, and minerals in order to survive. This statement shows that a living organism depends on

1 biotic factors
2 abiotic factors
3 symbiotic relationships
4 carnivore-herbivore relationships

56 Which statement best describes some organisms in the food web shown below?

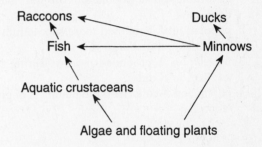

1 Minnows and fish are primary consumers.
2 Algae and floating plants are decomposers.
3 Aquatic crustaceans are omnivores.
4 Raccoons, fish, and ducks are secondary consumers.

---

57 Events that take place in a biome are shown in the diagram below.

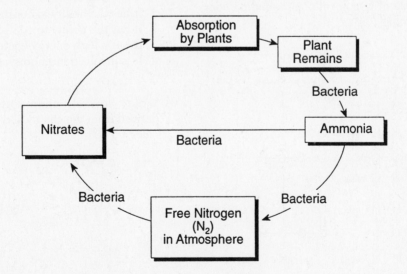

Which information is represented in the diagram?

1 Respiration and photosynthesis are interrelated.
2 Transpiration and condensation are related to the water cycle.
3 Decomposers release a material that is acted on by other organisms.
4 Predators and their prey are involved in many interactions.

58 The graph below shows the changes in two populations of herbivores in a grassy field.

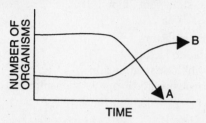

A possible reason for these changes is that

1 all of the plant populations in this habitat decreased
2 population *B* competed more successfully for food than population *A* did
3 population *A* produced more offspring than population *B* did
4 population *A* consumed the members of population *B*

59 The creation of wildlife refuges and the enforcement of game laws are conservation measures that promote increased

1 use of biocides
2 preservation of species
3 use of biological controls
4 exploitation of species

Part II

This part consists of five groups, each containing ten questions. Choose two of these five groups. Be sure that you answer all ten questions in each group chosen. Record the answers to these questions in accordance with the directions on the front page of this booklet. [20]

Group 1 — Biochemistry

If you choose this group, be sure to answer questions 60–69.

Base your answers to questions 60 and 61 on the structural formula of a molecule below and on your knowledge of biology.

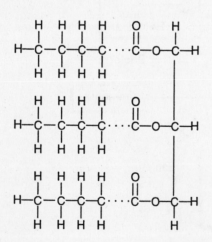

60 Which statement best describes this molecule?

1 It has the ability to control heredity.
2 It has the ability to control reactions.
3 It has a high energy content.
4 It is involved in photosynthesis.

61 Which formula represents an end product derived from the chemical digestion of this molecule?

(1) $O = C = O$

(2) $\begin{array}{l} H-C-OH \\ H-C-OH \\ H-C-OH \end{array}$ (with H above top and H below bottom)

(3) $H - O - H$

(4) $H - C - H$ (with H above and H below)

Base your answers to questions 62 and 63 on the two processes represented below and on your knowledge of biology.

Processes

(A) glucose + oxygen $\xrightarrow{\text{X}}$ water + carbon dioxide + energy

(B) glucose $\xrightarrow{\text{X}}$ alcohol + carbon dioxide + energy

62 Before the glucose in each process can be changed into the final products, it must first be converted to

1 pyruvic acid
2 lactic acid
3 glycogen
4 lipids

63 In both processes, the **X** represents

1 catalysts
2 hydrogen acceptors
3 monosaccharides
4 hormones

64 Which biological process is the main source of atmospheric oxygen?

1 respiration
2 photolysis
3 hydrolysis
4 deamination

65 An element found in all proteins but *not* found in carbohydrates and lipids is

1 carbon
2 hydrogen
3 oxygen
4 nitrogen

Base your answers to questions 66 and 67 on the diagram below and on your knowledge of biology.

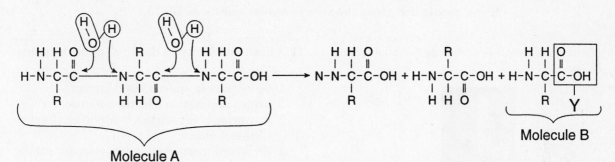

Molecule A   Molecule B

66 In molecule *B*, what type of group is contained in box *Y*?

1 an amino group
2 a variable group
3 a carboxyl group
4 a peptide group

67 How many peptide bonds are present in molecule *A*?

(1) 1
(2) 2
(3) 3
(4) 4

68 Which chemical reaction is represented by the diagram below?

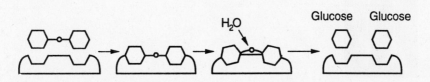

1 dehydration synthesis of a dipeptide
2 hydrolysis of a polypeptide
3 dehydration synthesis of a lipid
4 hydrolysis of a disaccharide

69 Which statement best describes the enzyme represented in the graphs below?

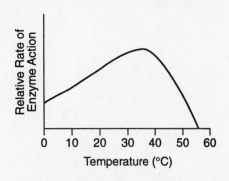
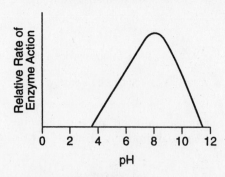

1 This enzyme works best at a temperature of 35°C and a pH of 8.
2 This enzyme works best at a temperature of 50°C and a pH of 12.
3 Temperature and pH have no effect on the action of this enzyme.
4 This enzyme works best at a temperature above 50°C and a pH above 12.

Group 2 — Human Physiology

If you choose this group, be sure to answer questions 70–79.

70 A human skeleton is shown in the photograph below.

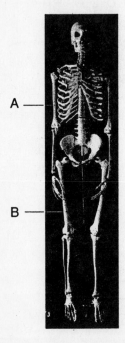

The elongation of structures *A* and *B* was stimulated by a hormone produced by the

1 islets of Langerhans   3 pituitary gland
2 liver   4 striated muscles

71 A heart attack may be due to all of the following *except*

1 an increase in arterial blood pressure
2 oxygen deprivation of cardiac muscle
3 narrowing of the arteries transporting blood to the heart muscle
4 decreased consumption of complex carbo-hydrates

72 Which food would provide the most roughage for the body?

1 baked fresh fish
2 lettuce-and-tomato salad
3 fried chicken breast
4 milkshake

Base your answers to questions 73 and 74 on the diagram below of the human heart and on your knowledge of biology.

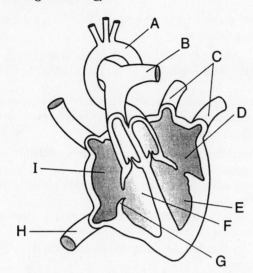

Base your answers to questions 77 through 79 on the diagram below of the human digestive system and on your knowledge of biology.

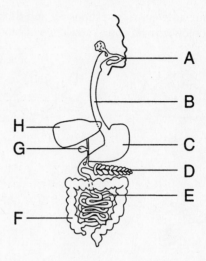

73 Which structures are most closely associated with the transport of deoxygenated blood?

(1) *A*, *B*, and *C*   (3) *C*, *D*, and *E*
(2) *B*, *F*, and *I*   (4) *D*, *H*, and *I*

74 A structure that prevents the backflow of blood into an atrium is indicated by letter

(1) *G*   (3) *C*
(2) *B*   (4) *H*

---

75 Which malfunction is most closely associated with connective tissue that is involved in human locomotion?

1 bronchitis   3 diabetes
2 tendinitis   4 meningitis

76 Hardened deposits of cholesterol that accumulate in the structure that stores bile are known as

1 gallstones   3 goiters
2 ulcers   4 allergies

77 In which structure does the initial hydrolysis of carbohydrates occur?

(1) *A*   (3) *C*
(2) *E*   (4) *D*

78 From which structure are glucose and amino acids normally absorbed into the circulatory system?

(1) *F*   (3) *C*
(2) *H*   (4) *E*

79 In which structure does extracellular chemical digestion of protein begin?

(1) *G*   (3) *C*
(2) *B*   (4) *E*

Group 3 — Reproduction and Development

If you choose this group, be sure to answer questions 80–89.

Base your answers to questions 80 and 81 on the diagrams below and on your knowledge of biology.

80 Which types of organisms usually develop from an egg containing an amnion?

(1) A and B   (3) C and D
(2) B and C   (4) A and D

81 Eggs that contain yolk are produced by

1 organisms A and B, only
2 organism B, only
3 organisms C and D, only
4 organisms A, B, C, and D

82 The endoderm in an embryo first forms during the process of

1 gametogenesis   3 blastula formation
2 zygote formation   4 gastrulation

83 Which sequence represents the correct order of events in the development of sexually reproducing animals?

1 fertilization → cleavage → differentiation → growth
2 cleavage → fertilization → growth → differentiation
3 growth → cleavage → fertilization → differentiation
4 fertilization → differentiation → cleavage → growth

84 In most mammalian species, which structure supplies food to the developing embryo?

1 amnion   3 placenta
2 ovary   4 allantois

85 A temporary suspension of the menstrual cycle normally occurs during

1 menstruation   3 ovulation
2 pregnancy   4 menopause

Base your answers to questions 86 through 89 on the diagrams below and on your knowledge of biology.

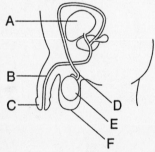

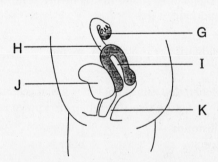

86 Which structures secrete hormones that regulate the development of secondary sex characteristics?

(1) A and J   (3) F and I
(2) D and H   (4) E and G

87 After sperm cells are deposited inside the female, the pathway they follow to reach the egg is from

(1) H to I to K   (3) K to I to H
(2) J to K to H   (4) G to H to I

88 Gametogenesis occurs within structures

(1) A and J   (3) B and I
(2) E and G   (4) D and H

89 Which structures are directly affected by hormones involved in the menstrual cycle?

(1) C and E   (3) G and I
(2) A and D   (4) I and J

Group 4 — Modern Genetics

If you choose this group, be sure to answer questions 90–99.

Base your answers to questions 90 through 92 on the diagram below of a biochemical process and on your knowledge of biology.

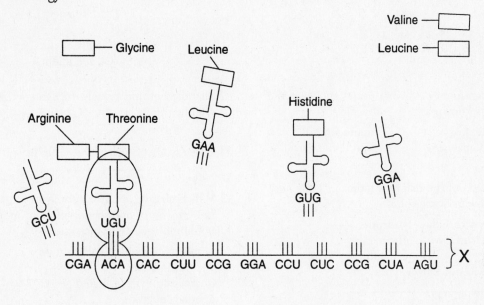

90 The synthesis of structure *X* occurred in the

1 nucleus 3 lysosome
2 cytoplasm 4 vacuole

91 Which amino acid would be transferred to the position of codon CAC?

1 leucine 3 valine
2 glycine 4 histidine

92 The biochemical process represented in the diagram is most closely associated with the cell organelle known as the

1 nucleolus 3 chloroplast
2 ribosome 4 mitochondrion

---

93 Which process represented by an arrow in the diagrams below is most similar to cloning?

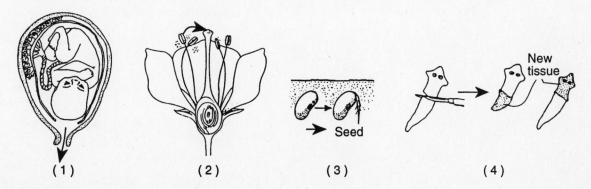

(1) (2) (3) (4)

Base your answers to questions 94 and 95 on the diagram below and on your knowledge of biology.

```
 1  2  3  4  5  6  7  8  9 10 11 12 13 14
```

```
15 16 17 18 19 20 21 22 XY
```

94 The arrangement of chromosomes shown in the diagram is known as

  1 a karyotype   3 amniocentesis
  2 a urine analysis   4 blood typing

95 Examination of the diagram indicates that these are the chromosomes of a

  1 female with Down syndrome
  2 male with Down syndrome
  3 female without Down syndrome
  4 male without Down syndrome

96 Which condition would most likely produce a change in the gene pool of a population?

  1 a large population
  2 random mating in the population
  3 migrations out of the population
  4 no mutations in the population

Directions (97–98): For *each* phrase in questions 97 and 98, select the genetic disorder, *chosen from the list below*, that is best described by that phrase. Then record its *number* on the separate answer paper.

Genetic Disorders
(1) PKU
(2) Tay-Sachs
(3) Sickle-cell anemia

97 Inability of individuals to metabolize phenyl-alanine

98 Directly affects cells involved in oxygen transport

99 Which change in chromosome structure involves the transfer of one section of a chromosome to a nonhomologous chromosome?

  1 nitrogenous base substitution
  2 translocation
  3 crossing-over of linked genes
  4 gene mutation

Group 5 — Ecology

If you choose this group, be sure to answer questions 100–109.

Directions (100–102): For *each* statement in questions 100 through 102, select the term, *chosen from the list below,* that is most closely associated with that statement. Then record its *number* on the separate answer paper.

Terms
(1) Mutualism
(2) Commensalism
(3) Parasitism
(4) Saprophytism
(5) Competition

100 Protozoans living in the intestine of a termite secrete enzymes that digest cellulose, providing digestive end products of value to both organisms.

101 The roots of a mistletoe plant absorb nutrients from living oak trees, causing some damage to the tissues of the trees.

102 Certain fungi use dead organic matter for food.

___

103 The diagram below represents a biomass pyramid.

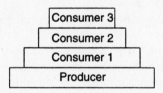

Consumer 3
Consumer 2
Consumer 1
Producer

Which statement concerning the energy in this pyramid is correct?
1 The producer organisms contain the least amount of stored energy.
2 Stored energy decreases from consumer 2 to consumer 3.
3 Consumer 3 contains the greatest amount of stored energy.
4 Stored energy increases from the producer to consumer 1.

104 One practice that has successfully increased the number of bald eagles in the United States is the
1 protection of their natural habitat
2 importation of food to their nesting sites
3 preservation of other eagle species that occupy the same niche
4 increased use of pesticides

105 Which statement concerning the climax stage of an ecological succession is correct?
1 It changes rapidly.
2 It persists until the environment changes.
3 It is the first community to inhabit an area.
4 It consists entirely of plants.

106 In a pond, which change would most likely lead to terrestrial succession?
1 a decrease in the number of suspended particles in the pond water
2 an increase in current velocity of the pond water
3 a decrease in the number of diverse organisms in the shallow water of the pond
4 an increase in sediment, fallen leaves, and tree limbs accumulating on the bottom of the pond

Directions (107–109): The map below illustrates the general location of various terrestrial biomes in selected areas of North, Central, and South America. For *each* statement in questions 107 through 109, select the biome, *chosen from the map below,* that is most closely associated with that statement. Then record its *number* on the separate answer paper.

Terrestrial Biomes

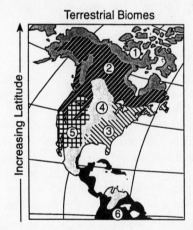

107 Snowy owls hunt mice that try to escape among the lichens growing on ground that has permanently frozen subsoil.

108 Prairie dogs hide in their burrows in a vast area of tall grasses that provide food for herds of pronghorn antelope and bison.

109 Deer nibble on low-lying shrubs while cardinals sit on branches of trees in a large deciduous forest.

Part III

This part consists of five groups. Choose three of these five groups. For those questions that are followed by four choices, record the answers on the separate answer paper in accordance with the directions on the front page of this booklet. For all other questions in this part, record your answers in accordance with the directions given in the question.   [15]

Group 1

If you choose this group, be sure to answer questions 110–114.

110 The diagram below represents a human cheek cell.

Select one of the lettered parts from the diagram and record the letter of the part chosen. Using one or more complete sentences, state a function of the part. You may use pen or pencil for your answer.

111 A new drug for the treatment of asthma is tested on 100 people. The people are evenly divided into two groups. One group is given the drug, and the other group is given a glucose pill. The group that is given the glucose pill serves as the

1 experimental group   3 control
2 limiting factor   4 indicator

112 A student used a compound light microscope to obtain data on the concentration of stomates in leaves. The student observed a small area of the lower epidermis of a leaf and counted two stomates in the high-power field of view. The student then observed an area of equal size from the upper epidermis of the same leaf and found no stomates in the high-power field of view. After making these observations, the student should

1 assume that leaves never have stomates on their upper surface
2 conclude that the lower epidermis of this leaf has a greater stomate concentration than the upper epidermis
3 conclude that the lower epidermis of all leaves has a greater stomate concentration than the upper epidermis
4 make additional observations before drawing conclusions about stomate concentration

113 Which statement correctly identifies the function and relative location of two structures shown in the diagram below?

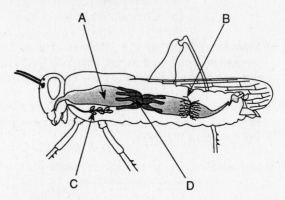

1 Digestive structure *A* is posterior to excretory structure *B*.
2 Digestive structure *C* is ventral to digestive structure *A*.
3 Excretory structure *B* is anterior to excretory structure *D*.
4 Circulatory structure *D* is dorsal to respiratory structure *C*.

114 A scientific study showed that the depth at which algae were found in a lake varied from day to day. On clear days, the algae were found as much as 6 meters below the surface of the water but were only 1 meter below the surface on cloudy days. Which hypothesis best explains these observations?

1 Light intensity affects the growth of algae.
2 Wind currents affect the growth of algae.
3 Nitrogen concentration affects the growth of algae.
4 Precipitation affects the growth of algae.

Group 2

If you choose this group, be sure to answer questions 115–119.

Base your answers to questions 115 through 118 on the information below and on your knowledge of biology.

A group of biology students extracted the photosynthetic pigments from spinach leaves using the solvent acetone. A spectrophotometer was used to measure the percent absorption of six different wavelengths of light by the extracted pigments. The wavelengths of light were measured in units known as nanometers (nm). One nanometer is equal to one-billionth of a meter. The following data were collected:

yellow light (585 nm) — 25.8% absorption
blue light (457 nm) — 49.8% absorption
orange light (616 nm) — 32.1% absorption
violet light (412 nm) — 49.8% absorption
red light (674 nm) — 41.0% absorption
green light (533 nm) — 17.8% absorption

115 Complete all three columns in the data table on the separate answer paper so that the wavelength of light either increases or decreases from the top to the bottom of the data table. The data table below is provided for practice purposes only. Be sure your final answer appears on your answer paper. You may use pen or pencil for your answer.

Color of Light	Wavelength of Light (nm)	Percent Absorption by Spinach Extract

Directions (116–117): Using the information in the data table, construct a line graph on the grid provided on your answer paper, following the directions below. The grid on the next page is provided for practice purposes only. Be sure your final answer appears on your answer paper. You may use pen or pencil for your answer.

116 Mark an appropriate scale on the axis labeled "Percent Absorption."

117 Plot the data from the data table. Surround each point with a small circle and connect the points.

Example:

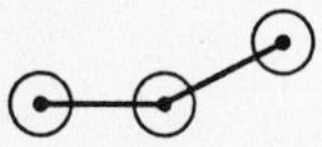

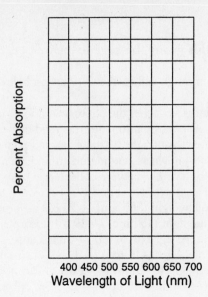

118 Which statement is a valid conclusion that can be drawn from the data obtained in this investigation?

1 Photosynthetic pigments in spinach plants absorb blue and violet light more efficiently than red light.
2 The data would be the same for all pigments in spinach plants.
3 Green and yellow light are not absorbed by spinach plants.
4 All plants are efficient at absorbing violet and red light.

---

119 Which set of laboratory equipment could a student use to determine whether or not apple juice contains simple sugars?

Set A	Set B	Set C	Set D
Safety goggles	Safety goggles	Safety goggles	Safety goggles
Bromthymol blue solution	Benedict's solution	Lugol's iodine solution	Lens paper
Test tubes	Test tubes	Scalpel	Hot water bath
Straw	Test tube holder	Forceps	Graduated cylinder
Water	Hot water bath	Graduated cylinder	Distilled water

(1) A   (3) C
(2) B   (4) D

Group 3

If you choose this group, be sure to answer questions 120–124.

120 The diagram below represents a hydra as viewed with a compound light microscope.

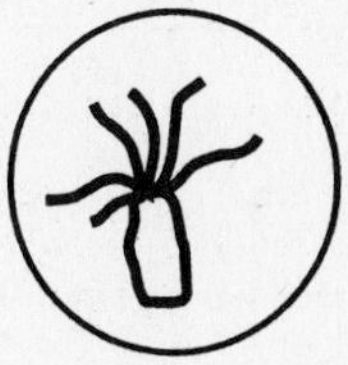

If the hydra moves toward the right of the slide preparation, which diagram best represents what will be observed through the microscope?

(1)

(2)

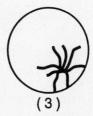
(3)

(4)

Base your answers to questions 121 and 122 on the diagram below and on your knowledge of biology.

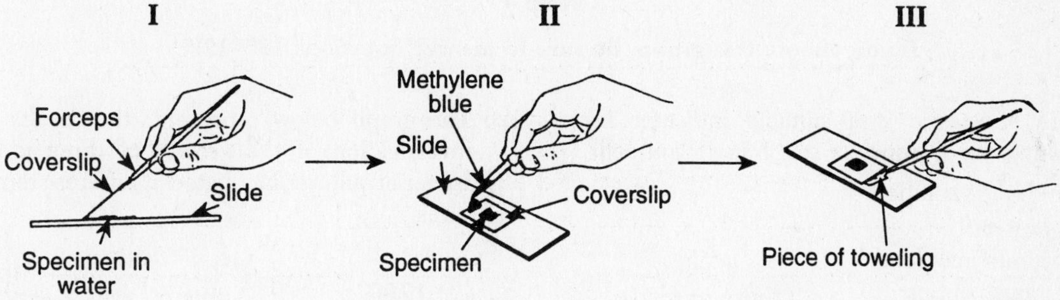

I   II   III

Forceps
Coverslip
Slide
Specimen in water

Methylene blue
Slide
Coverslip
Specimen

Piece of toweling

121 Which laboratory technique is illustrated in the diagram?

1 testing a specimen for amino acids
2 determining the pH of a specimen
3 measuring the photosynthetic rate in a specimen
4 preparing a wet mount of a specimen

122 Using one or more complete sentences, state a reason why methylene blue was used in the laboratory technique. You may use pen or pencil for your answer.

123 The diagram below shows a microscopic field containing a portion of the cross section of a root tip.

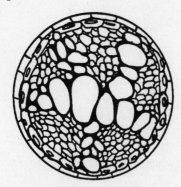

How should a student adjust the microscope in order to view a greater portion of the root tip?

1 stay at the same power and adjust the focus
2 stay at the same power but increase the size of the opening of the diaphragm
3 switch to a lower power and decrease the size of the opening of the diaphragm
4 switch to a higher power and adjust the focus

124 The diagram below represents two cells next to a metric measuring device under the low-power objective of a compound light microscope.

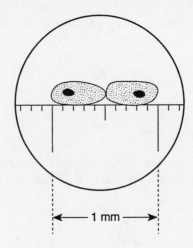

What is the approximate length of a nucleus of one of these cells?

(1) 100 μm
(2) 500 μm
(3) 1000 μm
(4) 1500 μm

Group 4

If you choose this group, be sure to answer questions 125–129.

125 Which substance is a suitable indicator for detecting the presence of starch in a plant cell?

(1) Fehling's solution
(2) pH paper
(3) bromthymol blue
(4) iodine solution

126 The graph below represents the results of an investigation of the growth of three identical bacterial cultures incubated at different temperatures.

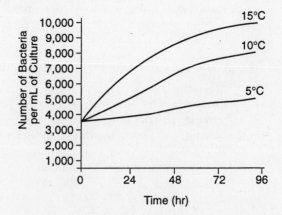

Which inference can be made from this graph?

1 Temperature is unrelated to the reproductive rate of bacteria.
2 Bacteria cannot grow at a temperature of 5°C.
3 Life activities in bacteria slow down at high temperatures.
4 Refrigeration will most likely slow the growth of these bacteria.

127 A study was conducted using two groups of 10 plants of the same species. During the study, the plants were placed in identical environmental conditions. The plants in one group were given a growth solution every 3 days. The heights of the plants in both groups were recorded at the beginning of the study and at the end of a 3-week period. The data showed that the plants given the growth solution grew faster than those not given the solution.

When other researchers conduct this study to test the accuracy of the results, they should

1 give growth solution to both groups
2 make sure the conditions are identical to those in the first study
3 give an increased amount of light to both groups of plants
4 double the amount of growth solution given to the first group

128 Using one or more complete sentences, explain why a test tube of material being heated over an open flame should *not* be stoppered. You may use pen or pencil for your answer.

129 The diagram below represents the measurements of two leaves.

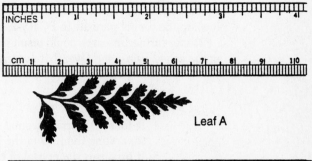

Leaf A

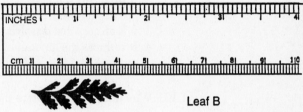

Leaf B

The difference in length between leaves *A* and *B* is closest to

(1) 20 mm
(2) 20 cm
(3) 0.65 m
(4) 1.6 μm

Group 5

If you choose this group, be sure to answer questions 130–134.

Base your answers to questions 130 through 133 on the reading passage below and on your knowledge of biology.

Take Two and Call Me in the Morning

Hippocrates observed that pain could be relieved by chewing the bark of a willow tree. We now know that this bark contains salicylic acid, which is similar to acetylsalicylic acid, the active ingredient in aspirin. Over 2,300 years after this observation by Hippocrates, scientists have learned how aspirin works.

When people get the flu or strain their backs, the body responds by making prostaglandins (PG), a group of hormonelike substances. The presence of certain prostaglandins may result in fever, headaches, and inflammation. Scientists have determined that aspirin interferes with prostaglandin H2 synthase (PGHS-2), an enzyme that the body uses to make pain-causing prostaglandins. In 1994, the structure of this enzyme was found to be a crystal with a tube running up the middle of it. Raw materials move through this tunnel to reach the core of the enzyme, where they are transformed into prostaglandin molecules. Research has shown that aspirin blocks this tunnel. Part of the aspirin molecule attaches to a particular place inside the tunnel, preventing the raw materials from passing through the tunnel. This blockage interferes with the production of prostaglandins, thus helping to prevent or reduce fever, headaches, and inflammation.

The body makes two forms of the enzyme. PGHS-1 is found throughout the body and has a variety of uses, including protecting the stomach. PGHS-2 usually comes into play when tissue is damaged or when infections occur. Its action results in pain and fever. Aspirin plugs up the tunnel of PGHS-1 completely and often causes stomach irritation in some people. Aspirin plugs up the tunnel partially in PGHS-2, thus helping to relieve pain and fever.

Perhaps further research could result in a drug targeting PGHS-2 but not PGHS-1, relieving the aches, pains, and fever, but not irritating the stomach as aspirin does now.

130 How does aspirin relieve the symptoms of the flu?
  1 It forms a barrier around the outer surface of PGHS-2 molecules, separating them from the prostaglandins.
  2 It dissolves the crystal of the enzyme, preventing it from producing prostaglandins.
  3 It is an acid that dissolves the prostaglandins that cause the symptoms.
  4 It reduces the amount of raw material reaching the active site of the enzyme that produces prostaglandins.

131 Why does aspirin irritate the stomach of some people who take it?
  1 It interferes with the activity of an enzyme that helps to protect the stomach.
  2 It is the only acid in the stomach and irritates the stomach lining.
  3 It stimulates prostaglandin production in the stomach.
  4 It is obtained from willow bark, which cannot be digested in the stomach.

132 Using one or more complete sentences, describe the molecular structure of prostaglandin H2 synthase. You may use pen or pencil for your answer.

133 Using one or more complete sentences, explain why chewing the bark of a willow tree could help relieve the symptoms of headache and fever. You may use pen or pencil for your answer.

134 Using one or more complete sentences, state one observation a student could make to determine that a slide preparation of unicellular organisms contained protists and *not* monerans. You may use pen or pencil for your answer.

BIOLOGY
JUNE 1998

ANSWER PAPER

Student . . . .

Teacher . . . . School . . . .

All of your answers should be recorded on this answer paper.

Part I (65 credits)

1	1 2 3 4		21	1 2 3 4		41	1 2 3 4
2	1 2 3 4		22	1 2 3 4		42	1 2 3 4
3	1 2 3 4		23	1 2 3 4		43	1 2 3 4
4	1 2 3 4		24	1 2 3 4		44	1 2 3 4
5	1 2 3 4		25	1 2 3 4		45	1 2 3 4
6	1 2 3 4		26	1 2 3 4		46	1 2 3 4
7	1 2 3 4		27	1 2 3 4		47	1 2 3 4
8	1 2 3 4		28	1 2 3 4		48	1 2 3 4
9	1 2 3 4		29	1 2 3 4		49	1 2 3 4
10	1 2 3 4		30	1 2 3 4		50	1 2 3 4
11	1 2 3 4		31	1 2 3 4		51	1 2 3 4
12	1 2 3 4		32	1 2 3 4		52	1 2 3 4
13	1 2 3 4		33	1 2 3 4		53	1 2 3 4
14	1 2 3 4		34	1 2 3 4		54	1 2 3 4
15	1 2 3 4		35	1 2 3 4		55	1 2 3 4
16	1 2 3 4		36	1 2 3 4		56	1 2 3 4
17	1 2 3 4		37	1 2 3 4		57	1 2 3 4
18	1 2 3 4		38	1 2 3 4		58	1 2 3 4
19	1 2 3 4		39	1 2 3 4		59	1 2 3 4
20	1 2 3 4		40	1 2 3 4			

PART I CREDITS

Directions to Teacher:

In the table below, draw a circle around the number of right answers and the adjacent number of credits. Then write the number of credits (not the number right) in the space provided above.

No. Right	Credits		No. Right	Credits
59	65		29	36
58	64		28	35
57	63		27	34
56	62		26	33
55	61		25	32
54	60		24	31
53	59		23	31
52	58		22	30
51	57		21	29
50	56		20	28
49	55		19	27
48	54		18	26
47	54		17	25
46	53		16	24
45	52		15	23
44	51		14	21
43	50		13	20
42	49		12	18
41	48		11	17
40	47		10	15
39	46		9	14
38	45		8	12
37	44		7	11
36	43		6	9
35	42		5	8
34	41		4	6
33	40		3	5
32	39		2	3
31	38		1	2
30	37		0	0

No. right . . . .

Part II (20 credits)

Answer the questions in only two of the five groups in this part. Be sure to mark the answers to the groups of questions you choose in accordance with the instructions on the front page of the test booklet. Leave blank the three groups of questions you do not choose to answer.

Group 1
Biochemistry

60 1 2 3 4
61 1 2 3 4
62 1 2 3 4
63 1 2 3 4
64 1 2 3 4
65 1 2 3 4
66 1 2 3 4
67 1 2 3 4
68 1 2 3 4
69 1 2 3 4

Group 3
Reproduction and Development

80 1 2 3 4
81 1 2 3 4
82 1 2 3 4
83 1 2 3 4
84 1 2 3 4
85 1 2 3 4
86 1 2 3 4
87 1 2 3 4
88 1 2 3 4
89 1 2 3 4

Group 5
Ecology

100 1 2 3 4 5
101 1 2 3 4 5
102 1 2 3 4 5
103 1 2 3 4
104 1 2 3 4
105 1 2 3 4
106 1 2 3 4
107 1 2 3 4 5 6
108 1 2 3 4 5 6
109 1 2 3 4 5 6

Group 2
Human Physiology

70 1 2 3 4
71 1 2 3 4
72 1 2 3 4
73 1 2 3 4
74 1 2 3 4
75 1 2 3 4
76 1 2 3 4
77 1 2 3 4
78 1 2 3 4
79 1 2 3 4

Group 4
Modern Genetics

90 1 2 3 4
91 1 2 3 4
92 1 2 3 4
93 1 2 3 4
94 1 2 3 4
95 1 2 3 4
96 1 2 3 4
97 1 2 3
98 1 2 3
99 1 2 3 4

Part III (15 credits)

Answer the questions in only three of the five groups in this part. Leave blank the groups of questions you do not choose to answer.

Group 1

110 _____

_____

111   1   2   3   4

112   1   2   3   4

113   1   2   3   4

114   1   2   3   4

Group 2

115

Color of Light	Wavelength of Light (nm)	Percent Absorption by Spinach Extract

116–117

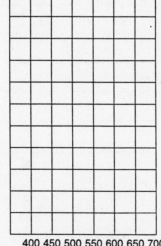

Percent Absorption

400 450 500 550 600 650 700
Wavelength of Light (nm)

118   1   2   3   4

119   1   2   3   4

Group 3

120   1   2   3   4

121   1   2   3   4

122   _____

_____

_____

_____

_____

123   1   2   3   4

124   1   2   3   4

Group 4

125   1   2   3   4

126   1   2   3   4

127   1   2   3   4

128   _____

_____

_____

_____

_____

129   1   2   3   4

Group 5

130   1   2   3   4

131   1   2   3   4

132   _____

_____

133   _____

_____

134   _____

_____

BIOLOGY
JANUARY 1999

Part I

Answer all 59 questions in this part.   [65]

Directions (1–59): For *each* statement or question, select the word or expression that, of those given, best completes the statement or answers the question. Record your answer on the separate answer paper in accordance with the directions on the front page of this booklet.

1 In which process are simple materials chemically combined to form more complex materials?

  1 synthesis   3 hydrolysis
  2 pinocytosis   4 cyclosis

2 Which reactions in the list below are associated with metabolism?

  (A) cellular reactions that release energy
  (B) photosynthetic reactions that store energy
  (C) muscle reactions that use energy

  (1) A and B, only   (3) C and A, only
  (2) B and C, only   (4) A, B, and C

3 Which scientist is correctly paired with his contribution to biological science?

  1 Miller — first to observe mitotic cell division
  2 Linnaeus — devised a binomial system for naming organisms
  3 Darwin — invented the electron microscope
  4 Watson — first to observe cells

4 The chart below indicates the elements contained in four different molecules and the number of atoms of each element in those molecules.

	Number of Atoms			
Element	Molecule A	Molecule B	Molecule C	Molecule D
Hydrogen	12	0	3	0
Carbon	6	1	0	1
Nitrogen	0	0	1	0
Oxygen	6	2	0	3
Calcium	0	0	0	1

Which molecule can be classified as organic?

  (1) A   (3) C
  (2) B   (4) D

5 According to the five-kingdom classification system, which two groups of organisms are classified as protists?

  1 bryophytes and tracheophytes
  2 coelenterates and annelids
  3 protozoa and algae
  4 bacteria and chordates

6 The shape, size, and internal structure of the mitochondrion have been revealed by

  1 studies of the chemical activity of enzymes
  2 the development of wet-mount techniques
  3 electron-microscope studies
  4 detailed studies of chromosomes

7 Lipase, maltase, and protease are members of a group of catalysts known as

  1 enzymes   3 carbohydrates
  2 hormones   4 fats

8 In the equations below, A represents a food substance, and B represents its completely digested end product. Which equation represents the change that takes place as a result of chemical digestion?

  (1) $A + water \rightarrow A + A + A$
  (2) $A + water \rightarrow B + B + B$
  (3) $B + B + B \rightarrow A + water$
  (4) $A + A + A \rightarrow A + water$

9 Which process is represented by the arrow in the diagram below?

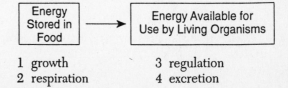

  1 growth   3 regulation
  2 respiration   4 excretion

10 In the setup shown below, which color light will cause the plant to produce the *smallest* number of gas bubbles?

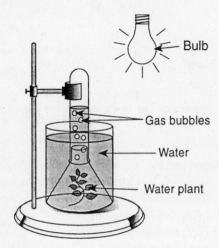

1 red
2 orange
3 blue
4 green

11 Which organisms are *not* able to make organic molecules from inorganic raw materials?

1 mushrooms
2 algae
3 bryophytes
4 tracheophytes

12 The diagram below represents a white blood cell engulfing some bacteria.

The structure labeled *X* is most likely a

1 nucleus
2 centriole
3 ribosome
4 vacuole

13 Freshwater protozoans excrete ammonia and mineral salts by means of

1 diffusion through the cell membrane
2 small vacuoles released through the cell membrane
3 small tubes leading from the cytoplasm to openings in the cell membrane
4 contraction of food vacuoles

14 Which organism lacks a specialized transport system?

1 earthworm
2 grasshopper
3 human
4 hydra

15 Which sequence best represents the pathway of a gas as it passes from the atmosphere into a leaf?

1 guard cell → xylem → palisade cell
2 stomate → air space → spongy cell
3 air space → phloem → palisade cell
4 cuticle → epidermis → spongy cell

16 The diagram below represents a unicellular organism.

This organism is able to survive without a specialized respiratory system because

1 it possesses a nucleus that controls the synthesis of respiratory enzymes
2 its vacuoles release oxygen from stored nutrients
3 its respiratory surface is in direct contact with a watery environment
4 it possesses chloroplasts that produce oxygen when exposed to sunlight

17 The lenticels of certain plants have the same function as

1 anthers
2 phloem
3 xylem
4 stomates

18 When a chemical is added to a slide containing a paramecium, the paramecium moves away from the chemical. This movement is an example of

1 passive transport of chemicals
2 a response to a stimulus
3 a tropic response
4 active transport of water

19 Which gas is excreted as a waste product of autotrophic nutrition in maple trees?

1 nitrogen
2 oxygen
3 carbon dioxide
4 methane

20 To aid in the transmission of an impulse, neurotransmitters are secreted

1 along an axon
2 by a dendrite
3 by a cyton
4 into a synapse

21 Plants bend toward light because cells on the dark side of the stem elongate. This elongation is influenced by hormones known as

1 auxins 3 adenines
2 antigens 4 amylases

22 Locomotion in chordates may be described as the interaction between

1 an endoskeleton and muscles
2 tentacles and contractile fibers
3 cilia and an exoskeleton
4 chitinous appendages and muscles

23 Which lettered structure in the diagram below produces enzymes for the digestion of nutrients in the small intestine?

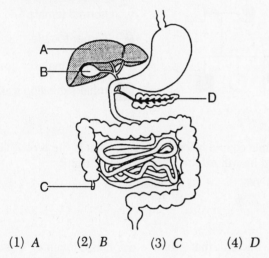

(1) *A*   (2) *B*   (3) *C*   (4) *D*

24 Which two activities in the chart below best describe the process of transport?

A	Walking from one place to another
B	Inhaling air into the trachea
C	Absorbing glucose into the villi
D	Distributing nutrients by means of blood vessels

(1) *A* and *C*   (3) *C* and *D*
(2) *B* and *C*   (4) *A* and *D*

25 Which part of the blood is correctly paired with its function?

1 red blood cells — fight infection
2 plasma — transports wastes and hormones
3 platelets — produce antibodies
4 white blood cells — carry oxygen

26 Choking on food is most likely caused by an interference with the proper functioning of the

1 diaphragm 3 bronchial tubes
2 nasal cavity 4 epiglottis

27 As urine is excreted, muscle contractions of the urinary bladder will cause the urine to pass into the

1 ureter 3 urethra
2 glomerulus 4 Bowman's capsule

28 Which statement best describes the chemical substances secreted by endocrine glands?

1 They are secreted in one place and most often act at another.
2 They are distributed by the nervous system.
3 They are found only in vertebrates.
4 They are secreted into specialized ducts for transport.

29 In the knee, the ends of the leg bones are held together primarily by

1 ligaments 3 tendons
2 smooth muscle 4 cardiac muscle

30 Which two diagrams show organisms reproducing by vegetative propagation?

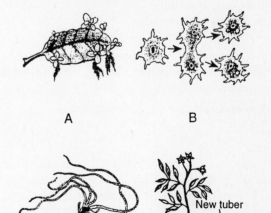

A   B

C   D

(1) *A* and *B*   (3) *C* and *D*
(2) *B* and *C*   (4) *A* and *D*

31 Which mitotic event in the chart below occurs after the other three events have taken place?

A	Appearance of spindle fibers
B	Separation of chromatids by the action of spindle fibers
C	Disintegration of the nuclear membrane
D	Replication of chromosomes

(1) *A* (3) *C*
(2) *B* (4) *D*

32 The production of motile monoploid gametes takes place in

1 ureters
2 ovaries
3 male gonads
4 gastric glands

33 The series of cellular divisions by which the zygote becomes a multicellular embryo is known as

1 gastrulation
2 cleavage
3 meiosis
4 disjunction

34 Which term best describes most organisms whose eggs are fertilized externally?

1 terrestrial autotrophs
2 terrestrial heterotrophs
3 aquatic autotrophs
4 aquatic heterotrophs

35 Which organisms do *not* receive direct nourishment from the parent during their internal development stage?

1 marsupials
2 mice
3 humans
4 cows

36 Scientists have been able to produce mutations in plants by irradiating their seeds with gamma rays. The result of one of the mutations was a plant that could not produce flowers. Because of this lack of flowers, the plant would *not* be able to

1 carry out photosynthesis
2 transport water
3 reproduce sexually
4 grow more than a few inches tall

37 A student placed some seeds on a moist paper towel in a petri dish. Another petri dish was filled with water and seeds. The petri dishes were covered and exposed to identical experimental conditions. After several days, the student noticed that the seeds submerged in water did not germinate, but those on the paper towel did. The best explanation for these results is that the seeds

1 on the towel were warmer than those under water
2 on the towel were able to receive more light
3 submerged in water built up carbon dioxide
4 submerged in water did not receive enough oxygen

38 The pedigree chart below shows the pattern of inheritance for a sex-linked trait.

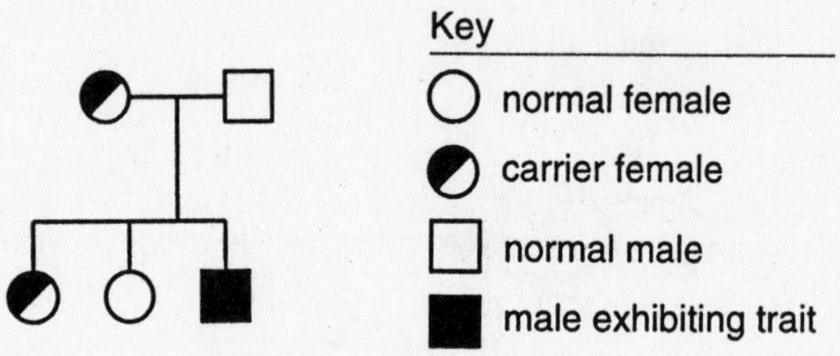
Key
normal female
carrier female
normal male
male exhibiting trait

If this couple has another son, what is the probability that he will exhibit this sex-linked trait?

(1) 0% (3) 50%
(2) 25% (4) 100%

39 Bacteria that produce colonies containing a red pigment were distributed on nutrient agar and exposed to ultraviolet light for several days. The colonies that developed were red, with the exception of one colony that was white. The appearance of this white bacterial colony most likely resulted from

1 a mutation
2 codominance
3 synapsis
4 multiple alleles

40 A garden hose that had been lying on a green lawn for several days was removed. Which statement best explains the presence of yellow grass in the area where the hose had been?

1 The lack of sunlight under the hose altered the genotype of the grass.
2 Gene expression is not affected by the environment.
3 The hose altered genes in the grass, causing the grass to switch from autotrophic to heterotrophic nutrition.
4 The lack of sunlight under the hose affected chlorophyll production.

41 Artificial selection is illustrated by

1 random mating taking place in a population
2 the appearance of a new species on an isolated island
3 a gardener producing a new hybrid by cross-pollinating plants
4 wind assisting the pollination of grass in a field

42 The gene-chromosome theory states that

1 chromosomes from both parents always have identical genes
2 genes exist at definite loci in a linear sequence on chromosomes
3 homologous chromosomes do not have alleles
4 Mendel's principles no longer apply to genetics

43 All of the offspring produced in a cross involving a brown mink and a silver-blue mink are brown. When these brown mink offspring were crossed with each other, the ratio of brown to silver blue was 3:1. The results of these crosses are best explained by

1 independent assortment and crossing-over
2 dominance, segregation, and recombination
3 codominance, segregation, and recombination
4 recombination and intermediate inheritance

44 In many breeds of cattle, the polled condition (absence of horns) is dominant over the presence of horns, and homozygous red coat color crossed with homozygous white coat color produces roan. Which cross will produce only horned roan offspring?

1 polled red × horned white
2 horned roan × horned roan
3 horned red × horned white
4 polled roan × horned roan

45 Which components of DNA are held together by weak hydrogen bonds?

1 phosphate and adenine
2 phosphate and deoxyribose
3 thymine and deoxyribose
4 cytosine and guanine

46 Biologically similar organisms have similar DNA and proteins. This statement supports the concept of

1 diversity in species
2 acquired characteristics
3 use and disuse
4 organic evolution

47 The embryos of fish, chickens, and pigs have gill slits and a tail. The presence of these features suggests that

1 all these animals can swim
2 pigs developed from chickens
3 these animals may have had a common ancestor
4 gill slits and tails are required for embryonic development

48 Characteristics of a species that make its members better able to live and reproduce in their environment are known as

1 favorable adaptations
2 homologous structures
3 abiotic factors
4 biotic factors

49 A large population of houseflies was sprayed with a newly developed, fast-acting insecticide. The appearance of some houseflies that are resistant to this insecticide supports the concept that

1 species traits tend to remain constant
2 biocides cause mutations
3 variation exists within a species
4 the environment does not change

50 Darwin's studies of finches on the Galapagos Islands suggest that the finches' differences in beak structure were most directly due to

1 acquired characteristics in the parent finches
2 the size of the island where the finches live
3 mating behaviors of the different finch species
4 adaptations of the finches to different environments

51 The fresh remains of an unknown vertebrate were discovered in the Amazon Basin. To help determine the vertebrate's possible relationship to other animals, scientists compared the external structure of its digestive organs to that of other vertebrates. This procedure is typical of work done in the field of comparative

1 cytology
2 anatomy
3 embryology
4 biochemistry

52 Which concept is most closely related to the cartoon shown below?

"Today's recipe for what I call 'the origin of life' requires a bit of hydrogen, nitrogen, compounds of sulfur, carbon, a smattering of metals: iron, magnesium. . ."

1 the heterotroph hypothesis
2 regeneration
3 speciation
4 survival of the fittest

53 A student set up a terrarium containing moist soil, several plants, and snails. The terrarium was placed in a sunny area. Which factor is *not* essential for the maintenance of the terrarium?

1 a constant source of energy
2 a living system capable of incorporating energy into organic compounds
3 a cycling of materials between organisms and their environment
4 the introduction of another heterotroph into the terrarium

54 A moss-covered log is overturned by a hungry bear looking for insects to eat. The bear disturbs an ant colony, and some chipmunks leave the hollow log to search for another home in the forest. Which relationship do these organisms have with each other?

1 They are all of the same species.
2 They all require the same type of food.
3 They are part of a community.
4 They are abiotic factors in a forest.

55 The diagram below represents a food web.

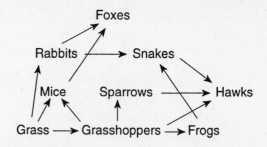

Which statement is supported by the information shown?

1 Foxes, snakes, and sparrows are secondary consumers.
2 Snakes eat grass, grasshoppers, and frogs.
3 Rabbits, mice, and grasshoppers contain the greatest amount of stored energy.
4 Sparrows and hawks are omnivores.

56 Humans often have not given much thought to the long-term impacts of technological change. As the 20th century comes to a close, most scientists would agree that humans should

1 use knowledge of ecology to consider the needs of future generations of humans and other species
2 use new technology to expand human influence on all natural communities
3 learn how to control every aspect of the environment so that damage due to technology will be spread evenly
4 develop the uninhabited parts of Earth for the human population increase

57 Respiration and photosynthesis have the *least* effect on the cycling of

1 carbon   3 oxygen
2 nitrogen   4 hydrogen

58 The diagram below represents an ecological process.

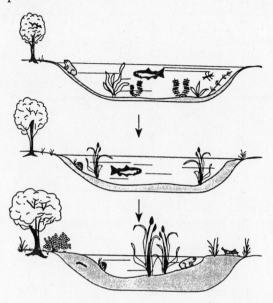

Which statement is most closely related to the process shown in the diagram?

1 Climax communities do not develop in aquatic habitats.
2 Ecosystems tend to change with time until a stable system is formed.
3 Humans have modified the environment through the use of technology and pollution.
4 Succession involves changes in plant species only.

59 An activity that would help to ensure a suitable environment for future generations is the increased use of

1 fossil fuels   3 biological controls
2 pesticides   4 chemical dumps

Part II

This part consists of five groups, each containing ten questions. Choose two of these five groups. Be sure that you answer all ten questions in each group chosen. Record the answers to these questions in accordance with the directions on the front page of this booklet. [20]

Group 1 — Biochemistry

If you choose this group, be sure to answer questions 60–69.

Base your answers to questions 60 through 62 on the chemical reaction represented below and on your knowledge of biology.

$$\underbrace{C_6H_{12}O_6 + C_6H_{12}O_6 + (C_6H_{12}O_6)_n}_{X} \xrightarrow{\text{Y}} \text{polysaccharide} + Z$$

60 Letter Y most likely represents

1 a neurotransmitter   3 a lipid
2 a hormone   4 an enzyme

61 Letter Z most likely represents molecules of

1 water   3 glycogen
2 plant hormones 4 nucleic acids

62 If this reaction takes place in an organism that requires sunlight to produce substance X, the organism must be

1 a heterotroph   3 an autotroph
2 an annelid   4 a fungus

Base your answers to questions 63 and 64 on the equation below and on your knowledge of biology.

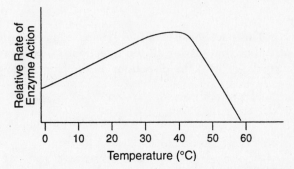

63 Which type of reaction is illustrated by the equation?

1 dehydration synthesis
2 hydrolysis
3 carbon fixation
4 photolysis

64 The structure in box *A* represents

1 an amino group
2 an oil molecule
3 a carboxyl group
4 a carbon dioxide molecule

Base your answers to questions 65 and 66 on the information in the chart below and on your knowledge of biology.

Class of Compound	Characteristic
A	Has glycerol as a building block
B	Contains both acid groups and amino groups
C	Formed from subunits containing a nitrogenous base, a phosphate, and ribose
D	Includes sugars and starches

65 What is another characteristic of the compounds in class *D*?

1 They are composed of basic subunits known as nucleotides.
2 They contain the atoms carbon, hydrogen, and oxygen, with the hydrogen and oxygen in a 2:1 ratio.
3 They transfer amino acids to ribosomes during protein synthesis.
4 They include chemical compounds such as insulin and hemoglobin.

66 Which class of compounds includes the compound represented in the diagram below?

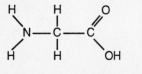

(1) *A*   (2) *B*   (3) *C*   (4) *D*

67 The effect of temperature on the relative rate of action of an enzyme is represented in the graph below.

The optimum temperature for the action of this enzyme is approximately

(1) 15°C   (3) 37°C
(2) 22°C   (4) 50°C

68 Most of the oxygen gas present in the atmosphere is produced as a result of

1 photochemical reactions
2 cellular respiration
3 dehydration synthesis
4 alcoholic fermentation

69 Oxygen serves as a hydrogen acceptor during aerobic respiration. This results in the production of

1 glucose   3 glycerol
2 lactic acid   4 water

Group 2 — Human Physiology

If you choose this group, be sure to answer questions 70–79.

Base your answers to questions 70 and 71 on the blood-typing chart below and on your knowledge of biology.

Individual	Antigens on Red Blood Cells	Antibodies in Plasma
1		anti-B
2	*B*	

70 Which antibodies, if any, are in the plasma of individual 2?

1 anti-A, only
2 anti-B, only
3 both anti-A and anti-B
4 neither anti-A nor anti-B

71 Individual 1 has blood type

(1) A　　　　　(3) AB
(2) B　　　　　(4) O

72 Arthritis and tendinitis differ in that arthritis is an inflammation of the joints and tendinitis is a

1 deposition of uric acid in the joints
2 tear in the connective tissue that attaches bone to bone
3 disorder involving connective tissue
4 type of arthritis found only in infants

73 Which foods should be included in a balanced diet as a good source of roughage?

1 red meat and poultry
2 fresh fruits and vegetables
3 eggs and milk products
4 animal fat and plant oil

74 Feces is usually about 40 percent water and 60 percent solid matter. Reducing the water content to 20 percent would most likely result in

1 ulcers　　　　3 diarrhea
2 appendicitis　　4 constipation

Directions (75–77): For *each* statement in questions 75 through 77, select the gland, *chosen from the list below*, that is best described by that statement. Then record its *number* on the separate answer paper.

Glands
(1) Adrenal
(2) Pancreas
(3) Parathyroid
(4) Hypothalamus

75 Cells within this gland secrete a hormone that, in times of emergency, increases the glucose level of the blood and speeds up the actions of the circulatory and respiratory systems.

76 Cells within this gland, which is part of the central nervous system, produce several hormones that affect the functioning of the pituitary gland.

77 Groups of cells within this gland secrete hormones that maintain normal levels of simple and complex carbohydrates in the body.

78 An individual who has had chicken pox rarely gets this disease again. This situation is an example of

1 biological control
2 negative feedback
3 active immunity
4 passive immunity

79 Which organic compounds are needed for the synthesis of the plasma membrane, contain a large amount of stored energy, and have been linked to cardiovascular diseases?

1 complex carbohydrates
2 saturated fats
3 simple sugars
4 polyunsaturated fats

Group 3 — Reproduction and Development
If you choose this group, be sure to answer questions 80–89.

Base your answers to questions 80 and 81 on the diagram below, which represents some stages in the development of an embryo, and on your knowledge of biology.

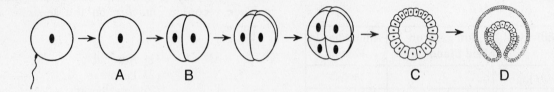

80 Which stage represents a zygote?

(1) *A* (3) *C*
(2) *B* (4) *D*

81 Which stage represents a blastula?

(1) *A* (3) *C*
(2) *B* (4) *D*

---

82 Which structures control the cyclic nature of menstruation?

1 oviduct and uterus
2 pituitary and testes
3 ovaries and umbilical cord
4 pituitary and ovaries

83 Which two processes are included in the prenatal development of a single human embryo?

1 gastrulation and differentiation
2 menopause and cleavage
3 puberty and gastrulation
4 menstruation and fertilization

84 Which techniques are sometimes used to help a woman who has blocked fallopian tubes have a child?

1 inbreeding and natural selection
2 in vitro fertilization and implantation
3 hybridization and vegetative propagation
4 synapsis and artificial selection

85 Hormones produced by the testes control the expression of traits for

1 hair color and eye color
2 beard development and number of fingers
3 hair color and voice quality
4 voice quality and beard development

Base your answers to questions 86 through 88 on the diagram below and on your knowledge of biology.

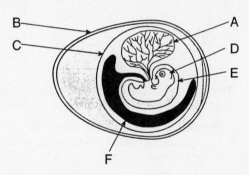

86 Which structure provides nourishment for the developing organism?

(1) *A* (3) *C*
(2) *B* (4) *D*

87 Which structure provides a watery environment and protects the embryo from physical shock?

(1) *A* (3) *E*
(2) *B* (4) *F*

88 Letter *C* indicates the

1 allantois 3 amnion
2 chorion 4 yolk sac

89 When asked to relate the terms "sperm," "scrotum," "testes," and "zygote," a student wrote the statements below.

Statements

(A) They all contain homologous pairs of chromosomes.

(B) The location of the testes within the scrotum aids in the production of sperm needed for zygote formation.

(C) Mitotic cell division is involved in the formation of the testes and scrotum, and meiosis is involved in the production of sperm, which is involved in the formation of a zygote.

(D) Formation of the testes, scrotum, and sperm occurs in human males; zygote formation occurs in females.

Which statements are correct?

(1) A, B, and D, only
(2) B, C, and D, only
(3) B and D, only
(4) A, B, C, and D

Group 4 — Modern Genetics

If you choose this group, be sure to answer questions 90–99.

Base your answers to questions 90 and 91 on the information below and on your knowledge of biology.

A large population of green aphids lives in a field and feeds on wild rose plants.

90 According to the Hardy-Weinberg principle, the stability of the aphid gene pool is maintained partly by the

1 type of food the aphids eat
2 type of habitat in which the aphids live
3 color of the aphids
4 large size of the aphid population

91 What will most likely result if exposure to insecticides causes mutations in the aphids over several generations?

1 Gene frequencies in the aphids will remain constant.
2 Gene frequencies in the aphids will change.
3 The number of gene alterations in the wild roses will increase.
4 The wild roses will become extinct.

Directions (92–93): For *each* statement in questions 92 and 93, select the genetic change, *chosen from the list below*, that is best described by that statement. Then record its *number* on the separate answer paper.

Genetic Changes

(1) Translocation
(2) Addition
(3) Deletion
(4) Gene mutation

92 A random change in the base sequence of DNA results in an alteration of a polypeptide.

93 A chromosomal rearrangement is formed after a section breaks off from one chromosome and becomes attached to a nonhomologous chromosome.

94 Recombinant DNA is presently used in the biotechnology industry to

1 eliminate all infectious disease in livestock
2 synthesize insulin, interferon, and human growth hormone
3 increase the frequency of fertilization
4 create populations that exhibit incomplete dominance

95 Oddly shaped red blood cells and severe pain are characteristics of a human genetic disorder known as

1 hemophilia   3 phenylketonuria
2 Tay-Sachs disease   4 sickle-cell anemia

96 Some events that take place during the synthesis of a specific protein are listed below.

(A) Messenger RNA attaches to a ribosome.
(B) DNA serves as a template for RNA production.
(C) Transfer RNA bonds to a specific codon.
(D) Amino acids are bonded together.
(E) RNA moves from the nucleus to the cytoplasm.

The correct order of these events is

(1) $B \rightarrow E \rightarrow A \rightarrow C \rightarrow D$
(2) $D \rightarrow A \rightarrow E \rightarrow C \rightarrow B$
(3) $B \rightarrow C \rightarrow E \rightarrow D \rightarrow A$
(4) $C \rightarrow B \rightarrow A \rightarrow E \rightarrow D$

97 What is the complementary messenger-RNA sequence for the DNA sequence shown below?

C A A G G T

(1) C–A–A–G–G–U   (3) G–U–U–C–C–A
(2) G–T–T–C–C–A   (4) C–A–A–G–G–T

Base your answers to questions 98 and 99 on the diagram of paired homologous chromosomes shown below and on your knowledge of biology.

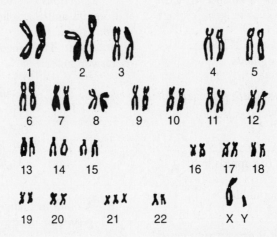

98 The genetic disorder shown in the diagram most likely resulted from

1 crossing-over   3 polyploidy
2 nondisjunction   4 segregation

99 Which technique was used to organize the chromosomes as shown in the diagram?

1 screening   3 karyotyping
2 chromatography   4 grafting

Group 5 — Ecology

If you choose this group, be sure to answer questions 100–109.

Base your answers to questions 100 and 101 on the diagram of the nitrogen cycle below and on your knowledge of biology. In the diagram, letters *A* through *E* represent organisms carrying on a process at that particular point in the cycle.

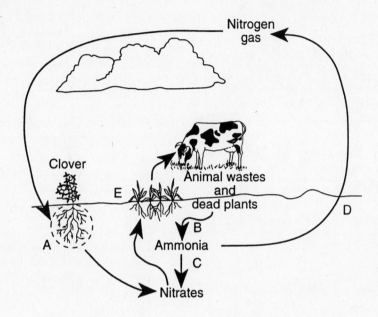

100 Letter *B* represents

  1 scavengers   3 autotrophs

  2 decomposers   4 carnivores

101 Nitrifying bacteria are represented by letter

  (1) *A*   (3) *C*

  (2) *E*   (4) *D*

---

102 The diagram below represents a food web.

If this food web is represented as a pyramid of biomass, the level of the pyramid with the *least* amount of biomass would contain the

1 grasshopper   3 mouse

2 grass   4 hawk

Base your answers to questions 103 and 104 on the diagram below of a biome and on your knowledge of biology.

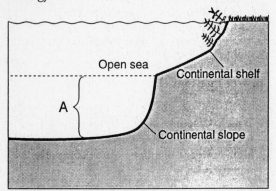

103 One characteristic that makes this biome the most stable aquatic environment is its

1 absorption and retention of large quantities of solar heat
2 lack of organisms that compete for nutrients
3 lack of autotrophs
4 high CO_2 level

104 Most of the organisms that live in region *A* are heterotrophs because

1 large quantities of salt are dissolved at this depth
2 oxygen does not dissolve in the water at this depth
3 water temperature varies greatly at this depth
4 sunlight cannot penetrate to this depth

105 If two different bird species in the same habitat require the same type of nesting site, both species will most likely

1 interbreed and share the nesting sites
2 compete for the nesting sites
3 change their nesting site requirements
4 use the nests of other bird species

Base your answers to questions 106 and 107 on the diagrams below, which represent the stages of an ecological succession in New York State, and on your knowledge of biology. The stages are *not* in order.

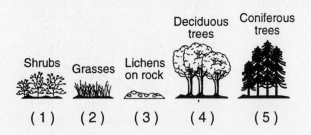

106 Which sequence represents a correct order of succession that would involve these stages?

(1) $2 \rightarrow 3 \rightarrow 1 \rightarrow 4 \rightarrow 5$
(2) $2 \rightarrow 1 \rightarrow 3 \rightarrow 5 \rightarrow 4$
(3) $3 \rightarrow 1 \rightarrow 2 \rightarrow 4 \rightarrow 5$
(4) $3 \rightarrow 2 \rightarrow 1 \rightarrow 5 \rightarrow 4$

107 In which stage would minerals be added during the formation of soil by a community composed primarily of pioneer organisms?

(1) 1   (3) 3
(2) 2   (4) 5

108 The taiga biome is characterized by

1 long, cold winters; frozen subsoil; and no trees
2 cold winters, coniferous trees, and much snow
3 heavy rainfall, broad-leaved trees, and hot temperatures
4 hot days, cool nights, and little precipitation

109 An organism that feeds on the blood of a live rabbit is known as

1 a parasite   3 an herbivore
2 a producer   4 a saprophyte

Part III

This part consists of five groups. **Choose three of these five groups.** For those questions that are followed by four choices, record the answers on the separate answer paper in accordance with the directions on the front page of this booklet. For all other questions in this part, record your answers in accordance with the directions given in the question. [15]

Group 1

If you choose this group, be sure to answer questions 110–114.

110 A new concept that is tested in a scientific investigation is known as

1 a theory 3 an inference
2 the hypothesis 4 an observation

111 To obtain the view of structure *A* shown in the diagram below, how was the cut most likely made?

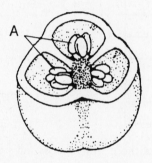

Lower Pistil Section

1 longitudinally through the anther, using a teasing needle
2 posteriorly through the filament, using a razor blade
3 horizontally through the ovary, using a scalpel
4 dorsally through the stigma, using a probe

112 Which structure in a stained cheek cell would most likely be visible when viewed through the high-power objective of a compound light microscope?

1 cell wall 3 chloroplast
2 ribosome 4 nucleolus

113 Which procedure is the most acceptable method for obtaining the accurate weight of a specimen in a laboratory experiment?

1 Make sure the balance weighs accurately before starting the measurement, and then record the weight for three trials and average the results.
2 Readjust the balance after weighing the specimen, and then weigh the specimen again.
3 Have two classmates use different balances to determine the weight of the specimen, and average the values they obtain.
4 Determine the weight of the specimen using one balance, and then measure the weight again using a different balance.

114 The diagrams below show the general appearance of five tree fruits that were used in an experiment to determine the length of time necessary for each type of fruit to fall a set distance. One hundred fruits of each type were used, and the average time of fall for each type of fruit is shown in the data table below.

Fruits

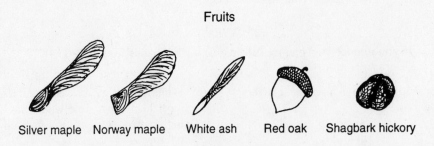

Silver maple   Norway maple   White ash   Red oak   Shagbark hickory

(Not drawn to scale)

Tree Type	Average Fall Time of 100 Fruits (seconds)
Silver Maple	3.2
Norway Maple	4.9
White Ash	1.5
Red Oak	0.8
Shagbark Hickory	0.8

What could a student correctly infer about the distribution of these fruits if they fell from branches 5 meters above the ground while the wind was blowing at 20 miles per hour?

1 A silver maple fruit would land closer to the base of its parent tree than would a shagbark hickory fruit.

2 A white ash fruit would land farther from the base of its parent tree than would a silver maple fruit.

3 A white ash fruit would land closer to the base of its parent tree than would a shagbark hickory fruit.

4 A Norway maple fruit would land farther from the base of its parent tree than would a silver maple fruit.

Group 2

If you choose this group, be sure to answer questions 115–119.

Base your answers to questions 115 through 118 on the data table below and on your knowledge of biology.

Human Body Surface Area as It Relates to Body Weight
(The figures are most accurate for people of average build.)

Weight (lb)	Surface Area (m²)
70	1.1
100	1.4
125	1.6
150	1.8
175	2.0
200	2.2
250	2.7

Directions (115–116): Using the information in the data table, construct a line graph on the grid provided *on your answer paper*, following the directions below. The grid on the next page is provided for practice purposes only. Be sure your final answer appears *on your answer paper.* You may use pen or pencil for your answer.

115 Mark an appropriate scale on each of the labeled axes.

116 Plot the data from the table. Surround each point with a small circle and connect the points.

Example:

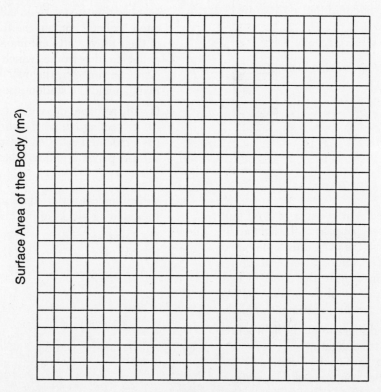

117 A normal, healthy individual requires about 1,500 milliliters of water each day for every square meter of body surface area. Approximately how much water will be required each day by a normal, healthy individual who weighs 100 pounds?

(1) 1,400 mL   (3) 1,800 mL

(2) 1,500 mL   (4) 2,100 mL

118 Using one or more complete sentences, state a relationship between body weight and body surface area. You may use pen or pencil for your answer.

119 Name one substance in the diagram below that would have a net movement out of the cell. You may use pen or pencil for your answer.

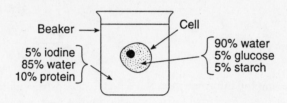

Group 3

If you choose this group, be sure to answer questions 120–124.

120 The volume of liquid shown in the graduated cylinder at the right is

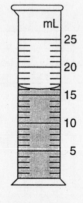

(1) 15.0 mL

(2) 16.0 mL

(3) 16.5 mL

(4) 17.0 mL

121 A water plant placed in bright light gives off bubbles. A student notes that placing the light at different distances from the plant causes the rate of bubbling to vary. The student decides to design an experiment to investigate the effect of light intensity on the rate of bubble production. An appropriate control for this experiment would be

1 a plant at a fixed distance from the light source

2 a plant exposed to sunlight

3 the addition of oxygen to the water

4 the use of blue light on some of the plants

122 After owls eat, they bring back up the indigestible remains of their meals. These regurgitated "pellets" contain the fur and skeletal parts of their prey. A student plans to examine an owl pellet to determine which small vertebrates were consumed by the owl. Which set of equipment should the student use?

(1) microscope, ultracentrifuge, and stain

(2) dissecting kit, petri dish, and gloves

(3) graduated cylinder, balance, and meterstick

(4) pH paper, liquid indicator, and beaker

123 Which indicator should be used to help identify the building blocks of maltose?

(1) Lugol's iodine   (3) Benedict's solution

(2) pH paper   (4) bromthymol blue

124 Using one or more complete sentences, state one safety precaution that should be used in the laboratory situation illustrated. You may use pen or pencil for your answer.

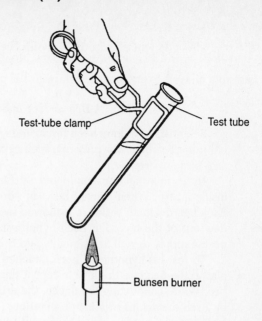

Test-tube clamp — Test tube

Bunsen burner

Group 4

If you choose this group, be sure to answer questions 125–129.

Base your answers to questions 125 and 126 on the diagram of a compound light microscope below and on your knowledge of biology.

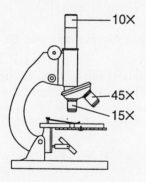

10×

45×

15×

125 Which parts of this compound light microscope with clean lenses should be used to improve the quality of the image being observed in the high-power field of view?

1 ocular and high-power objective
2 diaphragm and fine-adjustment knob
3 coarse-adjustment knob and low-power objective
4 ocular and diaphragm

126 The diameter of the low-power field of this compound light microscope measures 1,200 micrometers. What is the diameter of the high-power field in micrometers?

(1) 0.4   (3) 40
(2) 3.6   (4) 400

127 A student calculated the diameter of the high-power field of a compound light microscope to be 0.5 millimeter. If 10 plant cells fit end to end across the diameter of the high-power field, the average length of each plant cell would be

(1) 50 µm   (3) 200 µm
(2) 5 mm   (4) 20 mm

128 An unstained wet mount of epidermal cells shows few details. Which substance could be added to the slide to make the details more visible?

1 methylene blue   3 Benedict's solution
2 dilute acid   4 bromthymol blue

129 A student is making a wet-mount preparation of onion epidermis cells for observation with a compound light microscope. The student cuts off a slice of onion, places it on a slide, adds iodine, puts the slide on the stage, and rotates the nosepiece on the microscope to the high-power objective.

Using one or more complete sentences, state one error in the procedures followed by the student. You may use pen or pencil for your answer.

Group 5

If you choose this group, be sure to answer questions 130–134.

Base your answers to questions 130 through 133 on the reading passage below and on your knowledge of biology.

A Bee or Not a Bee, That Is the Question

Scientists have long been fascinated by the complex society of the bee. They have studied inherited behavior patterns, such as dances and other methods bees use to communicate basic information.

In an investigation conducted by Dr. Harold Esch, a small microphone was placed inside a hive. When a scout bee was communicating information in the form of a dance, Esch heard a loud "thththrr," followed by a short "beep," and then some of the worker bees flew out of the hive. Dr. Esch hypothesized that the sounds reported the distance to the nectar supply as well as its quality and quantity.

To test his hypothesis, Esch attached a tiny loudspeaker to an artificial scout bee and placed the bee into the hive to repeat the dance that had been performed by the live scout bee. While conducting the dance, the artificial bee emitted the "thththrr" sound recorded by Esch during his original observations. A ring of worker bees followed the performance with interest, but instead of flying out to seek the nectar, one of the worker bees flew over and stung the artificial scout bee. Smelling the odor of the venom, the other bees withdrew. This happened each time Esch repeated his experiment.

Dr. Esch eventually realized that he had neglected the short chirping beeps that followed the scout's "thththrr" sound. These beeps were apparently made by one of the worker bees to indicate that the message was understood. When the scout bee hears the beep, she is supposed to stop dancing so the workers can come close to her and smell the odor of the nectar she has found. When the artificial scout bee was once again placed into the hive to perform the dance and stopped the dance after the first beep, the worker bees approached the artificial scout bee and then left the hive in search of the nectar.

130 Scout bees communicate information to other bees by

1 the repeated blinking of their eyes
2 a dance performed in the hive
3 the number of times they sting
4 learned behavior patterns

131 Which statement correctly describes the reaction of the worker bees to the artificial bee when it continued to dance after the first beep?

1 One of the worker bees stung the artificial bee.
2 The worker bees appeared to ignore the artificial bee.
3 The worker bees appeared to accept the artificial bee.
4 One of the worker bees brought nectar to the artificial bee.

132 As a result of his investigations, Dr. Esch discovered that

1 artificial bees can be used to find food
2 worker bees can fly farther than scout bees
3 bees can communicate by means of sound
4 each hive has only one scout bee

133 Which statement best accounts for the stinging of the artificial scout bee by the worker bee?

1 Bees are not able to interpret recorded sounds.
2 Worker bees learn from other bees.
3 Scout bees are aggressive and unable to search for nectar.
4 Certain bee behavior is inherited.

134 A laboratory investigation was set up to determine if the hormone thyroxin increases metabolic activity in rats. Twenty rats of the same species, age, and weight were selected and divided into two equal groups. All the factors in the investigation were kept the same, except one group was given distilled water, and the other group was given distilled water containing thyroxin.

State the variable being studied in this investigation. You may use pen or pencil for your answer.

BIOLOGY
JANUARY 1999

ANSWER PAPER

Student ....

Teacher .... School ....

All of your answers should be recorded on this answer paper.

Part I (65 credits)

1	1 2 3 4	21	1 2 3 4	41	1 2 3 4
2	1 2 3 4	22	1 2 3 4	42	1 2 3 4
3	1 2 3 4	23	1 2 3 4	43	1 2 3 4
4	1 2 3 4	24	1 2 3 4	44	1 2 3 4
5	1 2 3 4	25	1 2 3 4	45	1 2 3 4
6	1 2 3 4	26	1 2 3 4	46	1 2 3 4
7	1 2 3 4	27	1 2 3 4	47	1 2 3 4
8	1 2 3 4	28	1 2 3 4	48	1 2 3 4
9	1 2 3 4	29	1 2 3 4	49	1 2 3 4
10	1 2 3 4	30	1 2 3 4	50	1 2 3 4
11	1 2 3 4	31	1 2 3 4	51	1 2 3 4
12	1 2 3 4	32	1 2 3 4	52	1 2 3 4
13	1 2 3 4	33	1 2 3 4	53	1 2 3 4
14	1 2 3 4	34	1 2 3 4	54	1 2 3 4
15	1 2 3 4	35	1 2 3 4	55	1 2 3 4
16	1 2 3 4	36	1 2 3 4	56	1 2 3 4
17	1 2 3 4	37	1 2 3 4	57	1 2 3 4
18	1 2 3 4	38	1 2 3 4	58	1 2 3 4
19	1 2 3 4	39	1 2 3 4	59	1 2 3 4
20	1 2 3 4	40	1 2 3 4		

PART I CREDITS

Directions to Teacher:

In the table below, draw a circle around the number of right answers and the adjacent number of credits. Then write the number of credits (not the number right) in the space provided above.

No. Right	Credits	No. Right	Credits
59	65	29	36
58	64	28	35
57	63	27	34
56	62	26	33
55	61	25	32
54	60	24	31
53	59	23	31
52	58	22	30
51	57	21	29
50	56	20	28
49	55	19	27
48	54	18	26
47	54	17	25
46	53	16	24
45	52	15	23
44	51	14	21
43	50	13	20
42	49	12	18
41	48	11	17
40	47	10	15
39	46	9	14
38	45	8	12
37	44	7	11
36	43	6	9
35	42	5	8
34	41	4	6
33	40	3	5
32	39	2	3
31	38	1	2
30	37	0	0

No. right ....

Part II (20 credits)

Answer the questions in only two of the five groups in this part. Be sure to mark the answers to the groups of questions you choose in accordance with the instructions on the front page of the test booklet. Leave blank the three groups of questions you do not choose to answer.

Group 1
Biochemistry

60 1 2 3 4

61 1 2 3 4

62 1 2 3 4

63 1 2 3 4

64 1 2 3 4

65 1 2 3 4

66 1 2 3 4

67 1 2 3 4

68 1 2 3 4

69 1 2 3 4

Group 3
Reproduction and Development

80 1 2 3 4

81 1 2 3 4

82 1 2 3 4

83 1 2 3 4

84 1 2 3 4

85 1 2 3 4

86 1 2 3 4

87 1 2 3 4

88 1 2 3 4

89 1 2 3 4

Group 5
Ecology

100 1 2 3 4

101 1 2 3 4

102 1 2 3 4

103 1 2 3 4

104 1 2 3 4

105 1 2 3 4

106 1 2 3 4

107 1 2 3 4

108 1 2 3 4

109 1 2 3 4

Group 2
Human Physiology

70 1 2 3 4

71 1 2 3 4

72 1 2 3 4

73 1 2 3 4

74 1 2 3 4

75 1 2 3 4

76 1 2 3 4

77 1 2 3 4

78 1 2 3 4

79 1 2 3 4

Group 4
Modern Genetics

90 1 2 3 4

91 1 2 3 4

92 1 2 3 4

93 1 2 3 4

94 1 2 3 4

95 1 2 3 4

96 1 2 3 4

97 1 2 3 4

98 1 2 3 4

99 1 2 3 4

Part III (15 credits)

Answer the questions in only three of the five groups in this part. Leave blank the groups of questions you do not choose to answer.

Group 1

110	1	2	3	4
111	1	2	3	4
112	1	2	3	4
113	1	2	3	4
114	1	2	3	4

Group 2

115 – 116

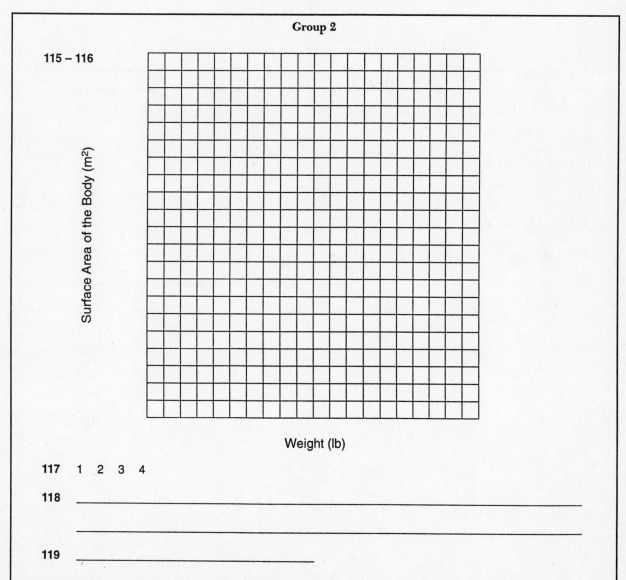

Surface Area of the Body (m²)

Weight (lb)

117   1   2   3   4

118 _____

_____

119 _____

Group 3

120   1   2   3   4

121   1   2   3   4

122   1   2   3   4

123   1   2   3   4

124 _____

_____

_____

_____

_____

Group 4

125   1   2   3   4

126   1   2   3   4

127   1   2   3   4

128   1   2   3   4

129 _____

_____

_____

_____

_____

Group 5

130   1   2   3   4

131   1   2   3   4

132   1   2   3   4

133   1   2   3   4

134 _____

_____

BIOLOGY
JUNE 1999

Part I

Answer all 59 questions in this part.   [65]

Directions (1–59): For *each* statement or question, select the word or expression that, of those given, best completes the statement or answers the question. Record your answer on the separate answer paper in accordance with the directions on the front page of this booklet.

1 When a duck dives into cold water, the capillaries in its skin constrict and move deeper below the surface of the skin. This reaction is an example of

1 homeostasis   3 respiration
2 synthesis   4 excretion

2 The remains of an organism are shown in the photograph below.

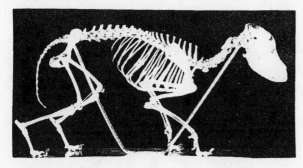

This organism is classified as

1 a coelenterate   3 a chordate
2 an annelid   4 an arthropod

3 Which instrument was used in the 18th and 19th centuries and helped scientists develop the cell theory?

1 light microscope
2 ultracentrifuge
3 electron microscope
4 microdissecting apparatus

4 Which organelle is correctly paired with its function?

1 nucleus — provides carbohydrates for fermentation
2 chloroplast — serves as a site for photosynthesis
3 centriole — synthesizes digestive enzymes
4 lysosome — packages cellular products

5 The phrase "is not a cell but has the ability to reproduce within a living cell" can be used to describe

1 an alga   3 a bacterium
2 a yeast   4 a virus

6 Which compound is inorganic?

1 glucose ($C_6H_{12}O_6$)
2 carbon dioxide (CO_2)
3 ethane (C_2H_6)
4 stearic acid ($C_{18}H_{36}O_2$)

7 Salivary amylase is an enzyme in humans that breaks down starch. The optimum pH for this reaction is 6.7. The rate of this reaction would *not* be affected by

1 decreasing the temperature of the reaction by 5°C
2 enzyme concentration
3 maintaining the pH of the reaction at 6.7
4 substrate concentration

8 Which process is a form of autotrophic nutrition?

1 transport   3 fermentation
2 regulation   4 photosynthesis

9 Which structure indicated in the diagram of a paramecium below is used for the process of egestion?

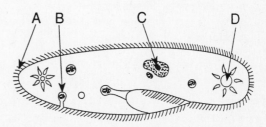

(1) *A*   (3) *C*
(2) *B*   (4) *D*

10 Which diagram best represents the fluid-mosaic model of a cell membrane?

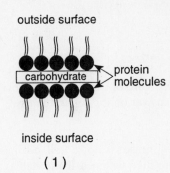

(1)

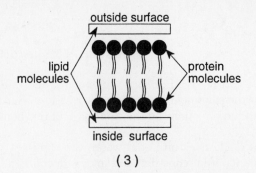

(3)

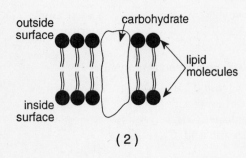

(2)

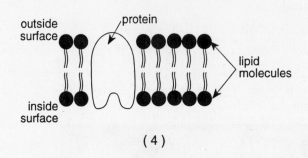

(4)

11 Under certain conditions, the openings of stomates in leaves become smaller. This process enables the plant to avoid excessive loss of

1 water   3 methane
2 salt   4 nitrates

12 Filaments known as rhizoids extend from bread mold, penetrate bread, and digest the bread by secreting substances known as

1 vitamins   3 hormones
2 minerals   4 enzymes

13 The root system of a grass plant is an adaptation that increases the ability of the plant to

1 absorb carbon dioxide for photosynthesis
2 ingest nutrient molecules
3 manufacture pigments for protection
4 carry on gas exchange and absorb inorganic substances

14 The diagram below represents the cross section of an earthworm.

Which letter indicates a structure that provides an increased surface area for the absorption of digestive end products?

(1) A   (3) C
(2) B   (4) D

15 A portion of a reflex arc is represented in the diagram below.

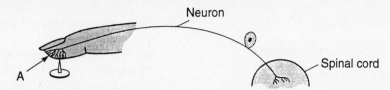

The function of structure A is to

1 synthesize neurotransmitters
2 detect changes in the external environment
3 carry messages away from the central nervous system
4 directly initiate an impulse in an effector

16 The diagram below represents a hydra.

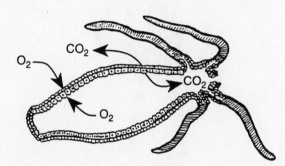

The movement of gases indicated by the arrows in the diagram takes place by the process of

1 pinocytosis
2 diffusion
3 active transport
4 dehydration synthesis

17 Which substances are metabolic waste products excreted by animals?

1 oxygen, ammonia, and salts
2 glucose, urea, and carbon dioxide
3 uric acid, oxygen, and water
4 water, urea, and carbon dioxide

18 In certain invertebrates, the function of Malpighian tubules and nephridia is to

1 collect waste materials
2 carry oxygen
3 transmit nerve impulses
4 synthesize proteins

19 In the diagram of a cell shown below, which number indicates the structure in which most of the enzymes involved in aerobic cellular respiration function?

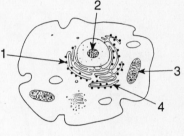

(1) 1   (3) 3
(2) 2   (4) 4

20 The diagram below represents the tip of a growing plant stem.

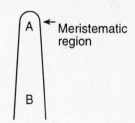

Which statement best describes the auxins in this stem?

1 They are produced at area A and only affect area A.
2 They are produced at area B and only affect area B.
3 They are produced at area A and transported to area B.
4 They are produced at area B and transported to area A.

21 Which row in the chart below contains a correct comparison between nervous regulation and chemical regulation?

Row	Nervous Regulation	Chemical Regulation
A	Slow response	Fast response
B	Long duration	Short duration
C	Involves neuro-transmitters	Involves hormones
D	Common to all organisms	Only in multi-cellular animals

(1) A   (3) C
(2) B   (4) D

22 Two organisms are represented in the diagram below.

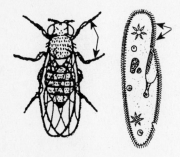

The arrows in the diagram indicate structures that help these organisms to

1 obtain food
2 carry out photosynthesis
3 carry out respiration
4 excrete wastes

23 Which substance is a nutrient in the human diet?

1 oxygen   3 water
2 carbon dioxide   4 roughage

24 After food enters the small intestine, lipases, proteases, and amylases are secreted into the small intestine by the

1 liver   3 salivary glands
2 gallbladder   4 pancreas

25 Structures specialized for returning blood to the heart are known as

1 arteries   3 lacteals
2 veins   4 bronchioles

26 An individual running a marathon may experience periods of oxygen deprivation that can lead to

1 anaerobic respiration in muscle cells, forming lactic acid
2 aerobic respiration in muscle cells, generating glycogen
3 anaerobic respiration in liver cells, producing glucose
4 aerobic respiration in liver cells, synthesizing alcohol

27 What is the principal function of the excretory structure indicated by letter X in the diagram below?

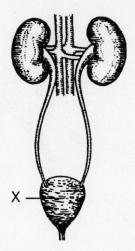

1 reabsorption   3 storage
2 filtration   4 egestion

28 When a child runs to his mother after hearing a clap of thunder, the child is using

1 the central nervous system, only
2 the peripheral nervous system, only
3 both the central and the peripheral nervous systems
4 neither the central nor the peripheral nervous system

29 The humerus, the bone in the upper arm of a human, is directly connected to other bones in the arm by

1 cartilage   3 extensors
2 tendons   4 ligaments

30 The chart below provides information about the flowers of three different plants.

Flower Characteristic	Flowers		
	Plant *A*	Plant *B*	Plant *C*
Petal color	white	purple	bright yellow
Aroma	none	rotting meat, strong	sweet, strong
Petal size	0.3 cm	10 cm	4 cm
Nectar amount	none	medium amount	large amount

Which inference is valid concerning the method of pollination for plants *A*, *B*, and *C*?

1 All three plants are insect pollinated.
2 Plant *A* is wind pollinated, but plants *B* and *C* are insect pollinated.
3 Plants *A* and *B* are insect pollinated, but plant *C* is wind pollinated.
4 All three plants are wind pollinated.

---

31 One difference between cell division in plant cells and in animal cells is that

1 plants form a cell plate between daughter cells but animals do not
2 more cytoplasm forms in animal cells than in plant cells
3 centrioles form in plant cells but not in animal cells
4 a double nucleus forms in animal cells but not in plant cells

32 Which human disorder is characterized by a group of abnormal body cells that suddenly begin to undergo cell division at a very rapid rate?

1 albinism   3 hemophilia
2 cancer   4 color blindness

33 Which process normally occurs during meiosis, but *not* during mitosis?

1 chromosomal replication
2 synapsis of chromosomes
3 spindle formation
4 centromere replication

34 Which process produces polar bodies that eventually degenerate?

1 oogenesis   3 cyclosis
2 spermatogenesis   4 cleavage

35 The bacterium *Clostridium tetani* is found on nearly all surfaces. A short time after one or two of these bacteria enter a wound, a large number of them may be found in the wound as a result of

1 regeneration
2 vegetative propagation
3 asexual reproduction
4 gametogenesis

36 The diagram below represents a microscopic structure observed during cell division.

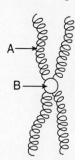

Which parts of the structure are indicated by arrows *A* and *B*, respectively?

1 centriole and tetrad
2 autosome and allele
3 homologous chromosome and spindle fiber
4 chromatid and centromere

37 A diagram of a flower is shown below.

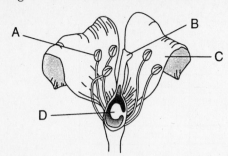

Fertilization occurs in region

(1) *A*   (3) *C*
(2) *B*   (4) *D*

38 A structure found in the nucleus of a cell is shown in the diagram below.

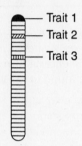

The information contained in the diagram best illustrates the

1 law of segregation
2 concept of nondisjunction
3 gene-chromosome theory
4 theory of natural selection

39 Which diagram illustrates fertilization that would most likely lead to the development of a normal human female?

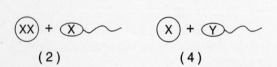

40 A mother with type B blood and a father with type A blood have four children, each with a different blood type. The best explanation for the occurrence of the four different blood types of the children is that blood type is

1 only determined by dominant alleles
2 determined by multiple alleles
3 influenced by environmental conditions
4 a sex-linked trait

41 Which statement best describes a chromosomal alteration?

1 It never affects the phenotype of an organism.
2 It may affect the phenotype of an organism.
3 It always produces a recessive genotype in an organism.
4 It never has an effect on the genotype of an organism.

42 A cattle breeder wished to develop a strain of cattle that would produce large quantities of meat per animal. He chose a bull and a cow that most nearly met his goals for breed size. From their calves, he again chose the male and female offspring that most nearly met his goals. After several generations of this style of breeding, the breeder developed a herd of high-yield cattle. In order to maintain this herd of high-yield cattle, which technique should the cattle breeder use?

1 vegetative propagation
2 hybridization
3 genetic recombination
4 inbreeding

43 A DNA nucleotide is composed of

1 carbon, hydrogen, oxygen, nitrogen, and phosphorus
2 carbon, hydrogen, nitrogen, sulfur, and calcium
3 calcium, hydrogen, oxygen, phosphorus, and iron
4 oxygen, hydrogen, phosphorus, sulfur, and iron

44 Two generations of offspring of four o'clock plants are shown in the diagram below.

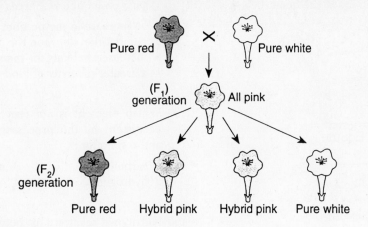

The phenotypic ratio of the F_2 generation is
(1) 3:1
(2) 2:1:2
(3) 2:1
(4) 1:2:1

---

45 When the bacterium *Serratia marcescens* is grown on a sterile culture medium in a petri dish at 30°C, the bacterial colonies will be cream colored. When this same bacterium is cultured under identical conditions, except at a temperature of 25°C, the colonies will be brick red. This difference in color is most likely due to the

1 type of nutrients in the culture medium
2 sterilization of the culture medium
3 effect of temperature on the expression of the gene for color
4 effect of colony size on the synthesis of color pigments

46 Fossils would most likely be found in

1 amber that is over 8 billion years old
2 icebergs that are 500 billion years old
3 sedimentary rocks that are 500 million years old
4 volcanic rocks that are 50 million years old

47 In some members of a species, inherited adaptations are combined in a way that makes these members more likely to survive than other members of the species. This statement is most closely associated with a theory of evolution proposed by

1 Darwin
2 Lamarck
3 Mendel
4 Miller

48 Which graph best illustrates the evolutionary concept of punctuated equilibrium?

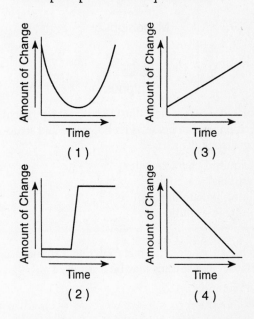

49 Blood proteins in horses are chemically similar to blood proteins in monkeys. This similarity suggests that horses and monkeys

1 can interbreed
2 evolved at the same time
3 live in the same habitat
4 may have a common ancestor

50 The diagram below shows the gradual change over time in the anatomy of the horse.

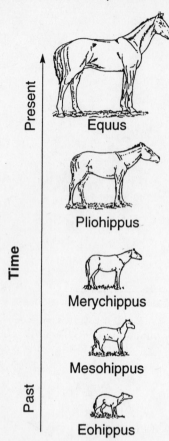

Which concept is best illustrated by the physical variations in the horse as its body size and structure change over time?

1 acquired characteristics
2 artificial selection
3 intermediate inheritance
4 organic evolution

51 A change in genetic material that produces a variation in a species may be a result of

1 a mutation
2 competition
3 overproduction of a species
4 a struggle for survival

52 According to the heterotroph hypothesis, the atmosphere of primitive Earth lacked

1 oxygen gas   3 ammonia
2 water   4 hydrogen gas

53 The most likely result of a group of squirrels relying on limited resources would be

1 an increase in the number of squirrels
2 competition between the squirrels
3 increased habitats for the squirrels
4 a greater diversity of food for the squirrels

54 Which element is *not* recycled throughout an ecosystem by the processes of photosynthesis and respiration?

1 carbon   3 nitrogen
2 hydrogen   4 oxygen

55 Nutritional relationships between organisms are shown in the diagram below.

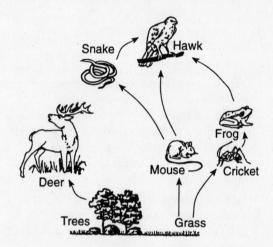

Which organisms are primary consumers?

1 mouse, snake, and hawk
2 snake, hawk, and frog
3 cricket, frog, and deer
4 mouse, deer, and cricket

56 Farmers sometimes release praying mantises into their fields to consume other insects that destroy crops. This action is an example of

1 biological control of insect pests
2 chemical control of insect pests
3 a technological oversight
4 exploitation of wildlife

57 The diagram below shows organisms in and around a pond.

Which ecological term refers to all the organisms shown in the diagram?

1 heterotroph
2 community

3 population
4 producer

58 Information relating to an ecosystem is contained in the diagram shown below.

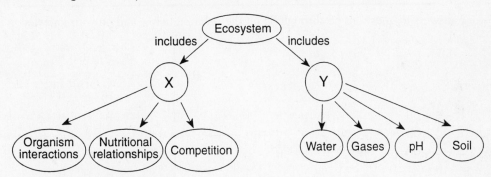

Which information belongs in areas *X* and *Y*?

(1) *X* — biotic factors; *Y* — abiotic factors
(2) *X* — ecological relationships; *Y* — biotic relationships
(3) *X* — abiotic factors; *Y* — interacting populations
(4) *X* — energy flow; *Y* — biotic factors

59 The diagram below represents a map showing different zones in an area once covered by a glacier.

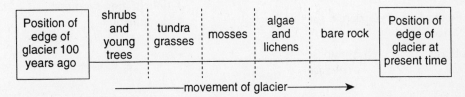

This map best represents

1 a food chain
2 ecological succession

3 a pyramid of energy
4 nutritional relationships

Part II

This part consists of five groups, each containing ten questions. Choose two of these five groups. Be sure that you answer all ten questions in each group chosen. Record the answers to these questions in accordance with the directions on the front page of this booklet. [20]

Group 1 — Biochemistry

If you choose this group, be sure to answer questions 60–69.

Base your answers to questions 60 through 62 on the biochemical reactions below and on your knowledge of biology.

$$\text{glucose} + \boxed{A} \xrightarrow{\boxed{B}} \text{4 ATP} + \text{2 pyruvic acid}$$

$$\text{2 pyruvic acid} + \boxed{C} \xrightarrow{\boxed{B}} \text{carbon dioxide} + \text{water} + \text{34 ATP}$$

60 Letter *A* represents

  (1) hydrogen   (3) carbon dioxide
  (2) 2 DNA   (4) 2 ATP

61 Letter *B* represents

  (1) 4 ADP   (3) 2 PGAL
  (2) enzymes   (4) starch

62 Letter *C* represents

  (1) oxygen   (3) 4 ADP
  (2) $2C_6H_{12}O_6$ (4) alcohol

Base your answers to questions 63 through 65 on the reaction below and on your knowledge of biology.

63 Which letter indicates a carboxyl group?

  (1) *A*   (3) *C*
  (2) *B*   (4) *D*

64 Which enzyme must be present for this reaction to take place?

  1 a protease   3 a lipase
  2 maltase   4 sucrase

65 This chemical reaction is known as

  1 enzymatic hydrolysis
  2 photolysis
  3 dehydration synthesis
  4 deamination

Base your answers to questions 66 through 68 on the table below and on your knowledge of biology.

Enzyme	Effective Temperature Range (°C)	Optimum pH
A	60–80	3
B	30–40	3.5
C	20–38	9
D	20–27	7

66 If enzyme *C* is functioning at 25°C and a pH of 7, under which conditions would the rate of enzyme action probably increase?

1 The temperature is decreased to 22°C and the pH is kept the same.
2 The temperature is increased to 30°C and the pH is increased to 8.
3 The temperature is kept the same and the pH is decreased to 6.
4 The temperature is increased to 44°C and the pH is kept the same.

67 At what temperature would enzyme *D* most likely be denatured?

(1) 15°C   (3) 25°C
(2) 20°C   (4) 39°C

68 Which enzyme would most likely be functional in bacteria living in a hot spring that is 35°C above normal human body temperature?

(1) *A*   (3) *C*
(2) *B*   (4) *D*

69 The diagram below represents some chemical events that take place in one type of autotrophic nutrition.

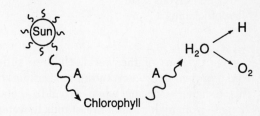

The arrows labeled *A* best represent

1 carbon dioxide   3 energy
2 glucose   4 lactic acid

Group 2 — Human Physiology

If you choose this group, be sure to answer questions 70–79.

Base your answers to questions 70 through 72 on the diagram below, which represents the pathway of blood throughout the body, and on your knowledge of biology.

70 Which structure carries oxygenated blood to the body?

(1) 1   (3) 7
(2) 2   (4) 8

71 Which sequence correctly represents blood flow known as pulmonary circulation?

(1) $4 \rightarrow 6 \rightarrow 2 \rightarrow 7$ (3) $6 \rightarrow 8 \rightarrow 1 \rightarrow 3$
(2) $5 \rightarrow 2 \rightarrow 7 \rightarrow 4$ (4) $3 \rightarrow 5 \rightarrow 8 \rightarrow 1$

72 Which structure represents the chamber of the heart that receives oxygenated blood directly from the lungs?

(1) 5   (3) 3
(2) 6   (4) 4

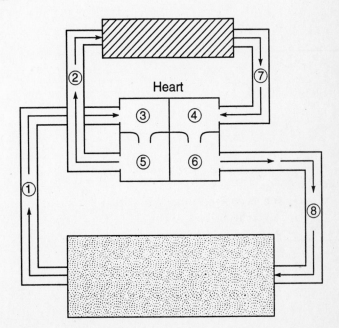

73 An allergic reaction characterized by the constriction of the bronchial tubes is known as

1 coronary thrombosis   3 asthma
2 arthritis   4 emphysema

74 A cerebral hemorrhage may result in

1 a stroke   3 polio
2 gout   4 meningitis

75 The contraction of the biceps and triceps muscles in the human arm is regulated by the

1 autonomic nervous system
2 pituitary gland
3 somatic nervous system
4 hypothalamus

76 In some regions of the world, children suffer from a protein deficiency known as kwashiorkor. This deficiency occurs when a child's diet is changed from high-protein breast milk to watery cereal. Even though the child is receiving calories, the child becomes sick and less active, and growth ceases. These symptoms are probably due to

1 too many nucleic acids in the diet
2 an overconsumption of complete protein foods
3 not enough carbohydrates in the diet
4 a lack of essential amino acids in the diet

Directions (77–78): For *each* phrase in questions 77 and 78, select the endocrine gland, *chosen from the list below*, that is best described by that phrase. Then record its *number* on the separate answer paper.

Endocrine Glands

(1) Thyroid
(2) Adrenal
(3) Islets of Langerhans
(4) Parathyroid

77 Secretes a hormone in times of emergency, accelerating metabolic activities

78 Requires a supply of iodine to synthesize its hormone

79 A photograph of a slide of human blood taken from a healthy individual is shown below.

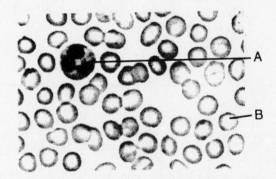

Which statement best describes the change that would be observed if the slide contained blood from an individual with anemia?

1 Cell type *A* would be fewer in number and larger in size.
2 Cell type *B* would be fewer in number and lighter in appearance.
3 Cell type *B* would be larger in size and greater in number.
4 Cell type *A* would be larger in size and darker in appearance.

Group 3 — Reproduction and Development
If you choose this group, be sure to answer questions 80–89.

Base your answers to questions 80 through 82 on the diagrams below and on your knowledge of biology.

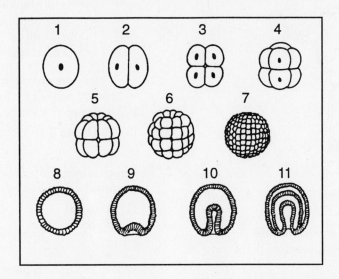

80 Which diagram shows the first appearance of the distinct layer of cells that will form the muscular, skeletal, and circulatory systems?

(1) 11   (3) 6
(2) 8   (4) 4

81 If stages 1 through 4 represent developmental stages of a human, where in the human female would these stages normally occur?

1 ovary   3 oviduct
2 vagina   4 uterus

82 Which events must occur immediately before the sequence represented in the diagrams can take place?

1 gametogenesis and fertilization
2 menstruation and menopause
3 prenatal development and gestation
4 placenta formation and metamorphosis

Base your answers to questions 83 through 85 on the diagram below and on your knowledge of biology.

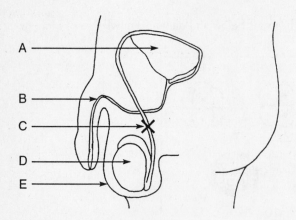

83 What would most likely happen if structure *C* was blocked at the **X**?

1 Sperm production would increase.
2 Sperm could not be transported to the outside of the body.
3 Urine could not be discharged from the urinary bladder.
4 Sex hormones would no longer be produced.

84 Which structure produces a hormone that is responsible for such characteristics as body hair, muscle development, and a deep voice?

(1) *A* (3) *E*
(2) *B* (4) *D*

85 Which structure is part of both the reproductive and excretory systems?

(1) *E* (3) *C*
(2) *B* (4) *D*

Base your answers to questions 86 and 87 on the organisms listed below and on your knowledge of biology.

Organisms
(A) Fish
(B) Amphibians
(C) Reptiles
(D) Birds
(E) Mammals

86 In which organisms are the embryos *least* dependent on yolk for food?

(1) *A* and *C* (3) *E*, only
(2) *C*, *D*, and *E* (4) *D*, only

87 Which organisms generally produce eggs that are fertilized externally and develop externally?

(1) *A* and *B* (3) *A* and *C*
(2) *B* and *D* (4) *B*, only

88 Which sequence represents the normal order of events that occur during the menstrual cycle?

1 menstruation → ovulation → corpus luteum → follicle stage
2 follicle stage → ovulation → corpus luteum → menstruation
3 ovulation → follicle stage → corpus luteum → menstruation
4 follicle stage → menstruation → corpus luteum → ovulation

89 Substances can diffuse from the mother's blood into the fetal blood through the structure known as the

1 amnion 3 yolk sac
2 fallopian tube 4 placenta

Group 4 — Modern Genetics

If you choose this group, be sure to answer questions 90–99.

Base your answers to questions 90 and 91 on the diagram below of two processes in the synthesis of proteins and on your knowledge of biology.

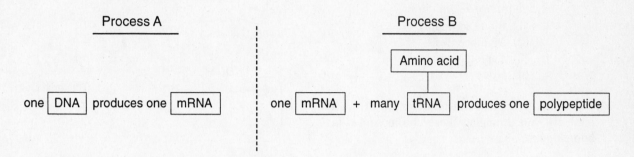

90 Process *B* involves the pairing of a codon with a triplet code on a transfer RNA molecule. A correct pairing would be

(1) CAT and GTA (3) GUG and UGU
(2) AAU and UUA (4) CAG and GUA

91 Process *A* occurs within the

1 mitochondrion 3 chloroplast
2 ribosome 4 nucleus

92 The diagram below shows some chromosomal alterations.

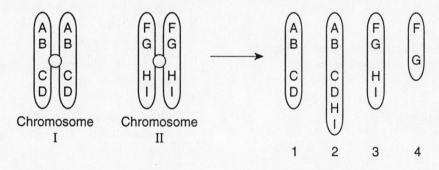

Which chromosome represents an alteration known as a deletion?

(1) 1 (3) 3
(2) 2 (4) 4

Directions (93–94): For *each* phrase in questions 93 and 94, select the laboratory technique, *chosen from the list below*, that is most closely associated with that phrase. Then record its *number* on the separate answer paper.

Laboratory Techniques
  (1) Blood screening
  (2) Amniocentesis
  (3) Karyotyping
  (4) Urine analysis

93 Enlarging photographs of chromosomes from a fetal cell and arranging these chromosomes in homologous pairs

94 Removal and examination of a sample of fluid surrounding the fetus

———————————

95 Which genetic disorder is characterized by a buildup of fatty tissue in the nervous system?

1 phenylketonuria   3 Down syndrome
2 sickle-cell anemia   4 Tay-Sachs

96 The total of the heritable factors for the traits in the deer population of New York State is an example of a

1 gene pool
2 phenotypic ratio
3 diploid number
4 chromosome number

Base your answers to questions 97 through 99 on the diagram below and on your knowledge of biology.

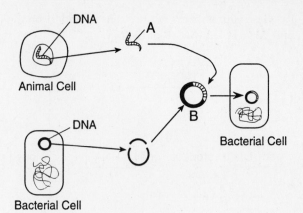

97 Structure *A* contains a

1 genetic code
2 single nucleotide, only
3 messenger RNA molecule
4 small polysaccharide

98 Structure *B* represents

1 a ribosome   3 recombinant DNA
2 transfer RNA   4 a male gamete

99 The technique illustrated in the diagram is known as

1 cloning
2 genetic engineering
3 protein synthesis
4 in vitro fertilization

Group 5 — Ecology

If you choose this group, be sure to answer questions 100–109.

Base your answers to questions 100 through 102 on the diagrams below of four stages of a biological process and on your knowledge of biology.

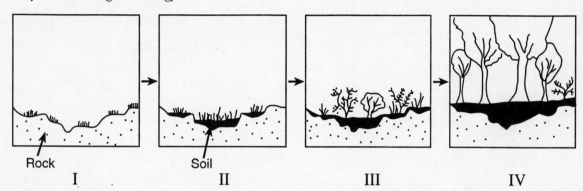

Rock   Soil

    I   II   III   IV

100 What would most likely be the predominant life-form found in stage 1?

   1 ferns   3 mushrooms
   2 tracheophytes   4 pioneer species

101 What is a major limiting biotic factor for animal succession in each stage?

   1 plant species   3 soil minerals
   2 sunlight   4 moisture

102 Stage IV will persist until it is altered by

   1 the growth in diameter of the trees
   2 a major change in an abiotic factor
   3 the reappearance of lichens and mosses
   4 seasonal dieback of vegetation

103 The pyramid below illustrates some feeding relationships in alpine meadows of Yellowstone National Park.

Grizzly bears

Chipmunks

Insects

Grasses

Which statement is best supported by the information shown in the pyramid?

1 Chipmunks and insects can occupy the same niche.
2 As the number of bears in this community increases, the number of chipmunks will increase.
3 Insects are classified as omnivores in alpine meadow communities.
4 Biomass decreases as energy is transferred from one level to another.

Base your answers to questions 104 through 106 on the map below, which shows the general location of some major biomes of Earth, and on your knowledge of biology. A different biome is represented by each of the following symbols:

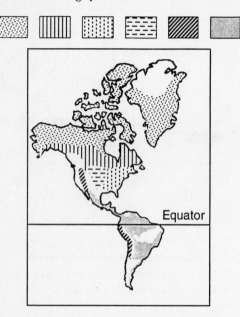

104 Which climax flora would be a major part of the biome indicated by the symbol ⊟⊟⊟ ?

1 mosses   3 grasses
2 succulent plants 4 lichens

105 Which symbol indicates an area with coniferous trees; long, severe winters; and black bears?

(1) ▨   (3) ▨

(2) ▥   (4) ▨

106 What is one characteristic of the biome indicated by the symbol ▨ ?

1 permanently frozen subsoil
2 extreme daily temperature fluctuations
3 drought-resistant shrubs
4 deciduous trees

Base your answers to questions 107 and 108 on the diagram below and on your knowledge of biology.

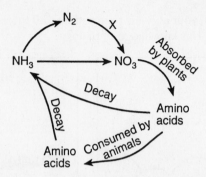

107 Which gas is released when the tissues of dead plants and animals are broken down by bacteria?

(1) NO_3 (3) NH_3
(2) N_2 (4) O_2

108 Bacteria responsible for process X are known as

1 nitrogen-fixing bacteria
2 nitrifying bacteria
3 denitrifying bacteria
4 autotrophic bacteria

———————————————

109 The American dogwood, a flowering tree of New York State's woodlands, has been attacked by a fungal disease specific to this tree species. Many dogwoods have died because fungicides have not proven effective in fighting the spread of this disease. Which term best describes the relationship between the dogwood trees and the fungus?

1 commensalism   3 parasitism
2 mutualism   4 saprophytism

Part III

This part consists of five groups. Choose three of these five groups. For those questions that are followed by four choices, record the answers on the separate answer paper in accordance with the directions on the front page of this booklet. For all other questions in this part, record your answers in accordance with the directions given in the question. [15]

Group 1

If you choose this group, be sure to answer questions 110–114.

Base your answers to questions 110 through 113 on the information below and on your knowledge of biology.

A student performed a laboratory investigation to determine the effect of temperature on the heart rate of Daphnia (water flea). The following temperatures and heart rates were recorded:

20°C — 270 beats/min; 10°C — 150 beats/min;
15°C — 180 beats/min; 25°C — 300 beats/min;
5°C — 108 beats/min

110 Organize the data by filling in the data table *provided on your answer paper*. Complete both columns in the data table so that the temperature either increases or decreases from the top to the bottom of the table. The data table below is provided for practice purposes only. Be sure your final answer appears *on your answer paper*. You may use pen or pencil for your answer.

Data Table

Temperature (°C)	Heart Rate (beats/min)

Directions (111–112): Using the information provided, construct a line graph on the grid *provided on your answer paper*, following the directions below. The grid on the next page is provided for practice purposes only. Be sure your final answer appears *on your answer paper*. You may use pen or pencil for your answer.

111 Mark an appropriate scale on each labeled axis.

112 Plot the data from your data table. Surround each point with a small circle and connect the points.

Example:

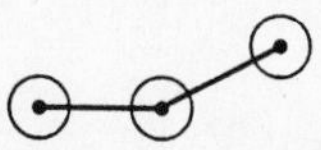

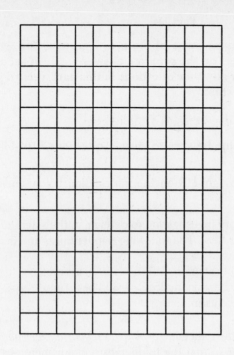

Heart Rate (beats/min)

Temperature (°C)

113 During which temperature interval did the greatest change in heart rate occur?

    (1) 5–10°C   (3) 15–20°C

    (2) 10–15°C   (4) 20–25°C

114 Which number indicates an acidic pH?

    (1) 14   (3) 3

    (2) 12   (4) 7

Group 2

If you choose this group, be sure to answer questions 115–119.

Base your answers to questions 115 through 118 on the passage below and on your knowledge of biology.

The Mystery of Deformed Frogs

Deformities, such as legs protruding from stomachs, no legs at all, eyes on backs, and suction cup fingers growing from sides, are turning up with alarming frequency in North American frogs. Clusters of deformed frogs have been found in California, Oregon, Colorado, Idaho, Mississippi, Montana, Ohio, Vermont, and Quebec.

Scientists in Montreal have been studying frogs in more than 100 ponds in the St. Lawrence River Valley for the past 4 years. Normally, less than 1% of frogs are deformed, but in ponds where pesticides are used on surrounding land, as many as 69% of the frogs were deformed. A molecular biologist from the University of California believes that the deformities may be linked to a new generation of chemicals that mimic growth hormones. The same kind of deformities found in the ponds have been replicated in laboratory experiments.

Some scientists have associated the deformities with a by-product of retinoid, which is found in acne medication and skin rejuvenation creams. Retinoids inside a growing animal can cause deformities. For this reason, pregnant women are warned not to use skin medicines that contain retinoids. Recent laboratory experiments have determined that a pesticide can mimic a retinoid.

A developmental biologist from Hartwick College in Oneonta, New York, questioned whether a chemical could be the culprit because there were no deformed fish or other animals found in the ponds where the deformed frogs were captured. He believes parasites are the cause. When examining a three-legged frog from Vermont, the biologist found tiny parasitic flatworms packed into the joint where a leg was missing. In a laboratory experiment, he demonstrated that the invasion of parasites in a tadpole caused the tadpole to sprout an extra leg as it developed. Scientists in Oregon have made similar observations.

115 Why are pregnant women advised not to use skin medicines containing retinoids?

1 Retinoid by-products may cause fetal deformities.
2 Retinoid by-products cause parasites to invade developing frogs.
3 Retinoid by-products mimic the effects of pesticides on fetal tissue.
4 Retinoid by-products reduce abnormalities in maternal tissue.

116 Some scientists argue that pesticides may *not* be the cause of the frog deformities because

1 pesticide use has decreased over the last 4 years
2 new pesticides are used in skin-care products
3 other animals in the ponds containing deformed frogs did not have abnormalities
4 laboratory experiments have determined that a pesticide can mimic retinoids

117 A possible reason for the absence of deformed fish in the ponds that contained deformed frogs is that

1 fish can swim away from chemicals introduced into the pond
2 parasites that affect frogs usually do not affect fish
3 fish cannot develop deformities
4 frogs and fish are not found in the same habitat

118 Which inference can be made from the information in the passage?

1 Only a few isolated incidents of frog deformities have been observed.
2 If frog parasites are controlled, all frog deformities will stop.
3 Deformities in frogs are of little significance.
4 Factors that affect frogs may also affect other organisms.

119 Using one or more complete sentences, state what substance a student could use to test for the presence of starch in a food sample *and* describe the positive result of this test. You may use pen or pencil for your answer.

Group 3

If you choose this group, be sure to answer questions 120–124.

120 Which sequence contains the correct order of steps for a student to follow to observe the nucleus of protozoa in a stained wet mount, using a compound light microscope?

	Begin by using the	Focus using the	Focus using the	Switch to the
(1)	low-power objective →	coarse adjustment →	fine adjustment →	high-power objective
(2)	low-power objective →	fine adjustment →	coarse adjustment →	high-power objective
(3)	high-power objective →	coarse adjustment →	fine adjustment →	low-power objective
(4)	high-power objective →	fine adjustment →	coarse adjustment →	low-power objective

---

121 A compound light microscope has a 10× ocular, a 10× low-power objective, and a 40× high-power objective. The diameter of the low-power field is 1,500 micrometers. Which information is *not* needed to calculate the diameter of the high-power field of this microscope?

1 diameter of the low-power field
2 magnification of the high-power objective
3 magnification of the low-power objective
4 magnification of the ocular lens

122 Which organelles would be most visible in a stained elodea leaf when viewed with the low-power objective of a compound light microscope?

1 endoplasmic reticula, chloroplasts, and nuclei
2 cell walls, nuclei, and ribosomes
3 chloroplasts, nuclei, and mitochondria
4 cell walls, chloroplasts, and nuclei

123 Which substance is used as a stain to make it easier to observe a wet mount of cheek cells with a compound light microscope?

1 Benedict's solution   3 bromthymol blue
2 methylene blue   4 salt solution

124 A plant cell is represented in the diagram below.

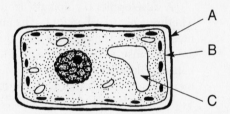

Select one of the lettered structures. Record the letter of the structure chosen in the space *provided on your answer paper* and, using one or more complete sentences, state the function of the structure. You may use pen or pencil for your answer.

Group 4

If you choose this group, be sure to answer questions 125–129.

125 The table below lists four groups of materials.

Group A	Group B	Group C	Group D
microscope	dissecting pan	hot plate	hydra culture
glass slide	dissecting pins	large beaker	depression slide
coverslip	hand lens	water	coverslip
water	razor blade	test tubes	microscope
dropper	scissors	test-tube rack	toothpick
pond water	earthworm	assorted food items	vinegar
		Benedict's solution	flashlight

Choose one of these groups. In the space *provided on your answer paper,* write the letter of the group chosen and, using one or more complete sentences, describe a laboratory activity for which that group of materials could be used. You may use pen or pencil for your answer.

---

126 A student measured an earthworm using a metric ruler, as shown in the diagram below.

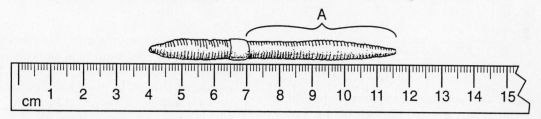

What is the length of section A?

(1) 7.6 cm

(2) 11.6 cm

(3) 46 mm

(4) 23 mm

---

127 An investigation was designed to determine the effect of ultraviolet light on mold spore growth. Two groups of mold spores were grown under identical conditions, except one group was exposed only to ultraviolet light, while the other group was grown in total darkness. In this investigation, the group of mold spores grown without receiving any ultraviolet light is known as the

1 experimental variable 3 control
2 hypothesis 4 limiting factor

128 Which pair of structures can be observed *without* dissecting an earthworm?

1 mouth and pharynx
2 skin and ventral nerve cord
3 anus and aortic arches
4 setae and excretory pores

129 Antibiotic X has a unique characteristic in that it fluoresces (glows) when exposed to ultraviolet light. An investigator added antibiotic X to a dish containing a culture of cells. She exposed the cells to ultraviolet light and found that antibiotic X was highly concentrated within mitochondria. Which assumption could the investigator make regarding the results of this experiment?

1 Antibiotic X could be used to identify mitochondria in living cells.
2 Antibiotic X could be used to stain nuclei of living cells.
3 All fluorescent materials will be absorbed by mitochondria.
4 All antibiotics will be absorbed by mitochondria.

Group 5

If you choose this group, be sure to answer questions 130–134.

130 Worker bees acting as scouts are able to communicate the distance of a food supply from the hive by performing a "waggle dance." The graph below shows the relationship between the distance of a food supply from the hive and the number of turns in the waggle dance every 15 seconds.

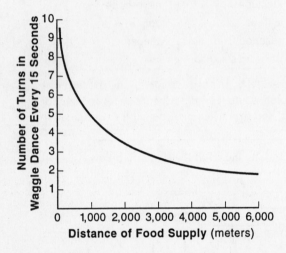

Using one or more complete sentences, state the relationship between the distance of the food supply from the hive and the number of turns the bee performs in the waggle dance every 15 seconds. You may use pen or pencil for your answer.

131 Based on experimental results, a biologist in a laboratory reports a new discovery. If the experimental results are valid, biologists in other laboratories should be able to perform

1 an experiment with a different variable and obtain the same results
2 the same experiment and obtain different results
3 the same experiment and obtain the same results
4 an experiment under different conditions and obtain the same results

132 As part of an investigation, 10 bean seedlings in one setup were grown in the dark, while 10 seedlings in another setup were grown in sunlight. All other growth conditions were kept the same in both setups. The seedlings grown in the dark were white with long, slender stems. These seedlings eventually died. The seedlings grown in the sunlight were green and healthy. Which hypothesis was most likely being tested in this investigation?

1 Plants grown in the dark cannot perform the process of respiration.
2 Sunlight is necessary for the normal growth of bean plants.
3 Light is necessary for the germination of bean seeds.
4 Light is necessary for proper mineral absorption by plants.

133 Male reproductive cells from numerous lubber grasshoppers, lake trout, and field mice were examined and found to have a flagellum. A valid conclusion that can be made based on this observation is that

1 only lubber grasshoppers, lake trout, and field mice are likely to produce reproductive cells with a flagellum
2 all organisms produce male reproductive cells with a flagellum
3 only male organisms produce reproductive cells with a flagellum
4 all male lubber grasshoppers, lake trout, and field mice most likely produce reproductive cells with a flagellum

134 Using one or more complete sentences, state one safety procedure that should be followed when an animal dissection is performed. You may use pen or pencil for your answer.

BIOLOGY
JUNE 1999

ANSWER PAPER

Student . . . .

Teacher . . . . School . . . .

All of your answers should be recorded on this answer paper.

Part I (65 credits)

1	1 2 3 4	21	1 2 3 4	41	1 2 3 4
2	1 2 3 4	22	1 2 3 4	42	1 2 3 4
3	1 2 3 4	23	1 2 3 4	43	1 2 3 4
4	1 2 3 4	24	1 2 3 4	44	1 2 3 4
5	1 2 3 4	25	1 2 3 4	45	1 2 3 4
6	1 2 3 4	26	1 2 3 4	46	1 2 3 4
7	1 2 3 4	27	1 2 3 4	47	1 2 3 4
8	1 2 3 4	28	1 2 3 4	48	1 2 3 4
9	1 2 3 4	29	1 2 3 4	49	1 2 3 4
10	1 2 3 4	30	1 2 3 4	50	1 2 3 4
11	1 2 3 4	31	1 2 3 4	51	1 2 3 4
12	1 2 3 4	32	1 2 3 4	52	1 2 3 4
13	1 2 3 4	33	1 2 3 4	53	1 2 3 4
14	1 2 3 4	34	1 2 3 4	54	1 2 3 4
15	1 2 3 4	35	1 2 3 4	55	1 2 3 4
16	1 2 3 4	36	1 2 3 4	56	1 2 3 4
17	1 2 3 4	37	1 2 3 4	57	1 2 3 4
18	1 2 3 4	38	1 2 3 4	58	1 2 3 4
19	1 2 3 4	39	1 2 3 4	59	1 2 3 4
20	1 2 3 4	40	1 2 3 4		

No. right . . . .

Part II (20 credits)

Answer the questions in only two of the five groups in this part. Be sure to mark the answers to the groups of questions you choose in accordance with the instructions on the front page of the test booklet. Leave blank the three groups of questions you do not choose to answer.

Group 1
Biochemistry

60	1	2	3	4
61	1	2	3	4
62	1	2	3	4
63	1	2	3	4
64	1	2	3	4
65	1	2	3	4
66	1	2	3	4
67	1	2	3	4
68	1	2	3	4
69	1	2	3	4

Group 3
Reproduction and Development

80	1	2	3	4
81	1	2	3	4
82	1	2	3	4
83	1	2	3	4
84	1	2	3	4
85	1	2	3	4
86	1	2	3	4
87	1	2	3	4
88	1	2	3	4
89	1	2	3	4

Group 5
Ecology

100	1	2	3	4
101	1	2	3	4
102	1	2	3	4
103	1	2	3	4
104	1	2	3	4
105	1	2	3	4
106	1	2	3	4
107	1	2	3	4
108	1	2	3	4
109	1	2	3	4

Group 2
Human Physiology

70	1	2	3	4
71	1	2	3	4
72	1	2	3	4
73	1	2	3	4
74	1	2	3	4
75	1	2	3	4
76	1	2	3	4
77	1	2	3	4
78	1	2	3	4
79	1	2	3	4

Group 4
Modern Genetics

90	1	2	3	4
91	1	2	3	4
92	1	2	3	4
93	1	2	3	4
94	1	2	3	4
95	1	2	3	4
96	1	2	3	4
97	1	2	3	4
98	1	2	3	4
99	1	2	3	4

Part III (15 credits)

Answer the questions in only three of the five groups in this part. Leave blank the groups of questions you do not choose to answer.

Group 1

110 **Data Table**

Temperature (°C)	Heart Rate (beats/min)

111 – 112

Heart Rate (beats/min)

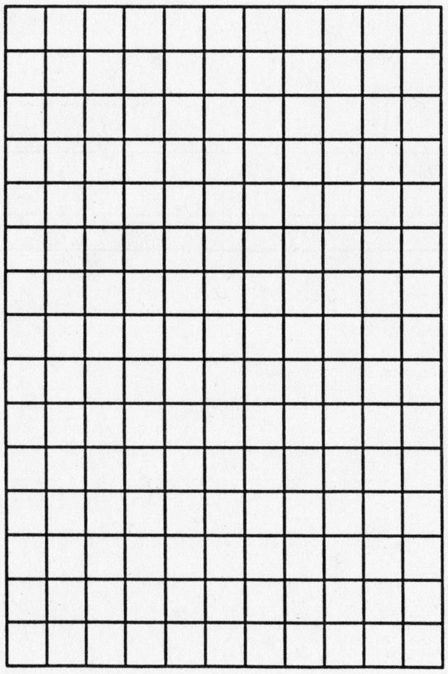

Temperature (°C)

113 1 2 3 4

114 1 2 3 4

Group 2

115 1 2 3 4

116 1 2 3 4

117 1 2 3 4

118 1 2 3 4

119 _____

_____

_____

_____

_____

_____

Group 3

120 1 2 3 4

121 1 2 3 4

122 1 2 3 4

123 1 2 3 4

124 _____

_____

_____

_____

_____

_____

Group 4

125 _____

_____

126   1   2   3   4

127   1   2   3   4

128   1   2   3   4

129   1   2   3   4

Group 5

130 _____

_____

131   1   2   3   4

132   1   2   3   4

133   1   2   3   4

134 _____

_____

BIOLOGY
JANUARY 2000

Part I

Answer all 59 questions in this part. [65]

Directions (1–59): For *each* statement or question, select the word or expression that, of those given, best completes the statement or answers the question. Record your answer on the separate answer paper in accordance with the directions on the front page of this booklet.

1 Which activity is necessary for the survival of a species of ameba but is *not* necessary for the survival of an individual member of that species?

1 elimination of water by a contractile vacuole
2 transport of oxygen through the cell membrane
3 ingestion of nutrients
4 process of binary fission

2 Which term is defined as all the chemical reactions that are required to sustain life?

1 metabolism   3 nutrition
2 regulation   4 synthesis

3 A classification scheme is shown below.

Classification	Examples
Kingdom — Animal	dolphin, house cat, songbird, lynx, wolf, earthworm, butterfly, hydra
Phylum — Chordata	dolphin, house cat, songbird, lynx, wolf
Genus — *Felis*	house cat, lynx
Species — *domestica*	house cat

This classification scheme indicates that the house cat is most closely related to the

1 dolphin   3 lynx
2 songbird   4 wolf

4 A structure that performs a specialized function within a cell is known as

1 a tissue   3 an organ
2 an organelle   4 a system

5 Which organism is considered an exception to the cell theory because it has a noncellular structure?

1 alga   3 virus
2 bacterium   4 moss

6 Which chemical compound makes up the greatest percentage of a protozoan?

1 nucleic acid   3 fatty acid
2 glucose   4 water

7 Which factor does *not* alter the rate of hydrolysis of maltose?

(1) temperature of the environment of the reaction
(2) pH of the environment of the reaction
(3) size of the substrate molecule
(4) number of enzyme molecules present

8 One immediate cause of a decrease in the rate of photosynthesis is a reduction in the availability of

1 carbon dioxide   3 hydrogen
2 carbon monoxide   4 nitrogen

9 The function of the gastric caecum in a grasshopper is most similar to the function of the

1 nephridium in an earthworm
2 pancreas in a human
3 anal pore in a paramecium
4 nerve net in a hydra

10 Which structure is most directly responsible for maintaining homeostasis in all cells?

1 chloroplast   3 centriole
2 cell membrane   4 cell wall

11 Vascular tissue that transports water in leaves connects directly to

1 meristems in the root tip
2 pistils in the flower
3 root hairs in the epidermis
4 xylem in the stem

12 Which two organisms represented below are heterotrophic?

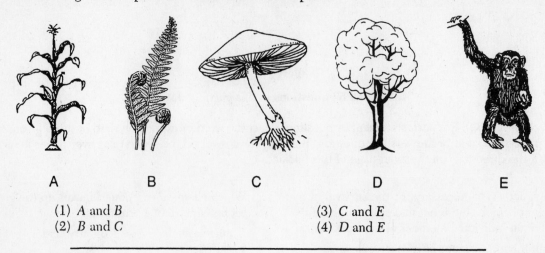

A   B   C   D   E

(1) *A* and *B*   (3) *C* and *E*
(2) *B* and *C*   (4) *D* and *E*

---

13 Which three processes are indicated by the arrows in the diagram below?

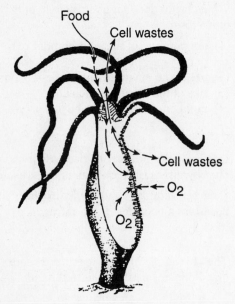

1 ingestion, diffusion, and excretion
2 ingestion, digestion, and egestion
3 cyclosis, meiosis, and mitosis
4 diffusion, active transport, and cyclosis

14 A biologist analyzed the liquid in the nephridia of earthworms and the liquid in the nephrons of humans. The liquid found in both organisms was most likely composed of water containing

1 sugar and uric acid
2 sugar and ammonia
3 salts and urea
4 salts and amino acids

15 Which letter in the diagram below indicates the structure that is most closely associated with excretion?

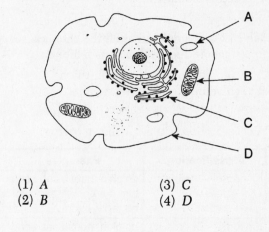

(1) *A*   (3) *C*
(2) *B*   (4) *D*

16 Which process is correctly paired with the waste it produces?

1 respiration — methane
2 protein metabolism — ammonia
3 dehydration synthesis — carbon dioxide
4 hydrolysis — urea

17 In grasshoppers and humans, locomotion is accomplished by means of

1 the interaction of muscles and jointed appendages
2 jointed chitinous appendages
3 a cartilaginous endoskeleton
4 the interaction of muscles and an exoskeleton

18 During aerobic respiration, the chemical energy of a glucose molecule is gradually released, producing 36 ATP and

(1) NH_3 and O_2 (3) H_2O and O_2
(2) NH_3 and CO_2 (4) H_2O and CO_2

19 In trees, shrubs, and other woody plants, the exchange of CO_2 and O_2 with the environment may occur through structures known as

1 spiracles   3 lenticels
2 anthers   4 rhizoids

20 Small hairs on the legs of certain insects have the ability to detect chemicals. These hairs function as

1 receptors   3 stimuli
2 effectors   4 responses

21 Which organism has a primitive brain, a ventral nerve cord, and antennae?

1 bryophyte   3 chordate
2 grasshopper   4 jellyfish

22 After several days near a window, a house plant began to grow toward the window. This growth pattern occurred because auxins

1 prevent the growth of cells on the light side of the plant
2 stimulate the growth of cells on the dark side of the plant
3 are activated when they are exposed to light
4 are distributed evenly throughout the plant stem

23 Which type of digestion occurs in the mouth when an individual chews a piece of bread?

1 mechanical digestion, only
2 chemical digestion, only
3 both mechanical and chemical digestion
4 neither mechanical nor chemical digestion

24 Which structure is lined with a ciliated mucous membrane that warms, moistens, and filters air?

1 pharynx   3 epiglottis
2 alveolus   4 nasal cavity

25 Which transport structures have specialized regions for filtering out bacteria and dead cells?

1 arteries   3 veins
2 capillaries   4 lymph vessels

26 In humans, the ureter transports urine from the

1 blood to the kidney
2 liver to the kidney
3 kidney to the urinary bladder
4 urinary bladder to outside the body

27 If a motor neuron involved in a reflex arc is damaged, which event in that arc is *least* likely to occur?

1 contraction of a muscle
2 stimulation of an interneuron
3 reception of a stronger stimulus by the sense organ
4 secretion of a neurotransmitter by the sensory neuron

28 Which system is most closely associated with the production of regulatory chemicals by glands?

1 nervous   3 circulatory
2 respiratory   4 endocrine

29 The inelastic connective tissue that attaches a muscle in the lower leg to a heel bone is known as

1 a tendon   3 cartilage
2 a ligament   4 epidermis

30 Which process results in offspring with a genetic makeup identical to that of the parent?

1 fusion of gametes
2 vegetative propagation
3 external fertilization
4 meiotic cell division

31 The uncontrolled division of certain body cells, which then invade the surrounding tissues and interfere with the normal functioning of the body, is known as

1 cancer   3 cleavage
2 regeneration   4 oogenesis

32 Corals reproduce by forming multicellular out-growths from the body wall that detach and develop into independent organisms. Which statement most closely describes this form of reproduction in another organism?

1 Molds reproduce by sporulation.
2 Hydras reproduce by budding.
3 Paramecia reproduce by binary fission.
4 Maple trees reproduce by seed formation.

33 Which reproductive process is correctly paired with the structure in which it occurs?

1 meiosis — liver
2 fertilization — gonad
3 gametogenesis — testis
4 pollination — stamen

34 A McIntosh apple tree branch was grafted to an Ida Red apple tree. The fruit produced by the newly grafted piece will be

(1) McIntosh apples, only
(2) Ida Red apples, only
(3) 50% McIntosh apples and 50% Ida Red apples
(4) apples that are a blend of McIntosh and Ida Red apples

35 Why is the release of 2,000 to 10,000 eggs by a female salmon during one season considered a favorable reproductive adaptation?

1 External fertilization increases the chance of sperm reaching the eggs.
2 Overproduction decreases the rate of embryo development.
3 The species is declining, so the reproductive rate has increased.
4 Unfavorable environmental conditions may destroy gametes.

36 Animals that produce embryos that are born small and relatively immature and must complete their development in a pouch are known as

1 hermaphrodites   3 marsupials
2 placental mammals 4 invertebrates

37 The brightly colored, highly scented flowers on a rosebush are an adaptation for

1 wind pollination
2 insect pollination
3 the production of spores
4 nutrition for developing rose embryos

38 Using the results of his experiments with pea plant crosses, Gregor Mendel discovered

1 the principles of dominance, segregation, and independent assortment
2 that pea plants develop mutations after exposure to radiation
3 intermediate inheritance and gene linkage
4 that DNA is involved in the inheritance of dominant traits

39 In a certain variety of chicken, the genes for black feather color and the genes for white feather color are codominant. This variety of chicken will most likely have

1 three possible phenotypes for feather color
2 white feather color, only
3 only two genotypes for feather color
4 black feather color, only

40 In fruit flies, red eye color (R) is dominant and white eye color (r) is recessive. The allele for eye color is carried on the X-chromosome. Which cross would most likely produce 50% white-eyed males and 50% red-eyed males?

(1) $X^R X^R \times X^R Y$ (3) $X^R X^r \times X^r Y$
(2) $X^R X^R \times X^r Y$ (4) $X^r X^r \times X^R Y$

41 A mutation may be passed on to future generations if it occurs within specialized cells of the

1 stomach   3 pancreas
2 liver   4 ovary

42 An example of a mutagenic agent is

1 an amino acid   3 acetylcholine
2 ultraviolet radiation 4 maltase

43 Kernel color in corn is a trait determined by two alleles. The dominant allele (*P*) produces a purple color, and the recessive allele (*p*) produces a yellow color. The diagram below shows an ear of corn produced by crossing two corn plants. The shaded kernels are purple, and the unshaded ones are yellow.

The yellow kernels can best be described as

1 homozygous dominant   3 hybrid
2 heterozygous   4 homozygous recessive

44 The results of a genetic process are represented in the diagram below.

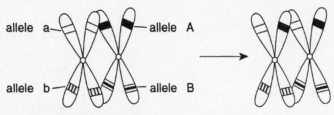

Homologous Chromosomes

Which process most likely produced these results?

1 chromosomal mutation during mitosis
2 nondisjunction during meiosis
3 independent assortment during mitosis
4 crossing-over during meiosis

---

45 A DNA nucleotide may contain

1 deoxyribose, cytosine, and a lipid
2 deoxyribose, thymine, and a phosphate group
3 ribose, uracil, and a polypeptide
4 ribose, adenine, and thymine

46 Fossils of an extinct species of giant armadillo were found to be similar to a smaller species of armadillo presently inhabiting the same region. This similarity could best be explained on the basis of

1 evolution from older forms
2 inheritance of acquired characteristics
3 use and disuse
4 the heterotroph hypothesis

47 A study of the position and shape of the bones in the forelimbs of a flying squirrel, a bat, and a beaver showed that the beaver and the flying squirrel appear to be most closely related. This determination was most likely based on a study in the field of comparative

1 embryology   3 anatomy
2 cytology   4 biochemistry

48 By simulating conditions thought to have existed on primitive Earth, Stanley Miller found that these conditions could result in the formation of

1 organic compounds   3 plant tissues
2 radioactive materials 4 animal embryos

49 The diagram below shows a comparison of nitrogen base sequences in the DNA of some organisms to those of a human.

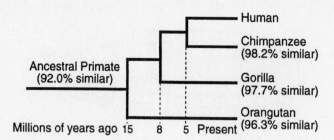

According to this diagram, humans may be most closely related to the

1 ancestral primate
2 chimpanzee

3 gorilla
4 orangutan

---

50 August Weismann conducted a series of experiments involving the removal of the tails from several generations of mice. Which concept of evolution did he help to *disprove*?

1 natural selection
2 gradualism
3 inheritance of acquired characteristics
4 geographic isolation

51 Modern evolutionary theory consists of the concepts of Darwin modified by knowledge concerning

1 overpopulation
2 the genetic basis of variation
3 survival of the fittest
4 competition

52 According to the heterotroph hypothesis, which gas was added to the environment by the first heterotrophs?

1 nitrogen
2 oxygen
3 water vapor
4 carbon dioxide

53 Which human activity would most likely result in the addition of an organism to the endangered species list?

1 cover cropping
2 use of pollution controls
3 use of erosion controls
4 habitat destruction

54 An aquarium ecosystem is shown below.

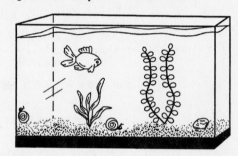

A community in this aquarium consists of the

1 plants and gravel
2 fish, water, and snails
3 fish, plants, and snails
4 water and gravel

55 The first organism in most natural food chains is

1 an herbivore
2 a decomposer
3 photosynthetic
4 carnivorous

56 Which factor is *not* necessary for an ecosystem to be self-sustaining?

1 a constant source of energy
2 living systems that incorporate energy into organic molecules
3 a cycling of materials between organisms and their environment
4 an equal number of producers and consumers

57 The diagram below provides some information concerning an ecosystem.

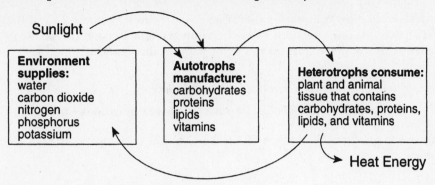

Which title is most appropriate for the diagram?

1 Energy Flow and Material Cycles in an Ecosystem
2 Evolution in an Ecosystem
3 Succession in an Ecosystem
4 The Water Cycle in an Ecosystem

58 The diagram below shows an example of interdependence among aquatic organisms. During the day, the organisms either use or give off substance *A* or *B*, as shown by the arrows.

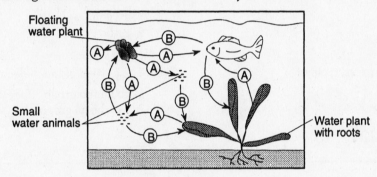

Which substances are represented by *A* and *B*?

(1) *A* represents oxygen and *B* represents carbon dioxide.
(2) *A* represents oxygen and *B* represents carbohydrates.
(3) *A* represents nitrogen and *B* represents carbon dioxide.
(4) *A* represents carbon dioxide and *B* represents oxygen.

59 The chart below lists four groups of factors relating to an ecosystem.

Group *A*	Group *B*	Group *C*	Group *D*
Sunlight	Sunlight	Sunlight	Sunlight
Green plants	Climate	Green plants	Rainfall
Rainfall	Rainfall	Rainfall	Consumers
Consumers	Minerals	Producers	Producers
Oxygen	Gases	Carbon dioxide	Water

Which group contains only abiotic factors?

(1) *A*   (3) *C*
(2) *B*   (4) *D*

Part II

This part consists of five groups, each containing ten questions. Choose two of these five groups. Be sure that you answer all ten questions in each group chosen. Record the answers to these questions in accordance with the directions on the front page of this booklet. [20]

Group 1 — Biochemistry
If you choose this group, be sure to answer questions 60–69.

Base your answers to questions 60 through 63 on the chemical reaction represented below and on your knowledge of biology.

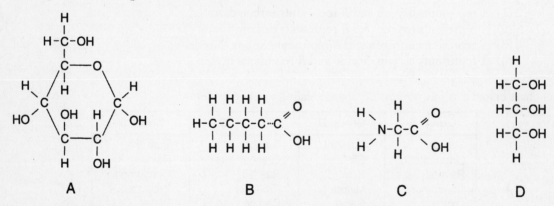

60 Amino acids are indicated by letters

(1) *A* and *B*   (3) *G* and *D*
(2) *A* and *G*   (4) *B* and *D*

61 This reaction is an example of

1 hydrolysis
2 aerobic respiration
3 dehydration synthesis
4 deamination

62 Letter *E* represents a molecule of

1 oxygen   3 glycerol
2 carbon dioxide 4 water

63 The portion of the molecule in box *F* is known as

1 an amino group   3 a polymer
2 a carboxyl group   4 a monosaccharide

---

64 The diagrams below represent four different molecules.

Which two diagrams represent the building blocks of lipids?
(1) *A* and *B*   (3) *C* and *D*
(2) *B* and *D*   (4) *A* and *C*

Base your answers to questions 65 through 67 on the diagram of a chloroplast below and on your knowledge of biology.

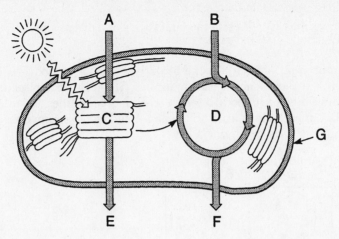

65 The process of photolysis in the grana occurs at letter

(1) *E* (3) *C*
(2) *G* (4) *D*

66 Carbon dioxide is represented by letter

(1) *E* (3) *C*
(2) *B* (4) *F*

67 The dark reactions in the stroma are represented by letter

(1) *A* (3) *C*
(2) *F* (4) *D*

---

68 Which statement is a valid conclusion based on the information in the graph below?

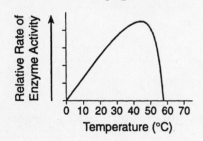

1 The maximum rate of human digestion occurs at about 45°C.
2 The maximum rate of human respiration occurs at about 57°C.
3 Temperature can influence the action of an enzyme.
4 Growth can be controlled by enzyme action.

69 What are the end products of the hydrolysis of a polysaccharide?

1 simple sugars 3 fatty acids
2 amino acids 4 nucleotides

Group 2 — Human Physiology
If you choose this group, be sure to answer questions 70–79.

Base your answers to questions 70 and 71 on the information and diagram below and on your knowledge of biology.

A technician needed to determine the blood type of four individuals. To do this, the technician set up four slides, one for each individual. The technician placed a drop of antibody A serum and a drop of antibody B serum on each of four slides. The technician mixed a drop of blood from each individual into the anti-A and anti-B serum on a different slide. The results of the four tests are shown below.

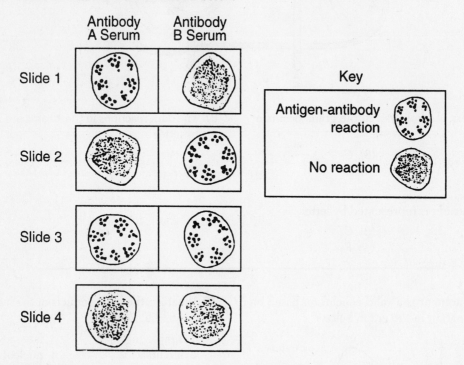

70 Which slide contains blood from the individual who has antigen A, but not antigen B?

    (1) 1   (3) 3

    (2) 2   (4) 4

71 Which slide contains blood from the individual who carries two recessive alleles for blood type?

    (1) 1   (3) 3

    (2) 2   (4) 4

Base your answers to questions 72 and 73 on the diagram below, which represents endocrine glands of both human sexes, and on your knowledge of biology.

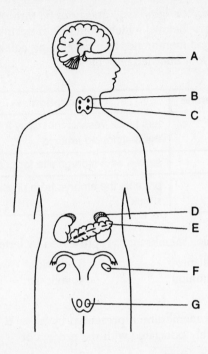

72 The secretion of hormones from gland *F* is regulated by hormones secreted from gland

(1) *A*   (3) *G*
(2) *B*   (4) *D*

73 The level of glucose in the blood is regulated by secretions from glands

(1) *A* and *G*   (3) *F* and *G*
(2) *B* and *C*   (4) *D* and *E*

_____

74 Pollen grains often stimulate an allergic response that produces

1 antigens   3 plasma
2 antibodies   4 platelets

Directions (75–76): For *each* phrase in questions 75 and 76, select the malfunction, *chosen from the list below,* that is best described by that phrase. Then record its *number* on the separate answer paper.

Malfunction

(1) Stroke
(2) Polio
(3) Cerebral palsy
(4) Meningitis

75 Congenital disease characterized by a disturbance of motor function

76 Inflammation of the membranes surrounding the central nervous system

_____

77 The flow of blood to and from the lungs is referred to as

1 pulmonary circulation
2 systemic circulation
3 autonomic circulation
4 somatic circulation

78 A source of roughage in the human diet is supplied by certain

1 saturated lipids
2 complete proteins
3 complex carbohydrates
4 nucleic acids

79 Which set of symptoms would most likely lead to a diagnosis of asthma?

1 enlargement and degeneration of the alveoli
2 constriction of the bronchial tubes and wheezing
3 inflammation and swelling of the epiglottis
4 constriction of the nasal cavity and watery eyes

Group 3 — Reproduction and Development
If you choose this group, be sure to answer questions 80–89.

Base your answers to questions 80 through 82 on the diagram below, which suggests an event in human reproduction, and on your knowledge of biology.

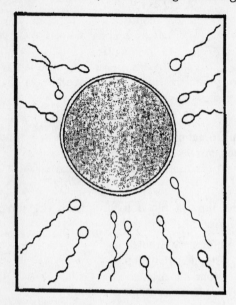

80 In humans, which process would normally *not* occur within the first two months after the completion of the process suggested in the diagram?

1 mitosis   3 menstruation
2 implantation   4 differentiation

81 In humans, the process suggested in the diagram usually occurs in the

1 follicle   3 vagina
2 uterus   4 oviduct

82 Which statement concerning all of the cells shown in the diagram is correct?

1 They contain the same amount of cytoplasm.
2 They normally contain the monoploid number of chromosomes.
3 They were formed by the process of mitosis.
4 They were formed by asexual reproduction.

Base your answers to questions 83 through 85 on the chart below, which contains descriptions of embryonic membranes in a developing chicken egg, and on your knowledge of biology.

Membrane	Description
A	has blood vessels that carry food to the developing embryo
B	serves as a storage site for uric acid
C	protects the embryo from physical shock

83 Which membrane is represented by letter *A*?

1 allantois   3 chorion
2 amnion   4 yolk sac

84 The membrane represented by letter *B* is most closely associated with the process of

1 excretion   3 nutrition
2 regulation   4 synthesis

85 The membrane represented by letter *C* is the

1 allantois   3 chorion
2 amnion   4 yolk sac

---

86 In which organ are female primary sex cells produced?

1 ovary   3 testis
2 urethra   4 placenta

87 A third cell layer in the human embryo is formed during the

1 zygote stage   3 gastrula stage
2 blastula stage   4 cleavage stage

88 Which adaptations do most reptiles have for fertilization and development?

1 internal fertilization and internal development
2 internal fertilization and external development
3 external fertilization and internal development
4 external fertilization and external development

89 Which hormone stimulates and controls the development of secondary sex characteristics in human males?

1 estrogen
2 progesterone
3 insulin
4 testosterone

Group 4 — Modern Genetics

If you choose this group, be sure to answer questions 90–99.

Directions (90–92): For *each* phrase in questions 90 through 92, select the genetic disorder, *chosen from the list below*, that is most closely associated with that phrase. Then record its *number* on the separate answer paper.

Genetic Disorders

(1) Tay-Sachs
(2) Phenylketonuria
(3) Sickle-cell anemia
(4) Down syndrome

90 Changes in speech patterns and mental retardation due to the presence of an extra chromosome

91 A decrease in the ability of the blood to carry oxygen due to the presence of abnormal hemoglobin

92 Inability of the body to manufacture the enzyme needed to metabolize a specific amino acid

___

93 A single change in the sequence of nitrogenous bases in a DNA molecule would most likely result in

1 crossing-over
2 polyploidy
3 nondisjunction of chromosomes
4 a gene mutation

94 Which base is normally used in the synthesis of RNA but *not* in the synthesis of DNA?

1 adenine
2 uracil
3 cytosine
4 guanine

95 A sequence of three nitrogenous bases in a messenger-RNA molecule is known as a

1 codon
2 gene
3 polypeptide
4 nucleotide

Base your answers to questions 96 and 97 on the information below and on your knowledge of biology.

Some geneticists are suggesting the possibility of transferring some of the genes that influence photosynthesis from an efficient variety of crop plant to a less efficient crop plant to produce a new variety with improved productivity.

96 To produce this new variety, the project would most likely involve

1 amniocentesis
2 genetic screening
3 genetic engineering
4 inbreeding

97 Which technique would most likely be used to produce large numbers of genetically identical offspring from this new variety of plant?

1 cloning
2 karyotyping
3 cross-pollination
4 chromatography

___

98 According to the Hardy-Weinberg principle, the gene pool of a population will remain stable if

1 no mutations occur
2 the population is small
3 individuals migrate into and out of the population
4 nonrandom mating occurs by artificial selection

99 In the synthesis of proteins, what is the function of messenger-RNA molecules?

1 They act as a template for the synthesis of DNA.
2 They carry information that determines the sequence of amino acids.
3 They remove amino acids from the nucleus.
4 They carry specific enzymes for dehydration synthesis.

Group 5 — Ecology
If you choose this group, be sure to answer questions 100–109.

Base your answers to questions 100 and 101 on the biomass pyramid below of a community containing a variety of producers and consumers and on your knowledge of biology.

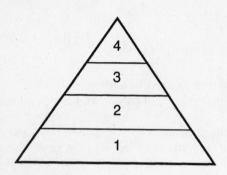

100 Primary consumers would be found at

1 levels 1 and 2   3 level 3, only
2 level 2, only   4 levels 2 and 3

101 At which level would organisms capable of autotrophic nutrition be found?

(1) 1   (3) 3
(2) 2   (4) 4

---

102 Some characteristics of four different biomes are represented in the chart below.

Biome	Characteristic Plant Life	Characteristic Animal Life
A	succulent plants	kangaroo rat, lizard
B	grasses	antelope, bison
C	deciduous trees	fox, deer
D	conifers	moose, black bear

Which biome is characterized by moderate precipitation, cold winters, warm summers, and climax plants that lose their leaves in the winter?

(1) A   (3) C
(2) B   (4) D

Base your answers to questions 103 through 105 on the chart below and on your knowledge of biology.

Stage	Dominant Flora
A	None (freshly plowed land)
B	Annual grasses
C	Various shrubs
D	Birch and cherry trees
E	Beech-maple forest

103 Which stage represents a pioneer community?

(1) A   (3) C
(2) B   (4) D

104 The replacement of stage B by stage C and the replacement of stage C by stage D in a particular location is known as

1 exploitation
2 cover cropping
3 ecological succession
4 punctuated equilibrium

105 In New York State, which fauna would most likely be associated with stage E?

1 caribou   3 leopards
2 prairie dogs   4 gray squirrels

---

106 Which statement does *not* describe a marine biome?

1 It is the most stable aquatic environment.
2 It has very few species of fauna.
3 It absorbs and holds large quantities of solar heat.
4 It contains a relatively constant supply of nutrients.

107 The diagram below represents a tree containing three different species of warbler, *A*, *B*, and *C*. Each species occupies a different niche.

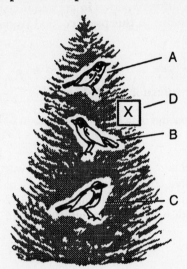

A fourth species, *D*, which has the same environmental requirements as species *B*, enters the tree at point *X*. Members of species *B* will most likely

1 live in harmony with species *D*
2 move to a different level and live with species *A* or species *C*
3 stay at that level but change their diet
4 compete with species *D*

108 A symbiotic relationship exists between two organisms of different species. If only one organism benefits from the relationship and the other is not harmed, the relationship is known as

1 commensalism
2 mutualism
3 parasitism
4 saprophytism

109 Nodules on the roots of legumes contain

1 nitrogen-fixing bacteria, which help produce nitrates
2 denitrifying bacteria, which produce amino acids
3 bacteria that release uric acid into the soil
4 bacteria that produce protein for absorption by plants

Part III

This part consists of five groups. Choose three of these five groups. For those questions that are followed by four choices, record the answers on the separate answer paper in accordance with the directions on the front page of this booklet. For all other questions in this part, record your answers in accordance with the directions given in the question. [15]

Group 1
If you choose this group, be sure to answer questions 110–114.

Base your answers to questions 110 through 113 on the information and data table below and on your knowledge of biology.

One milliliter of a solution containing an even distribution of a species of bacterium was spread on the surface of a nutrient medium in each of five culture dishes. The nutrient medium in each dish was the same, except for pH. The dishes were then incubated at 37°C for 24 hours. The number of bacterial colonies in each dish was then counted, and the results are represented in the data table below.

Data Table

pH of Nutrient Medium	Number of Bacterial Colonies on Nutrient Medium
5	10
6	50
7	60
8	70
9	5

Directions (110–111): Using the information in the data table, construct a line graph on the grid provided *on your answer paper,* following the directions below. The grid on the next page is provided for practice purposes only. Be sure your final answer appears *on your answer paper.* You may use pen or pencil for your answer.

110 Mark an appropriate scale on each labeled axis.

111 Plot the data for the number of bacterial colonies on the grid. Surround each point with a small circle and connect the points.

Example:

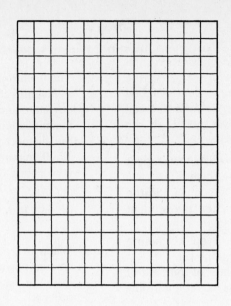

pH

112 The limiting factor in this investigation is the

(1) pH of the nutrient medium
(2) species of bacterium in each culture dish
(3) color of the colonies of bacteria
(4) amount of nutrient medium in each culture dish

113 Using one or more complete sentences, state a conclusion that relates the number of colonies of this species of bacterium to pH. You may use pen or pencil for your answer.

114 The graph below shows the results of an investigation in which an unknown species of bacteria was cultured for 24 hours. With the exception of temperature, all conditions influencing the growth of this bacterium remained constant.

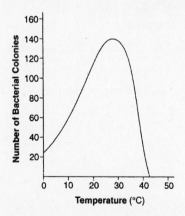

What is the experimental variable in this investigation?

1 time   3 number of colonies
2 size of each bacterium   4 temperature

Group 2

If you choose this group, be sure to answer questions 115–119.

115 A student used a light microscope to observe a cell under low power. After the student switched to high power and attempted to focus, the cell was no longer visible. What was most likely the cause of the disappearance of the cell?

  1 The diaphragm was open while the student observed the cell under low power.
  2 The distance between the specimen and the objective lens decreased after the student switched to high power.
  3 The student focused the eyepiece before observing the cell under high power.
  4 The cell was not in the center of the field of view when the student observed it under low power.

116 A unicellular organism is represented in the diagram below.

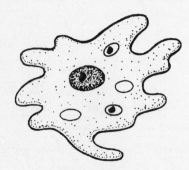

On the copy of the diagram *on your answer paper*, draw an arrow to the structure where deoxyribonucleic acid is synthesized. The point of the arrow must touch the structure. You may use pen or pencil for your answer.

117 The ocular of a compound light microscope has a magnification of 10×, and the low-power objective and high-power objective lenses have magnifications of 10× and 30×, respectively. If the diameter of the low-power field measures 1,500 micrometers, the diameter of the high-power field will measure

  (1) 100 μm   (3) 500 μm
  (2) 300 μm   (4) 4,500 μm

118 When preparing a wet mount of onion cells, a student put a drop of Lugol's iodine solution on the slide. Lugol's iodine solution was applied in order to

  1 prevent air bubbles
  2 make cell structures more visible
  3 increase the magnification
  4 increase respiration in the cells

119 A student is viewing a protist under the low-power objective of a compound light microscope. Using one or more complete sentences, describe an adjustment the student would need to make to see the protist clearly after switching from low power to high power. Include the name of the part of the microscope that would be used to make the adjustment. You may use pen or pencil for your answer.

Group 3

If you choose this group, be sure to answer questions 120–124.

120 An environmental change causes the contractile vacuoles of a paramecium to stop functioning, while most of the other cell structures appear to be unaffected. Which environmental change would most likely produce this result?

(1) temperature change from 20°C to 25°C
(2) pH change from 7.0 to 6.5
(3) large decrease in the amount of light
(4) slight increase in salt concentration in the environment

121 A student is studying the internal structures of an earthworm. To examine a cross section of the part of the earthworm's digestive tract that is specialized for mechanical digestion, the student should

1 observe the ventral side of the crop with a compound light microscope
2 make a longitudinal cut through the mouth and view the result with a dissecting microscope
3 make a vertical cut through the gizzard and view the result with a dissecting microscope
4 observe a thin section of the intestine with a compound light microscope

122 A student added 10 mL of a yeast suspension and 10 mL of 30°C water to each of two test tubes. Five grams of sugar was then added to one of the test tubes. Both test tubes were gently swirled to mix the contents, and then the test tubes were placed in a warm water bath for 15 minutes. The student made observations of any bubbles that formed in the test tubes and recorded the data in a table.

This experiment was most likely carried out to investigate the

1 effect of sugar on a metabolic activity of yeast
2 effect of temperature on a metabolic activity of yeast
3 solubility of yeast in water at 30°C
4 solubility of sugar in a yeast suspension

123 A biologist plans to spend a year investigating the mating behavior of a certain species of frog. To make meaningful observations, the biologist should observe

1 a small number of frogs in their natural habitat
2 a large number of frogs in their natural habitat
3 several groups of frogs maintained in different temperatures in the laboratory
4 several groups of frogs maintained on different diets in the laboratory

124 When a fish opens and closes its mouth, water is forced over the gills, which act as the sites of gas exchange. Four teams of students investigated the effect of temperature on the rate of mouth openings in a certain species of fish. Proper experimental procedure was followed throughout the investigation. The results are shown in the data table below.

Data Table

TEAM	Number of Mouth Openings per Minute			
	30°C	28°C	26°C	24°C
Team 1	105	105	103	102
Team 2	109	105	103	101
Team 3	112	105	102	96
Team 4	104	103	103	100
Team Average	107.5	104.5	102.8	99.8

Using one or more complete sentences, predict what will most likely happen to the rate of respiration in this species of fish if the temperature is decreased to 22°C. You may use pen or pencil for your answer.

Group 4

If you choose this group, be sure to answer questions 125–129.

Base your answers to questions 125 through 128 on the passage below and on your knowledge of biology.

Ibuprofen Helps Patients with Cystic Fibrosis

A faulty version of the CFTR gene causes the disease cystic fibrosis (CF). This gene is found in 1 in 25 Caucasians in the United States. A person who inherits a copy of this gene from each parent develops CF. Thick mucus builds up in the lungs of CF patients, leaving them vulnerable to infections. Over time, this repeated cycle of illness and inflammation causes structural damage to the lungs of the patient.

In a recent study, the common pain reliever ibuprofen significantly reduced lung damage caused by cystic fibrosis. This study included 85 CF patients between the ages of 5 and 39. Half of those participating in the study were given a tablet containing ibuprofen, and the other half were given a placebo (a tablet containing no ibuprofen). Ibuprofen, taken along with other treatments, most benefited CF patients between the ages of 5 and 13. Patients taking ibuprofen suffered less inflammation of the bronchial tubes. Lung deterioration in the children taking ibuprofen was nearly 90% slower than expected. Among those patients taking ibuprofen, lung capacity declined by only 2%, while those taking the placebo experienced a decline of 16%.

Researchers recommend that doctors begin the new therapy with their cystic fibrosis patients. However, the treatment involves taking large doses of ibuprofen, which can cause serious side effects, including stomach and kidney damage. The researchers warn people with cystic fibrosis not to take ibuprofen without talking with their doctors first.

Thirty years ago, most CF patients died before the age of 5. Today, many CF patients live into their 30's. A new drug for CF, DNase, was approved in 1994. Trials are also being done using gene therapy to correct the faulty gene found in cystic fibrosis patients. Since ibuprofen therapy delays the progression of the disease, it is hoped that more patients will be able to benefit from gene therapy when it becomes available for general use.

125 Which statement regarding the use of ibuprofen in the treatment of cystic fibrosis is correct?

1 Lung deterioration in individuals taking ibuprofen was about 16% slower than in those taking the placebo.
2 Although initially promising, problems with stomach and kidney damage have made most doctors unwilling to prescribe ibuprofen for the treatment of cystic fibrosis.
3 Large doses of ibuprofen can be dangerous, but under the care of a doctor the benefits of ibuprofen for individuals with cystic fibrosis can be significant.
4 The most significant reduction in the swelling of the bronchi due to ibuprofen therapy occurred in individuals 15 to 35 years of age.

126 A valid conclusion that can be drawn from this information is that

1 ibuprofen is now considered the drug of choice, replacing DNase in treating cystic fibrosis
2 because of ibuprofen, gene therapy and the use of DNase are no longer considered effective ways to treat cystic fibrosis
3 ibuprofen, with its serious side effects, is too dangerous to use in the treatment of cystic fibrosis
4 in combination with other drugs, ibuprofen reduces lung damage and slows the progress of cystic fibrosis

127 Cystic fibrosis results when an individual is

    1 homozygous for the faulty CFTR gene
    2 heterozygous for the faulty CFTR gene
    3 given an overdose of ibuprofen
    4 exposed to a person with this disease

128 Using one or more complete sentences, state one possible result of the buildup of mucus in the lungs of individuals with cystic fibrosis. You may use pen or pencil for your answer.

---

129 A single protist was placed in a large test tube containing nutrient broth. The tube was then kept at room temperature for 24 hours. Samples from the tube were observed periodically during the 24 hours, using the low power of a compound light microscope. The data are summarized in the table below.

Data Table

Age of the Population in Hours	Number of Protists in the Population
0	1
6	2
8	3
10	4
13	8
16	16
18	32
20	64
22	128
24	256

Which graph best represents the data?

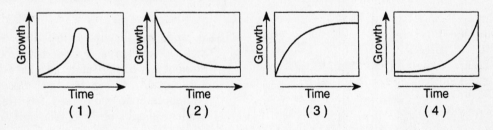

Group 5

If you choose this group, be sure to answer questions 130–134.

130 A student wanted to determine if plants grow better under blue light than under yellow light. The student obtained two genetically identical plants of the same size and placed each in a growth chamber. One plant was grown in blue light, and the other was grown in yellow light. All other experimental conditions were the same. The student measured the height of the plants after 2 weeks. To test the reliability of the data, the student repeated the experiment with two plants of the same species that were not genetically related to the first set of plants. The results were similar to those of the first experiment.

To make a valid conclusion regarding these results, the student should

1 repeat the experiment using other species of plants
2 conduct another experiment using only blue light
3 repeat the experiment using different variables
4 publish the results of the experiments

131 Record the letter that indicates the apparatus that serves as the control for the experiment in the diagram below. You may use pen or pencil for your answer.

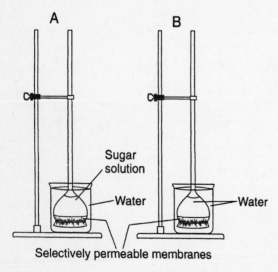

132 The diagram below shows a wasp positioned next to a centimeter ruler.

What is the approximate length of a wing of this wasp?

(1) 10 mm
(2) 1.4 cm
(3) 3.5 cm
(4) 35 mm

133 A blue solution turns yellow when it is exposed to a weak acid. A small amount of this blue solution was added to a test tube of water containing an aquatic snail. The color of the water in the tube changed from blue to yellow after 30 minutes. A possible explanation for this color change is that the

1 body of the snail is slightly basic
2 snail is absorbing carbon dioxide from the water
3 excretions of the snail have affected the pH of the water
4 snail ingested some of the blue solution

134 A student is heating a test tube containing a crushed cracker and Benedict's solution. The student is wearing safety goggles and a laboratory apron. Using one or more complete sentences, state one other safety precaution the student should observe. You may use pen or pencil for your answer.

BIOLOGY
JANUARY 2000

Part I Score (Use table below)	. . . .
Part II Score	. . . .
Part III Score	. . . .
Total Score	. . . .

Rater's Initials: . . . .

ANSWER PAPER

Student . . . .

Teacher . . . . School . . . .

All of your answers should be recorded on this answer paper.

Part I (65 credits)

1	1 2 3 4	21	1 2 3 4	41	1 2 3 4
2	1 2 3 4	22	1 2 3 4	42	1 2 3 4
3	1 2 3 4	23	1 2 3 4	43	1 2 3 4
4	1 2 3 4	24	1 2 3 4	44	1 2 3 4
5	1 2 3 4	25	1 2 3 4	45	1 2 3 4
6	1 2 3 4	26	1 2 3 4	46	1 2 3 4
7	1 2 3 4	27	1 2 3 4	47	1 2 3 4
8	1 2 3 4	28	1 2 3 4	48	1 2 3 4
9	1 2 3 4	29	1 2 3 4	49	1 2 3 4
10	1 2 3 4	30	1 2 3 4	50	1 2 3 4
11	1 2 3 4	31	1 2 3 4	51	1 2 3 4
12	1 2 3 4	32	1 2 3 4	52	1 2 3 4
13	1 2 3 4	33	1 2 3 4	53	1 2 3 4
14	1 2 3 4	34	1 2 3 4	54	1 2 3 4
15	1 2 3 4	35	1 2 3 4	55	1 2 3 4
16	1 2 3 4	36	1 2 3 4	56	1 2 3 4
17	1 2 3 4	37	1 2 3 4	57	1 2 3 4
18	1 2 3 4	38	1 2 3 4	58	1 2 3 4
19	1 2 3 4	39	1 2 3 4	59	1 2 3 4
20	1 2 3 4	40	1 2 3 4		

PART I CREDITS

Directions to Teacher:

In the table below, draw a circle around the number of right answers and the adjacent number of credits. Then write the number of credits (not the number right) in the space provided above.

No. Right	Credits	No. Right	Credits
59	65	29	37
58	64	28	36
57	63	27	36
56	62	26	35
55	61	25	34
54	60	24	33
53	59	23	32
52	59	22	31
51	58	21	30
50	57	20	29
49	56	19	28
48	55	18	27
47	54	17	26
46	53	16	25
45	52	15	25
44	51	14	23
43	50	13	22
42	49	12	20
41	48	11	18
40	48	10	17
39	47	9	15
38	46	8	13
37	45	7	12
36	44	6	10
35	43	5	8
34	42	4	7
33	41	3	5
32	40	2	3
31	39	1	2
30	38	0	0

No. right . . . .

Part II (20 credits)

Answer the questions in only two of the five groups in this part. Be sure to mark the answers to the groups of questions you choose in accordance with the instructions on the front page of the test booklet. Leave blank the three groups of questions you do not choose to answer.

Group 1
Biochemistry

60   1   2   3   4

61   1   2   3   4

62   1   2   3   4

63   1   2   3   4

64   1   2   3   4

65   1   2   3   4

66   1   2   3   4

67   1   2   3   4

68   1   2   3   4

69   1   2   3   4

Group 3
Reproduction and
Development

80   1   2   3   4

81   1   2   3   4

82   1   2   3   4

83   1   2   3   4

84   1   2   3   4

85   1   2   3   4

86   1   2   3   4

87   1   2   3   4

88   1   2   3   4

89   1   2   3   4

Group 5
Ecology

100   1   2   3   4

101   1   2   3   4

102   1   2   3   4

103   1   2   3   4

104   1   2   3   4

105   1   2   3   4

106   1   2   3   4

107   1   2   3   4

108   1   2   3   4

109   1   2   3   4

Group 2
Human Physiology

70   1   2   3   4

71   1   2   3   4

72   1   2   3   4

73   1   2   3   4

74   1   2   3   4

75   1   2   3   4

76   1   2   3   4

77   1   2   3   4

78   1   2   3   4

79   1   2   3   4

Group 4
Modern Genetics

90   1   2   3   4

91   1   2   3   4

92   1   2   3   4

93   1   2   3   4

94   1   2   3   4

95   1   2   3   4

96   1   2   3   4

97   1   2   3   4

98   1   2   3   4

99   1   2   3   4

Answer the questions in only three of the five groups in this part. Leave blank the two groups of questions you do not choose to answer.

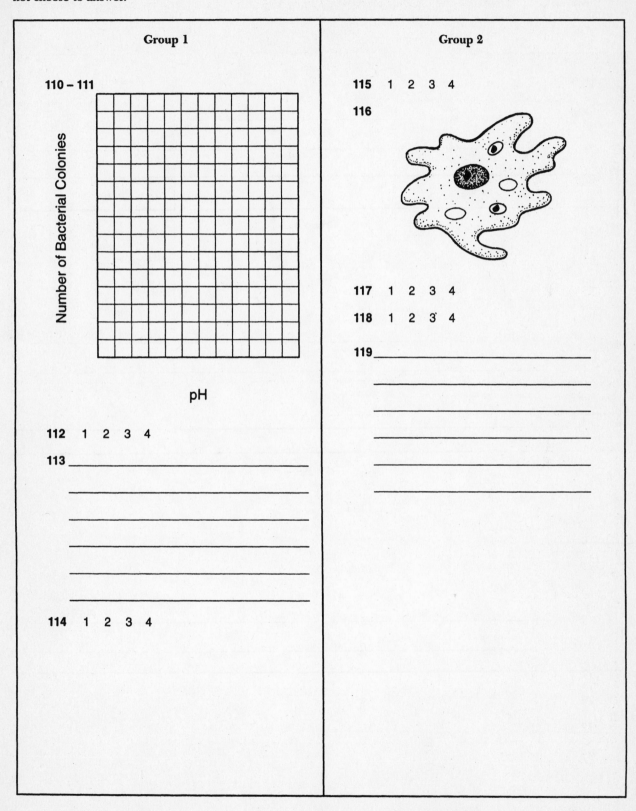

Group 1

110 – 111

Number of Bacterial Colonies

pH

112   1   2   3   4

113 _____

_____

_____

_____

_____

114   1   2   3   4

Group 2

115   1   2   3   4

116

117   1   2   3   4

118   1   2   3   4

119 _____

_____

_____

_____

_____

Group 3

120   1 2 3 4

121   1 2 3 4

122   1 2 3 4

123   1 2 3 4

124 _____

_____

Group 4

125   1 2 3 4

126   1 2 3 4

127   1 2 3 4

128 _____

_____

129   1 2 3 4

Group 5

130   1 2 3 4

131   _____

132   1 2 3 4

133   1 2 3 4

134 _____

_____